MEN OF SPACE

Volume 5

Profiles of the Leaders in Space Research, Development, and Exploration

Advisory Committee

Chairman:

DONALD L. PUTT
Lieutenant General,
United States Air Force (Ret.)
President, United Technology Corporation

Members:

DR. EUGENE M. EMME
Historian,
National Aeronautics and Space Administration

MARVIN W. MCFARLAND
Guggenheim Chair of Aeronautics,
Library of Congress

GRAYSON MERRILL
Captain, United States Navy (Ret.)
Vice-President—Electronics,
Harris-Intertype Corp.

FRANK PACE, JR.
Director, General Dynamics Corp.

DR. FRANK E. SORENSON
Chairman, Department of Educational Services, University of Nebraska

THE HONORABLE STUART SYMINGTON
United States Senator from Missouri
Member, Senate Committee on Aeronautical and Space Sciences

DR. E. C. WELSH
Executive Secretary, National Aeronautics and Space Council

Volume 5

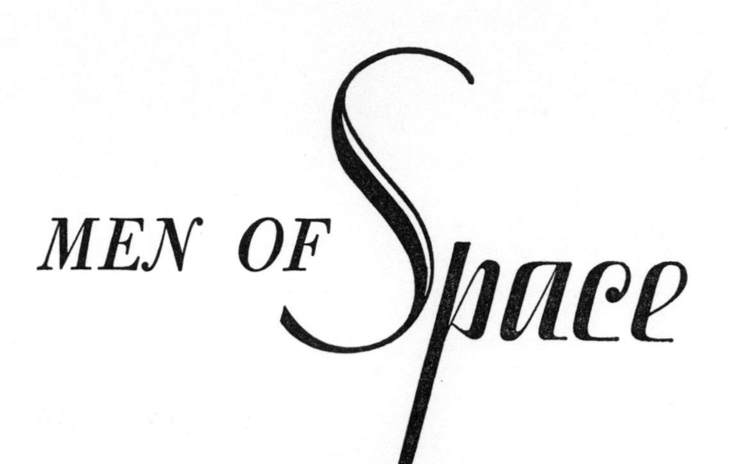

Profiles of the Leaders in Space Research, Development, and Exploration

By SHIRLEY THOMAS

Illustrated

CHILTON BOOKS

A DIVISION OF CHILTON COMPANY

Publishers

PHILADELPHIA AND NEW YORK

First Edition

Published in Philadelphia by Chilton Company, and simultaneously in Toronto, Canada, by Ambassador Books, Ltd.

Library of Congress Catalog Card Number 60-15720

Research Associate: Margaret R. Annis

Designed by William E. Lickfield

Manufactured in the United States of America by Quinn & Boden Company, Inc., Rahway, N. J.

To B. and W.

Foreword

Excitement and fast-moving drama characterize the Space Age which the world has so recently entered. There is, however, much more to space activity than the courageous and skilled achievements of men rocketing out of the earth's atmosphere and returning heroically to earth. There is a movement in depth throughout our whole economy—only a portion of which is revealed on the screen of spectacular action. Shirley Thomas has, with skill and judgment, brought to the threshold of understanding a treasure of knowledge about those who have furthered this movement toward outer space. In so doing, she is writing not only about space pioneers, but also as a space pioneer herself.

As one reads the published volumes of *Men of Space,* and as one anticipates the future volumes of this series, he cannot but be impressed with the program's vitality. The outstanding features of this space revolution are its great speed of progress and its emphasis on the mental competence of dedicated individuals. It is relatively easy to be enthusiastic about a spectacular success, such as a manned flight at fantastic speeds in earth orbits. It is extremely difficult, however, to keep in proper perspective the millions of man-hours, the disappointments, the solutions to hitherto unsolvable problems, and the unheralded but basic decisions which of necessity preceded the glamorous successes. The quality of man is tested no less in the preparation than it is in the final performance.

The spotlight of attention has been directed most frequently toward the astronaut as an individual and then to the scientists and the engineers as a dual category. This is understandable, and such credit is certainly well merited. However, from the President down, there are also those who take responsibilities, make decisions, administer staffs, formulate policy, and, in fact, mold space competences into a viable space program. Such persons and their actions make possible what would otherwise be impossible, even if every needed scientific breakthrough had become fact.

Second place for the United States in space is unacceptable. Our goal is space leadership in maintaining the peace and in improving peaceful living. The individuals honored in this book have contributed toward that goal.

E. C. Welsh
Executive Secretary,
National Aeronautics and
Space Council

Author's Introduction

In the *Men of Space* books, each chapter tells a story of the most powerful force on earth. This is not some advanced and exotic rocket propellant. This power is *man*.

His mind can exert a force without limitation, provided that it is supported with effort, energy, and dedication. His thoughts reach farther than the most fanciful missions yet projected.

The scientific mind, in particular, is a wondrous instrument. While investigating the known, it constantly speculates on the unknown. Though operating in complex areas of fact and truth, it still must contend with the possibility that the axioms may be false. The scientific mentality is capable of unbelievable discipline, but it functions best in an atmosphere of freedom.

Space had its beginning in the minds of men. It will continue as their ideas and concepts expand. Therefore, the most fascinating view of today's history-making developments is seen through the eyes of the *Men of Space*.

All of the various projects and accomplishments are but manifestations of their dreams. The astounding progress that is occurring can be directly pinpointed to a relatively small, highly selective, and enormously gifted group—the *Men of Space*.

SHIRLEY THOMAS

MEN OF SPACE
Advisory Committee

Chairman

DONALD L. PUTT

Lieutenant General, United States Air Force (Ret.)

Though a retired Air Force Lieutenant General, Donald L. Putt remains closely affiliated with the service by acting as Chairman of the Air Force Scientific Advisory Board. The scope of his activities reaches beyond this nation, for he serves also as the United States National Delegate to the NATO Advisory Group for Aeronautical Research and Development. He is a member of the Defense Science Board, a member of the Board of Trustees of the System Development Corporation and Carnegie Institute of Technology. These important activities are adjuncts to the General's current position, which is President of the United Technology Corporation, a subsidiary of the United Aircraft Corporation.

General Putt's thirty-year military service embraced a wide range of assignments. His last appointment before retirement in 1958 was as Deputy Chief of Staff for Development. His decorations include: Distinguished Service Medal, Legion of Merit with Oak Leaf Cluster, Bronze Star with Oak Leaf Cluster, *Croix de Guerre avec Palme.*

DR. EUGENE M. EMME

Historian, National Aeronautics and Space Administration

As the historian for the National Aeronautics and Space Administration, Dr. Emme is absorbed in setting down an accurate and authoritative chronicle of this era. He has written a very remarkable and useful volume, *Aeronautics and Astronautics: An American Chronology of Science and Technology in the Exploration of Space, 1915–1960,* which he points out is clearly but a beginning. His doctoral dissertation was entitled *German Air Power, 1919–1939. The Impact of Air Power* (1959), edited by Dr. Emme, has become a standard anthology on aerospace affairs.

Dr. Emme was a research historian at the Air University Research Studies Institute. He was awarded a Commendation for Meritorious Civilian Service by the Department of the Air Force. He has served as Director of the Graduate Study Group and as Civilian Research Advisor on the faculty of the Air War College.

MARVIN W. McFARLAND

Guggenheim Chair of Aeronautics, Library of Congress

This writer, editor, and well-known authority on aeronautics and aeronautical history is the incumbent of the Guggenheim Chair of Aeronautics in the Library of Congress, where he fills the position of Head of the Aeronautics Section in the Science and Technology Division. The twofold purpose of this position is to assure the development of a collection of aeronautical—and, now, of space—literature "second to none in the world" and to "interpret" that collection for members of the Congress, for other Government agencies, for scholars, and for the public.

Mr. McFarland has had more than twenty years of library, archival, and editorial experience. His best-known publication is his monumental two-volume edition of *The Papers of Wilbur and Orville Wright,* which appeared in 1953.

GRAYSON MERRILL

Captain, United States Navy (Ret.)

A retired Captain of the United States Navy, Grayson Merrill is editor of a comprehensive, ten-volume work entitled *Principles of Guided Missile Design,* editor of the *Dictionary of Guided Missiles and Space Flight,* and co-author of an undergraduate textbook, *Fundamentals of Guided Missiles.* He is Vice-President—Electronics of Harris-Intertype Corporation.

Captain Merrill's experience in guided missile research and development dates from the very first pilotless aircraft operated by the Navy. He has been awarded two commendations from the Secretary of the Navy as well as the Legion of Merit for his work in the missile field. He formulated the Navy's first program for launching a guided missile from a sub and was named first Technical Director of the Fleet Ballistic Missile (*Polaris*) program in 1956, the position he held prior to his retirement from the Navy.

FRANK PACE, JR.

Director, General Dynamics Corporation

As Vice Chairman of the President's Commission on National Goals, this executive lent his vigorous thinking to the drafting of *Goals for Americans.* He now serves on the President's Foreign Intelligence Advisory Board and has been chairman of, or a member of, several NATO groups. He attended both Princeton and Harvard and has been honored with degrees from many other outstanding colleges and universities. When serving as Secretary of the Army, he warned Major General H. N. Toftoy, who was enthusiastic about the potential of missile development, "Don't oversell me. If I get going on this, I'm going to be hard to stop." His persistence and leadership have proved to be an important adjunct to this nation's advancement in rocket and missile technology.

DR. FRANK E. SORENSON

Chairman, Department of Educational Services, University of Nebraska

As one of the nation's most outstanding leaders in aerospace education, Dr. Sorenson travels widely from his post at the University of Nebraska. He serves as the vigorous Chairman of the Technical Assistance Board of the Link Foundation, is Administrator of the Nebraska Aerospace Education Division, is a member of the U.S. Air Force Air Training Command Advisory Board, and is Chairman of the Aerospace Education Council of the Air Force Association.

For his outstanding contribution to Aerospace Education, Dr. Sorenson has received the Frank G. Brewer Trophy, the University Aviation Association Award, a special citation from the Arnold Air Society, and the Hoyt S. Vandenberg Award for 1959. In 1962, he was awarded the U.S. Air Force Scroll of Appreciation—an honor which is bestowed upon but twelve civilians each year.

THE HONORABLE STUART SYMINGTON

United States Senator from Missouri
Member, Senate Committee on Aeronautical and Space Sciences

The Senator from Missouri was the nation's first Secretary of the Air Force in 1947 and has long been one of the nation's strongest influences for a positive air/space program. He is a vocal and highly regarded member of the Aeronautical and Space Sciences Committee.

His responsibilities with Government date from 1941 when he went to England at the request of the War Department to study airplane armament. Other appointments have been: Chairman, Surplus Property Board; Assistant Secretary of War for Air; Chairman, National Security Resources Board; and Administrator, Reconstruction Finance Corporation. Senator Symington was approved by the Senate six times for high office without a single dissenting vote, Democratic or Republican. He was awarded the Medal of Merit in 1947 and the Distinguished Service Medal in 1952.

DR. E. C. WELSH

Executive Secretary, National Aeronautics and Space Council

Appointed in 1961 as the Executive Secretary of the National Aeronautics and Space Council, Dr. Welsh had served previously as Legislative Assistant to Senator Stuart Symington since 1953. While in this position, Welsh also held the positions of Staff Director of the airpower hearings in 1956, and Staff Director for President Kennedy's Defense Reorganization Committee in 1960.

Prior assignments for this holder of a Ph.D. in Economics have included: Chief of the Antitrust and Cartels Division in the General Headquarters of General Douglas MacArthur, 1947; Assistant to the Chairman of the National Security Resources Board; and Assistant to the Administrator of the Reconstruction Finance Corporation. On April 13, 1962, Dr. Welsh received the Arnold Air Society's Paul T. Johns Trophy, which is awarded annually to an individual for "Distinguished contributions to science and defense technology."

Contents

First American to orbit the earth

JOHN H. GLENN, JR.

"The way to do is to be."

A man is greater than the sum of all his deeds. Yet, when one of those accomplishments includes the orbiting of the earth, an avalanche of adjectives is likely to submerge this truth and smother the true man.

It is to John H. Glenn, Jr.'s great credit that the strength of his personality and the depth of his character have dominated even the hero-image that has been superimposed since that historic day of February 20, 1962, when he flew *Friendship 7* in three earth orbits.

A tense, watching world suffered through a drama more suspenseful than any that ever flowed from the pen of the great Bard—a drama played in ten acts. Glenn's own clear tones echoed the countdown: "Ten, nine, eight, seven, six, five, four, three, two, one, zero!" At "ignition," the world paused. A hundred million people stared transfixed at television screens. No wind could rustle the agonizing four seconds of the build-up of thrust. At "lift-off," the *Mercury* capsule was propelled by more than the flame-gushing *Atlas*—it had in addition the massive power of human hope and urging.

"We are under way." Glenn's firm voice reassured the waiting world, and the frieze of suspended animation shattered. With the capsule's rising trajectory, the momentum of mass exhilaration mounted. "It is bumpy along about here . . . coming into high Q . . . we are smoothing out some now." Vicariously, a billion passengers were riding in *Friendship 7*.

Never had technical achievement stood as a greater symbol of pride and prestige. Never had the burden of fulfillment rested more squarely upon one man. Never was an individual more thoroughly prepared, or more voraciously eager to perform a mission. John Glenn had channeled every thought and action of his life toward that moment—since long before he knew what the moment would be.

"We are placed here with certain talents and capabilities. It is up to each of us to use those talents and capabilities as best we can. If we do that, I think there is a power greater than any of us that will place the opportunities in our way . . . if I use the talents and capabilities I happen to have been given to the best of my ability, I think there is a power greater than I am that will certainly see that I am taken care of. . . ."[1] Radiating boundless spirit and confidence, Glenn made that statement on the day it was announced that he had been selected as an Astronaut.

Soon, the Astronaut team of seven men* found an undesignated but acknowledged leader—a role not unfamiliar to Glenn. Says his commanding officer of World War II days, John P. Haines, Jr. (now Colonel, USMC, Ret.), "Overseas in the Marshall area, when something really had to be done, it was not unusual for me to ask John to lead a strike with senior pilots behind him. And the interesting thing here is not that I might have chosen him, because that was the obvious selection, but that the pilots would without question accept John's leadership."[2]

Leadership—what is it? Is it clarity of thought? Are the indicators such manifestations as the quickness to comprehend and respond? Does it relate to formal IQ, or accumulated experience? Self-reliance? Decisiveness? Initiative? In an age where the most abstruse elements can be reduced to specific formulae, the quality of leadership is better felt than defined. When present, it registers like a charge of electricity, and all the reasons for its being seem but rationalization. When absent, no words will instill it. Leaders seem to be born, rather than made.

But the quality can undergo development that broadens both scope and capability. Ideally, the background for this should include parents endowed with solid thinking, and an upbringing reinforced with firm teaching

* The six other original Astronauts are: Malcolm S. Carpenter; Leroy G. Cooper; Virgil I. Grissom; Walter M. Schirra; Alan B. Shepard; and Donald K. Slayton. It was announced on September 17, 1962, that nine other men had been designated as Astronauts: Neil A. Armstrong; Frank Borman; Charles Conrad, Jr.; James A. Lovell, Jr.; James A. McDivitt; Elliott M. See, Jr.; Thomas P. Stafford; Edward H. White, 2d; and John W. Young.

of important fundamentals. Such elements were present in Mr. and Mrs. John H. Glenn, Sr., and the schools of New Concord, Ohio. At the first crossroads of John Glenn's life, the direction was clear—the United States Marine Corps.

"If the Army and the Navy ever look on heaven's scenes, they will find the streets are guarded by United States Marines." This closing line of the *Marines' Hymn* would appear to reflect a certain bias, yet it certainly conveys the Marines' fierce, traditional pride.

The roots of this confidence reach back into history, to the time of their service on the ships of John Paul Jones, to the battles in Tripoli which vanquished Mediterranean pirates, to service with such figures as General Jackson, General Fremont, Commodore Perry, Admiral Farragut, and Admiral Dewey. Epitomizing their bravery is the legendary photograph of a small group implanting the American flag on Iwo Jima. Of this gallant action, Fleet Admiral Chester W. Nimitz said, "Uncommon valor was a common virtue."

Semper Fidelis—Always Faithful. To a Marine, this means "faithful" to his buddy, his company, his squadron, the Corps—but above all, faithful to his immediate comrades in arms. The motto has covered the encompassing area of their fields of operation—on land, on sea, and in the air. Now, a Marine has gone into space. For the achievement, John Glenn wears the Marine Corps Astronaut Insignia, and the Navy Astronaut Wings.

Twenty years ago, Glenn won his Naval Aviator Wings. Lieutenant Colonel Thomas H. Miller, USMC, has enjoyed a close friendship with Glenn since that date. He recalls, "I first met John in 1942 at Corpus Christi during basic and advanced flight training. At that time, he was not an extremely social individual, because he was primarily interested in his studies. He was a perfectionist in getting the most out of the training."

Throughout his life, Glenn's application had been total—in studies and sports at New Concord High School, at Muskingum College, and in affairs that related to his community. But at the period of his flight training, there was additional reason for avid attention to study: there was immediate prospect of using that skill in the war that had just disploded.

He was learning more than the handling of a joy stick, the control of rudders and ailerons and the reading of air-speed indicators; he was absorbing one of the greatest lessons the Marine Corps has to teach—teamwork. Says Miller, "This is basic to the spirit. The individual is only a part of the team, and he can do no job by himself. Only through the help and cooperation of his buddies can he accomplish the mission. And once a mission is assigned, you can be sure that the 'gung ho' spirit will prevail, and the objective *will be accomplished*.

"No one more completely personifies the spirit than our own Marine

Commandant, General David M. Shoup. The Congressional Medal of Honor was bestowed upon him for his leadership and courage displayed at Tarawa. Countless Marines deserve medals for having given their lives to save their buddies."

All of this attitude was being stored in John Glenn's consciousness during his early Marine training—stored for the day when he would draw upon it as a member of the most famous seven-man team ever assembled.

Graduation from the Naval Air Training Center brought Glenn an assignment to Cherry Point, North Carolina. He made the trip by way of New Concord, where he and Anna Castor were married. Soon, Tom Miller deserted the ranks of the bachelor lieutenants, and followed suit; he married Ida Mai Giddings, a childhood playmate.

Glenn and Miller both had gone through multi-engine flight training in school as a form of "insurance"—should the Corps no longer require their services after the War, they would be equipped to become airline pilots. From the B-25 medium twin-engine bomber they had flown at Cherry Point, their next assignment to Camp Kearney, California, brought even less exhilarating flying in transports. Both men grew restive. This was not the kind of airplane for young and spirited men.

The solution was nearby—just across the field! There, one fighter squadron was stationed. Though this physical distance of separation was not great, it lay like an unattainable plateau by the route of official channels. Undaunted, Glenn set about to effect a transfer.

His first move was to determine if Major (now Colonel, USMC, Ret.) J. P. "Pete" Haines, Jr., who was Commanding Officer of the fighter squadron, would be in favor of the switch. Haines was. He needed pilots, and he liked the enthusiasm that he saw in Glenn. The squadron leader had returned from his first tour overseas to build up a new squadron to take back, and he realized the value of this quality.

Delighted that this first hurdle was surmounted, Glenn charged ahead in his effort and went to the Group Commander, Lieutenant Colonel Dean C. Roberts—entirely forgetting to see his own Commanding Officer in the Transport Squadron. Miller explains, "John had intended no disrespect, but was merely a little green in the ways of the military. I was trying for a transfer also, and even though I had properly seen our own Commanding Officer, he was so irked that John had by-passed him that he squelched both our transfers."

It was a hard lesson for Glenn. To have failed was a disappointment—but to have failed through his own error was unforgivable. Eagerness was supplanted with calm resolve and careful planning, for he was not content to be blocked. Persistence triumphed. Through Haines' intercession, Glenn won his transfer to VMF-155 Squadron. His first craft was the SNJ—a two-seat trainer airplane.

Glenn's natural aptitude was more evident in the faster and more maneuverable craft. Recalls John S. Griffith (now Captain, USMC, Ret.), "I consider it fortunate that I served with John for two years. From the first, it was obvious that he would be one of the leaders among the pilots. He was skillful, conscientious, and had a pleasing, straightforward personality. He was soon selected to lead a division of planes."

Griffith continues, "Competition among the young 'hot' pilots was keen, and all of us were anxious to show our superiority. In our training, we frequently went out to the gunnery range in the Chocolate Mountains to make firing runs on towed cloth targets. I had a degree of 'beginner's luck' in my scores. However, I quickly gave way to John Glenn."

Haines, Glenn's Commanding Officer, provided him with stiffer competition. Haines recently recalled, "the rivalry that built up in our aerial gunnery was fierce. Just before John made his orbital flight, I sent him a note, and told him I was sure he would have no trouble in orbit as long as he didn't have to shoot."

Despite the tremendous pressures of work in preparing for that flight, Glenn took the time to reply to Haines, and in mock-seriousness wrote: "Now, as to your caustic and unwarranted comments regarding my gunnery ability! All I can say is if I can get a gunsight on this capsule, I will have to prove once *again* to you and T. H. [Tom Miller] that science, skill and ingenuity will always triumph over ignorance, superstition and luck. As a matter of fact, I haven't had sore knees from crawling up and down a gunnery banner for some time now. That would be a lot of fun. If I ever have ulcers in this work, it will probably be from arguing who got how many of what colors on gunnery hops."

Haines adds, "This running argument has persisted over the years, though truthfully the only time I ever came close to beating John was when I shot off the banner that was being towed behind another fighter. But I have never let him forget that one incident, over the many, many he won over me!"

Excellence was not happenstance with Glenn. He worked for it. He drilled in every phase. One of his aims was to make more loops than anyone else, and he would perform 25 without stopping. He was operations officer in a number of squadrons, and always set about trying to improve things—never being content to continue in a routine manner just because it was custom.

The squadron was moved to El Centro Air Station, and Glenn graduated into the F4F Grumman *Wildcat,* the airplane used by such remarkable fliers as Joe Foss and Marion Carl to achieve victories in the early part of World War II. The next airplane Glenn flew was the F4U Chance-Vought *Corsair,* which became the Navy's famous fighter. Working schedules at El Centro extended around the clock; because the heat of summer days caused frequent blow-outs of the small airplane tires, there was much night flying.

The fliers and their families grew very close, as frequently happens in wartime. The wives passed many of these evenings playing bridge or gin rummy at the Officers Club. Only on weekends could they all gather—perhaps for a barbecue or a picnic.

This interlude soon ended for Glenn. He got his wish to become an active part of the conflict in February, 1944, when Marine Fighter Squadron 155 set sail for the Pacific area. The destination, via Hawaii, was Midway Islands.

The great Battle of Midway had taken place the previous June. This strategic victory for the Allies which returned some semblance of naval parity is regarded by some historians to be the turning point of the war in the Pacific theater. Haines' squadron, which included Glenn, was sent on a three-month tour to protect the Midway submarine base—the largest one in the Pacific at that time.

Every overseas squadron had to have an appropriate name, so ideas were sought for this one. Glenn's eager attitude evinced itself in his suggestion: "Ready Teddy." Haines felt it too flippant, but his protest was not heeded. The other pilots voted for Glenn's choice, and also adopted his sketch for the emblem—a figure of a Teddy bear running, as though on scramble! The symbol was painted on all of their F4U *Corsair* fighters.

The mission of the squadron called for a constant alert. Aircraft were airborne at dawn and dusk, and four airplanes stood on strip alert. The pilots kept a vigil in the ready room, and bounded into action when the order came to "Scramble two." Relates Miller, "Since there were four of us to answer the call for two, the competition was keen. The first to get airborne would be the ones who had the chance to fly. John was always well prepared in the way he set up his cockpit, and had all the switches on the instrument panel positioned for a quick take-off. John was pretty adept at beating the rest of us off the ground."

Between scrambles, time was spent studying navigation, with interludes of table tennis—a sport which trains the quick response so valuable in a pilot. At Midway, also, Glenn first entered into a sport that still remains a favorite—that of spear fishing. Glenn and his buddies would don nose masks, round eye masks, and swim fins. Their weapon was a bamboo tube, in which was a steel spear, propelled by a rubber band. They would swim underwater, holding it in a cocked position, until the target fish was spotted.

Many native Hawaiians, who were on Midway with the construction battalion, gave the fliers helpful instructions on the art, and tips on what to do if they encountered sharks, barracuda, squid, octopus, or eel. The latter were their special targets, for they are fish-of-prey. The edible fish the fliers speared were taken to the cooks, who obligingly prepared them into tasteful meals.

Miller makes the interesting comparison, "Swimming and flying give the same feeling of freedom—in water on the one hand, in the air on the other. One of the primary emotions which an aviator experiences is, in essence, this great freedom. Many people have commented that when John was orbiting in space, there must have been a feeling of fear. This, I think, is completely false. If he had a moment to be conscious of any reaction, I would bet it was this feeling of freedom, intensified in space beyond anything that can be experienced within the atmosphere."

Midway was the location of an underwater incident that provided Glenn with a different kind of experience—one that he has never forgotten. A submarine came into the base for replenishment of supplies and replacement of personnel between patrols. Glenn and the torpedo officer aboard the *USS Barb,* Lieutenant Eastman, became friends. The Navy officer expressed a desire to see what his submarine looked like from the vantage point of the air. Glenn and Miller gave Eastman rides on several occasions.

Eastman then wanted to reciprocate, so he invited the two fliers to go aboard the *Barb* and dive with them. The visit was arranged on a day when new crews were being indoctrinated and torpedoes were being fired at practice targets. A depth charge was fired, and the *Barb* made a maximum depth dive to determine the state of the submarine. It was found to be considerably less than watertight, as Miller describes:

"We were on the bridge and observed a tremendous leak stemming from around the periscope, it looked like a gushing fire hose. There was great hollering for the cook to bring pots and pans—which reminded me of when I was a kid and the roof of our house always leaked in a rainstorm. When the submarine finally surfaced, John said one experience like that was enough. That was not the life for him. He was quite happy to concentrate his activities on getting above the earth's surface and not below it!"

Not all of Glenn's energies could be used up on the patrols, however. He still had some left over which diverted into a little mild mischief. The construction battalion was building a new runway on Midway and had many pieces of equipment scattered about. One huge grader, which was sitting behind the bachelor officers' quarters, proved a great temptation for Glenn.

He managed to get the grader started, and with one of his pals, Lieutenant Monte Goodman, had a wonderful time pushing sand around. But when word of the escapade reached Haines, the Commanding Officer, both men received a severe "chewing out."

Though Glenn's resilient spirit was not appreciably dampened by the reprimand, one truly sad note did exist on that Island, and that was the moaning birds. Their night nesting place was beneath the floor of the bachelor officers' quarters, and this proved an unendurable situation to one of the fliers, John Griffith. It was not unusual to hear him stumble out of his bed at about 2 A.M., grab a stick, then crawl around under the building and beat the ground in an effort to scare away the moaning birds. Glenn and the others had grown accustomed to the birds, and found Griffith's attempts to achieve quiet to be a pretty noisy operation!

Glenn's fondness for the game of bridge nearly led to trouble in May, 1944. His squadron was ordered from Midway to the Marshall Islands, but Glenn and several other pilots were diverted first to Honolulu to test fly the airplanes.

While there, Glenn stayed at the Moana Hotel, and ended up one evening at the home of a friend, playing bridge. Haines and Miller were also involved, and the competition became so engrossing that a minor detail like time did not occur to them until the clock chimed two. Hawaii, under wartime conditions, had a 9 P.M. curfew.

A severe logistics problem suddenly arose: How could three officers transport themselves for the distance of the five blocks to get back to their hotel without being apprehended by the alert military police patrols? The best available solution necessitated the unaccustomed behavior of creeping behind hedges, darting into dark doorways, and racing across streets, until the rear entrance of the hotel was finally reached.

In November, 1943, Admiral Nimitz sent forces into the Gilbert Islands. Once secured, at heavy toll to the Marines, the Islands became a springboard for attacks on the Japanese-held Marshall Islands. In January, 1944, invasion of some of the Marshall atolls began. In mid-February, Nimitz moved his forces on to Eniwetok, leaving remaining atolls of the Marshalls and Gilberts to be taken by other forces.

The carrier transported the squadron to which Glenn belonged to that area, anchored in the lagoon, and catapulted the fighter planes off the deck for a landing at Majuro Atoll. This remained the squadron's base of operations until September, 1944.

The Fleet pool of airplanes was kept at Majuro; when airplanes were lost—as many were in the battle of the Philippine Sea—pilots were sent to Majuro for replacements. The atoll, therefore, became a special target for attack, so it was necessary to fly cover over it. Two airplanes were kept in the air at all times. About every fifth day, Glenn and his wingman, Lieutenant Edward Taylor, drew this duty. After three hours, they were relieved for refueling and brief rest, as Miller and his wingman, Lieutenant Edward "Tyrone" Powers, took over the watch.

From Majuro, daily attacks were flown against those islands of the Marshall group which were still held by the Japanese; among them were the heavily fortified atolls of Mille and Maloelap. Our losses on Kwajalein influenced the decision not to try to occupy the other atolls. Rather, it was decided to prevent any build-up behind the Allied fleet, which had moved on to bases approaching Guam and Okinawa, by carrying on continuous bombing operations against these Japanese bases.

Glenn seemed destined not to participate in the air-to-air combat flying he so earnestly desired. Haines points out, "Like all fighter pilots, John preferred to work at his trade. But in the Marshall–Gilbert area, during a period when you were liable to get killed in the rush if you ever saw a Jap plane in the air, the task was dive bombing. John joined in with a typical enthusiasm, a desire for perfection, and a disregard for the added risk of true dive bombing."[2]

The knack of using fighter aircraft for this purpose required specialized technique, as Haines explains: "With a *Corsair,* you drop the wheels and they act as dive brakes so that you hit terminal velocity at around 400 miles an hour in a vertical position, and you can trim your plane so it flies practically hands-off. Then your flight path is the gun barrel, and you can get pin-point accuracy. John would truly disdain outfits that would try to bomb wheels-up in fighter swoops with increased speeds that diminished their accuracy and forced higher release and high pull-outs."[2]

Of all the missions flown, Haines recalls as perhaps the most important strike from the Marshall–Gilbert area the one that transpired when Allied intelligence decided it was no longer satisfactory to isolate the capital of the Japanese empire in this area, located on Jaluit Atoll. Haines, whose squadron was selected to carry the top punch, relates:

"This target dictated two close-knit twelve-plane sections in the squadron. It was just natural to call John to fly the other one—to lead the other section—because we had to have four squadrons to cover and keep down the enemy fire. When you have that total expenditure, and have that one chance for a total surprise, you can't miss."[2]

Significantly, Haines adds, "When you have something to do where you can't miss, John is the one you select. If John were digging a ditch or if he were President, he would do the job! That's the lesson John's example can teach everyone."[2]

Since Marine Squadron 155 had been overseas a year, in February, 1945, it was ordered back to the States.

An English minister, Canon Wescott, has said, "Great occasions do not make heroes or cowards; they simply unveil them to the eyes of men. Silently and imperceptibly, as we wake or sleep, we grow strong or weak; and at last some crisis shows us for what we have become."[3]

War, with its conditions of crises and stress-creating events, prove a man to the world—and to himself. Confidence is not a structure that can be fabricated entirely within the mind—it gains reinforcement with the accomplishment of deeds.

One of the great contributors to Space Age advancements is Colonel John Paul Stapp, USAF (MC). This doctor, who demonstrated incredible fortitude by riding a rocket sled to such speeds that he subjected himself to peaks of 46 g, expresses personal thoughts of great significance: "Courage for living comes from the realization that every difficulty overcome brings increased equanimity toward lesser distresses that daily beset us. The worst one could be called upon to bear can be no more than what has already been borne, and having survived that, why succumb to lesser ills? From the totality of events, let good experience be refined and accumulated as a memory of happiness and a beginning of wisdom."[4]

When considered from Stapp's standpoint, it becomes clear that there is a salvation to suffering that helps to justify the pain, and a strengthening with trial that tempers capacity. An important phase of John Glenn's training for his orbital mission transpired on flights when his capability was pitted against enemy attack. Without this experience, there could be today a different John Glenn.

Upon Glenn's return to the States, he was assigned to the 9th Marine Aircraft Wing. He soon became heavily involved in flight testing—the phase of his career that subsequently has proved to be of such importance. Accelerated testing was being conducted at the Naval Air Station at Patuxent River, Maryland. Alternating shifts had the responsibility of taking over an airplane and subjecting it to as many hours of flying as was possible. Generally, Glenn flew two 3½-hour hops in the 8-hour shift; his shifts rotated around the clock, and gave him a proportionate share of night flying. His primary aircraft was the F8F Grumman *Bearcat*. Flying with various high-power settings for these long periods of time, simulating fleet usage of the airplane, a year's normal flying was duplicated in three months. Basic weaknesses were readily revealed under such stringent conditions.

At Patuxent, Glenn served with his long-time friend, R. H. Rainforth (now Lieutenant Colonel, USMC). "Glenn, Rainforth, and Miller were known as tremendous 'tigers,' to use the Marine Corps expression of respect for an aviator," says F. K. Coss (now Colonel, USMC, Ret.).

The trio had other nicknames, acquired while living together overseas during World War II, Miller recalls: "Our initials were R. H., J. H., and T. H., and somewhere along the line we picked up the tag of 'Purity Kids' —I suppose because we didn't smoke, and we drank only when it seemed socially required."

But it most certainly is not implied that the trio ever lacked the capacity to have fun. At Patuxent, the married men of the old VMF-155 gang lived with their families at a rambling inn named The Gables. The Glenns affectionately called the place "The Stables." It was located in low country on the Patuxent River, and was surrounded by bays. John Griffith recalls, "One day, several of us decided to go on a picnic. My fiancée, Lorna Bohan, the Glenns, Eva Rainforth (whose husband was on flying duty), and I piled into a rowboat and headed for a nearby island. The girls had planned the menu, and John bought the food at the commissary. However, when the basket was unpacked, the meat for hamburgers was missing—left by accident at the commissary. We substituted cheese, melted over an open fire. Needless to add, John took a lot of ribbing for having forgotten it."

The trip back from the island proved somewhat eventful. Griffith and Glenn each manned an oar on the rather large rowboat, and Griffith confesses, "As boys—and sometimes young men—are apt to do, we started competing. This is not unusual, because all one had to do was pull an oar with an ounce more strength than John was giving, and the fight to show superiority was on, in gay spirits. His wonderful competitive desire to win showed up even in a boat ride! Soon we were both pulling frantically. It all came to a sudden halt when my oar came out of the oarlock and I fell over backward into the bottom of the boat. The hilarious laughter in the boat at eleven at night must have resounded to many of the nearby islands."

Griffith adds, "Great loud laughter is always an important ingredient in any memory of John, because he's certainly a man with whom we all have had wonderful times. And from the competitive aspect, it was not until long after the War was over that I learned John had beaten me in another way. I had been known as a very 'eager' pilot. I took all flights assigned to me and bummed flights from other pilots who didn't want to fly as much as I did. I managed to pile up 53 missions in the Pacific, and this seemed to be as many as anyone could get in that time span. Imagine my surprise to find out recently that John Glenn flew 59 missions!"

Glenn's outstanding record earned him two Distinguished Flying Crosses and ten Air Medals, as a pilot in Marine Fighter Squadron 155, Marine Aircraft Group 31, 4th Marine Aircraft Wing.

At the War's end, Glenn had a major decision to make as to what direction his life should take. From the first period in the Marine Corps, he had chosen the training that would equip him to become an airline pilot. It had always been his father's hope that he would return to New Concord and take over the family business of plumbing contracting. The third alternative was to remain in the service—an opportunity extended to him because of an outstanding record.

There really was never a serious question in Glenn's mind which choice it would be. He savored flying, challenge, adventure. Deep-seated was pride in the prestige of the Corps. This not only was the place he wanted to be, but the place where he should be. His conviction was firm. Haines wrote a letter of recommendation for a regular commission in the Marine Corps, and Glenn was integrated in March, 1946.

For the remainder of that year he was assigned to El Toro in California, serving as Operations Officer of VMF-323. Comments Samuel F. Martin (now Lieutenant Colonel, Division of Aviation, Headquarters, USMC), "John was looked upon by most of his fellow pilots as 'an aviator's aviator.' Although only a Captain at that time, he was respected by us junior officers for both his officer qualities and flying abilities. This was especially apparent in the exacting techniques of carrier qualifications. Whenever John was in the pattern, you could be sure he would fly a 'Roger pass' that would serve as an example for those of us with less experience and considerably less skill."

Glenn earned respect as a flier, and as a man. Those who have known him over a period of years call to mind many incidents indicative of his character. Relates a friend: "John's religious convictions are well known to the country at this time. During World War II, also, he was 'living' his religion. At one of the interminable bull sessions at the BOQ at the Ewa Air Station, Hawaii, an argument among the pilots arose over religion in the squadron. John and one of his close friends maintained that the skipper should conduct religious services, and lead the squadron in prayers.

"Being an agnostic, I rose to the issue and argued heatedly that we would be much better off spending this time in ground and flight training for the battles with the enemy that we expected soon. John's suggestions were never adopted, but it shows his courage in proposing ideas he believes in. And time has proved that John's strong convictions have been important to his career. The tremendous popularity he has enjoyed, his friendly smile and genuine love for his fellow man must certainly be based, in part, on these religious foundations."

December, 1946: destination, China.

Glenn left the States for two years' duty with Marine Aircraft Group 24, 1st Marine Aircraft Wing, to join the Marine Fighter Squadron 218 in Peiping. He became flight officer of the squadron, which had as its duty North China patrol.

Donald L. May (now Major, Personnel Department, Headquarters, USMC) has a clear memory of that period: "I joined the squadron as a brand new second lieutenant fresh from flight training. John Glenn was extremely patient and understanding of my inexperience, and devoted a considerable amount of time both on the ground and in the air explaining flying techniques and correcting my mistakes.

"His easy manner, keen sense of humor, and excellent ability as an informal instructor did much to build my confidence in my flying ability. John 'knew the airplane' better than anyone in the squadron. A question concerning any of the aircraft systems frequently resulted in blackboard diagrams depicting all the components of the system, accompanied by a detailed explanation of the operation of the item in question."

This thorough knowledge was gathered from great application and boundless interest. Haines recalls, "From the beginning of his training, John was interested in engineering. He got his first training in engineering in Squadron 155 under the finest and most practical engineer I ever knew, Bill Lewis—a man who is a story in himself."[2]

If there exists a single thread linking people of achievement, it may well be that they do not waste the commodities of either time or opportunity. They demonstrate unusual facility to glean ultimate benefit from every situation, and to link together the fragments of knowledge from unrelated experiences. Whereas, even a giant brain can become stultified from lack of application, the smallest muscle will expand with use. Discipline, development, and dedication may have a closer tie than mere alliteration.

Those who understand Glenn best will say he is neither a genius nor an "egghead." But, they will qualify significantly, the telling factor is the manner in which Glenn uses the abilities he has. Equipped with the usual virtues and qualities, he has consistently applied them in an extra-usual fashion. The credit that must be acknowledged for this application has dissipated any envy or jealousy that might tend to be incurred in other circumstances.

A great, pervading characteristic of Glenn's is his "common touch." Some Marine buddies would dub him "all-American boy," while others termed him "jug head." Either way, the kinship was there—with pilots, with people, at all times.

One of his most "human" moments, as legend has it, occurred in China.

Glenn had been called back to the States on emergency leave. Annie had been most seriously ill following the birth of their daughter, Carolyn Ann. Upon his return, the squadron had moved to Tsingtao. A number of United States Army personnel stationed there had been allowed to have their families join them. But the Marines, traditionally, because they are considered a "force in readiness," seldom are permitted the encumbrance of families.

It has to be that way. But Marines are still husbands and fathers, and sometimes the missing of wives and children becomes acute. A group of Marines including John, so the story goes, were occupying a table at a joint service dance one night, and were happy for the Army men that their wives and children were present—but a little sorry for themselves because they were alone. Toward the end of the evening, the Marines had eaten many Chinese wafers, each of which contained a marble. The marbles were all accumulated in a hat. Suddenly, with a flick of the wrist, the marbles were rolling all over the dance floor. The party was thrown into a state of slight confusion, and the group of lonely Marines were escorted out. Of course, China is very big and very old. So it may be that this tale was first told of Marco Polo's men.

Families were happily reunited when the Marine Fighter Squadron 218 was transferred to Guam. Quarters were constructed for wives and children to join their husbands. But these "quarters" were something less than elaborate, as Donald May explains: "They were Quonset huts, resurrected from the jungle by Seabees, set up on concrete feet in the housing area, wired and piped. The prospective occupant then supplied his own labor to finish the interior. John, of course, was a participant in this unique dual existence—a professional Marine aviator by day, a wielder of hammer and paintbrush by night."

May continues, "Despite these conditions, a thriving community of wives and children gradually blossomed. I recall that it was a most compatible group of families, due in large part, perhaps, to the close friendship built up between the men while they were in China. Annie and John, with their children, Lyn and David, were integral members of this close community on Guam, and many continuing friendships were established."

In what is a great tribute, Haines reflects upon the Glenns in this vein: "If you had to live the rest of your life on an isolated island, there are few people you really know with whom you could unquestionably live, and live a full and rounded life. Well, John and Annie Glenn are the types with whom you could do this."[2]

Of the millions of words that have been uttered and written about friendship, from Sophocles to Shakespeare and since, none appears to have meaning more pertinent to these times than a thought from Woodrow Wilson: "Friendship is the only cement that will ever hold the world together."[5]

In this era when the seams are rent with rivalry and distrust, the world yet may be humbled into accepting such a simple truth. The reality of space flight has opened vistas into the universe, and implied a unification of the earth's people. The common goal can unify no less solidly than the common enemy. Space flight will surely prove one, and possibly both, instances—unification in search for knowledge of the universe, and for protection of man in this new environment.

John Glenn had many assignments before his venture into space. He knew every dive in Corpus Christi in 1949. He made it his business to learn about them, as methodically as he might memorize readings on an instrument panel, so that he would be better able to fulfill his duties as a Shore Patrol Officer. Men in trouble learned they could get help from Glenn. They also learned the strength of will within this man. He would be no more nor less tolerant of others than of himself. Reaction from others could never be far from the area of respect.

His new assignment brought much kidding from Miller, a native Texan, who accused him of being a displaced Yankee. Glenn responded by sending a letter to Hawaii in which he related a joke to Miller: A Californian and a Floridian were arguing about which of the two states had the best qualities. The man from Florida finally conceded, "Well, I guess we shouldn't be bragging too much, because Texas lies between us and they have a little bit of everything." The man from California thought a moment, then protested, "No, they don't. They don't have the Pacific Ocean." The Floridian responded, "If you will just give them time to dig a ditch and lay a pipe line, and if they can suck as hard as they can blow, they'll also have some of that!"

Glenn completed the course at the Instructors' Advanced Training Unit, Naval Auxiliary Air Station, Cabaniss Field, Corpus Christi, with distinction, and he was retained as a Flight Instructor. Later he was transferred to the Naval Air Station as an Instrument Flight Instructor, and there was reunited in duty with his friend, Miller.

At intervals, the instructors took cross-country flights to retain their proficiency. Miller recalls, "We would leap off for three days at a time, going wherever we could find the worst weather possible. Since we were teaching all-weather flying, this was the best practice."

On one occasion, the men encountered fog that was nearly their undoing. Approaching the field at Biloxi, Mississippi, Glenn was being "talked down" on a ground-controlled approach, GCA. Even Miller, whose confidence in his friend's flying skill was unshakable, grew nervous when they kept dropping and dropping altitude—yet could see absolutely nothing. When the radar operator said they had reached their minimum altitude, he instructed them to pull up if the runway were not in sight.

Glenn circled and again got onto the glide path. They dropped down, down, down. Again the operator instructed a pull-up if the runway were not visible. Glenn kept dropping, watching his instruments. At the intuitive moment, he pulled back on the yoke a little to flare it, and the tires screeched in a perfect landing. Haines, who does not handle words extravagantly, says, "John is a superb pilot."

At the Marine Corps' impressive base at Quantico, Virginia, are several schools for the training of officers. In July, 1951, Glenn attended the

Amphibious Warfare School, and upon completion was retained on the staff of the Commandant, serving in the responsible position as Assistant G-2/G-3.

In his work he encountered primarily aviation problems that were vital to the operation of the Marine Corps schools. One problem which occupied much of his attention was in maintaining reserve air space over Quantico's artillery firing areas. There was constant controversy between the military and civilian personnel on this point. Commercial airlines wanted the freedom to fly over the area, but the Corps required that air space as a range for firing artillery shells in their ground-forces training.

In assignments such as this, where the personal element has figured importantly, Glenn's capability to stand by what he believes to be right, to maintain respect, yet to "get along with people" has been evident. As modern flight and modern communications are bringing peoples into ever closer contact, such qualities are a particularly desirable lubricant.

Civilization seemed to be surging forward. In 1948, the giant 200-inch telescope at Palomar opened an extended avenue into the universe, with its capability to peer 1000 million light years into space. In 1949, the Nobel Prize for Physics was presented to Hideki Yukawa for his theoretical work on the meson. But on June 25, 1950, bright hope was dimmed. People everywhere looked at their atlases to see where the 38th Parallel crossed Korea, and the United Nations took decisive action against the aggression.

Glenn was not ordered to duty in Korea until February, 1953—yet even with that late entry, he still accumulated the remarkable record of flying 90 combat missions. Holding the rank of major, he was first assigned to Marine Fighter Squadron 311, Marine Aircraft Group 33.

Relates F. K. Coss (now Colonel, USMC, Ret.), who was the Commanding Officer of the 311th: "At the time John joined, our jet fighter-bomber squadron was running a full schedule of strikes every day. Morale was very high and we had a collection of experienced pilots. Our Modex Number (Navy tail number) was WL. From that, we were called the 'Willing Lovers,' and all wore sky blue scarfs polka-dotted with half-dollar-sized red hearts."

With many friends in the squadron, Glenn was enthusiastically welcomed aboard, and immediately put on the flight schedule, flying F9F5 Grumman *Pantherjets*. Coss says, "Before his initial area check-outs were completed, he was assigned to lead my second section on a division strike. I had an engine malfunction shortly after climb-out. The normal procedure would have been to abort the whole flight, but I left the option up to John, and he unhesitatingly requested permission to lead the strike. Though we had inexperienced lieutenants on our wings, the mission was carried out to perfection. This combat lead was thrust upon him suddenly and unexpectedly. But John was complete master of the situation."

Thereby qualified immediately as a flight leader, he subsequently effected many devastating strikes. Ted Williams, the former Red Sox left fielder, was Glenn's wing man during part of this period. Even the intrepid Williams was abashed at the spirit Glenn displayed in his flying, for he declared, "The man is crazy."[6]

Coss endeavored to set a reasonably sane pace, he explains: "In the 'Willing Lovers,' I had a written policy that essentially stated that no North Korean target in itself was worth the life of an American pilot or an aircraft, both of whom could return again and again on repeated strikes. When the 'calculated risk' position was reached, the pilot was to take appropriate action to save his life and preserve his plane.

"John allowed his aggressiveness to exceed this policy on one mission, however. A machine gunner fired on him at low altitude. He saw the gun and whipped around in a low-level attack. His strafing attack destroyed the machine gun, but at the instant of passing, John took a 90mm shell in his airplane's tail section when it was about 15 feet altitude. He told me later that for a second or two he was sure he was going to 'buy the farm,' but finally succeeded in hauling the nose up and returned the badly-shot-up bird to base."

Coss admits, "I'm certain that I gave him a bad time over risking his aircraft and his valuable hide on such a foolhardy venture. This is one of the 'joys' of being a squadron commander, for I well remembered other such actions that did not turn out so fortunately."

There were many "hairy" episodes during Glenn's Korean tour. One of the Marine Corps' famed photographs was taken by Sergeant Curt Giese in Korea on March 25, 1953. With the caption, "Clobbered in Korea," it showed Glenn standing beside his *Pantherjet* after a low-flying bombing mission. The airplane had been sieved with 375 bullet holes, and a gaping section—which appeared large enough to accommodate a basketball —had been ripped out of his tail section. But the photo shows Glenn's countenance as confident and smiling. "He got his target," the caption confirmed.

Across his jet was inscribed "Lyn, Annie, Dave." In the letters he wrote home to them, he related in a detached and somewhat poetic vein how the bullets sparkled when they hit the airplane. He had many opportunities to observe.

For Glenn's actions in the 63 missions he flew with VMF-311 from February until May, 1953, he was awarded a third Distinguished Flying Cross and six Air Medals. Subsequently, he was selected as an exchange pilot to the Fifth Air Force. With the 25th Fighter Squadron, 51st Fighter Interceptor Wing, he flew an F-86 North American *Sabre* up along the Yalu River.

On one mission, his wing man got badly shot up. With the remainder of the squadron gone, Glenn successfully protected him against six attacking MIG fighters. It has been evident that within Glenn is an instinct, more forceful than any that could be implanted with teaching or indoctrination of Corps spirit. It has surmounted even the powerful drive toward self-preservation, when supreme action could mean the saving of another's life.

This was demonstrated most incredibly when Glenn's Air Force Commanding Officer, Lieutenant Colonel Giraudo, was shot down in enemy territory. Glenn "capped him," stayed over him and protected him, until the last possible instant that his airplane had sufficient remaining fuel to gain altitude and get back to base; he made it only by dead-sticking it part of the way. The moment his fuel-dry craft had stopped rolling on the runway, he jumped out and clambered into a fresh airplane. He zoomed back to the spot he had been forced to leave, but too late. Giraudo had been captured. (He was subsequently returned during the prisoner of war exchange known as "Operation Big Switch.")

Glenn was awarded for this effort, which was most certainly "beyond the call of duty," and for his destroying of three MIG's in nine days, his fourth Distinguished Flying Cross, and his seventeenth and eighteenth Air Medals; these were presented by the Air Force.

Although personally Glenn appears easygoing, Coss speaks of a deeper quality, "John has a grim determination, and is fully capable of exerting tremendous pressures on both his superiors and subordinates in a quiet, but effective, manner." Haines fills in another aspect by saying, "John is daring to the ultimate, when it is warranted. Otherwise, he is solid in discipline and not at all a 'wild blue yonder' type."[2]

Balance for this great seriousness is not lacking. If there is any activity that may rival flying in Glenn's preference, it would be singing! Donald May relates of his days in VMF-218 in China, "John was the accepted leader of the 'Little Madrigal Society,' a self-styled harmonic group consisting of any squadron mates present. We harmonized, composed parodies, sang the 'good old songs,' and generally provided ourselves with many hilarious moments of relaxation."

The habit continued in Korea, as Coss can attest: "Almost every evening, John could be found 'harmonizing' in someone's hut with Joe Mitchell, Mark Jones, Ted Williams, Jerry Hendershot, or Hal Newendorp. He knew every song in creation, it seemed. One of his favorites was 'Mrs. Murphy's

Lye Soap'—a very jovial song. We had a lot of good records which John loved and played regularly."

With this long-standing penchant, it is not surprising that Glenn, teamed with Eddie Hodges, won a very substantial cash prize on the television program, "Name that Tune." A large share of the money was spent on a beautiful home organ for Annie—who is an accomplished musician.

Glenn's "home life," which had undergone long periods of interruption during World War II, overseas duty, and Korea, became more stable with his assignment early in 1954 to the Navy Test Pilot Training School at the Naval Air Station, Patuxent River.

A part of his work at this installation was in optimizing the flight path to get the maximum altitude out of an airplane on a climb. This testing entailed much zoom-flight work, and a curiously interesting thought kept coming into Glenn's mind—if only he had the power to continue that zoom into a loop! But he did not have in mind a loop like one performs with an airplane. Rather, his dreaming was of earth-looping—orbiting. In his orderly, appraising mind he conjured just how he would feel to keep going out and out. The seed was there, taking firm root, toward the day when this powerful inclination would blossom into achievement.

Flying did not consume all of Glenn's time at Patuxent. Water sports had always held a special interest, so he built a home in Town Creek, on a little lagoon where he could dock his motorboat. A fun-filled routine was soon established. As soon as he arrived home from work, the family would head for the boat and some pre-dinner water-skiing. Glenn quickly became proficient at it, as might be expected.

The trait was pronounced. Whatever the activity, Glenn always excelled. When the normal competition between organized groups was not present, he created it from another source. Hal W. Vincent (now Major, USMC, Executive Officer, Marine All-Weather Fighter Squadron 314, El Toro Base) attended the Test Pilot Training School at the same time, and clearly recalls, "John typified most Marines in that he is a terrific competitor. He scrambles for everything and never cares to be topped. When the units there chose their 'best' men to test a new high-performance jet, the F8U Chance-Vought *Crusader,* John was chosen to represent Armament Test. In view of their later association, it is interesting that Al Shepard was also among the group; he and I represented Flight Test." In Glenn's testing of the ordnance capability of the weapons system of this airplane, problems were encountered. He flew the airplane to Edwards Air Force Base, to take advantage of their unequalled test facilities, and solutions were soon found.

Glenn's association with the *Crusader* continued after he had been transferred to the Bureau of Aeronautics, Navy Department, in Washington. As Project Officer on the F8U in the Fighter Design Branch, he influenced some of the changes in design and characteristics of this shipboard fighter. It is noteworthy that the elapsed time from its first flight until its full acceptance for operational service was a remarkably short period.

Glenn's first wide publicity came on July 16, 1957, with Operation Bullet. It has been said that he was selected to make this first supersonic transcontinental flight. More accurately, it should be stated that it was he who proposed the flight—not once, but four times. Because of his perseverance and detailed preparation, the Navy and the Defense Department finally agreed to the flight. For its time, it was most advanced; the average speed at which Glenn flew the F8U far exceeded the muzzle velocity of a .45 caliber bullet. Glenn selected the name. Operation Bullet, feeling it would be a comparison of speed which the taxpayer could readily understand.

In this achievement was evinced his strong point—advanced planning. At least 90 per cent of his effort was directed at the meticulous working out of every detail. Course and fuel consumption were figured precisely, every sensible short cut was utilized, and a single radio frequency was selected on which he would receive all stations en route.

In the mechanics of its execution, the flight was so demanding that Glenn said it was more like sitting inside an IBM calculator than sitting in a cockpit. Acting as his own navigator, check points were taken every 3½ minutes. He devised an ingenious "how goes it" chart to keep a running tally on location, speed, altitude, and fuel.

It was necessary to refuel three times—at Albuquerque, New Mexico; Olathe, Kansas; and Indianapolis, Indiana. For this critical procedure, he had to reduce speed and descend from 50,000 to 25,000 feet at the moment designated for the rendezvous, and approach the tankers at an exact 205 knots. Should the approach speed not be accurate, the drogue trailing from the tanker would damage the F8U by oscillating or by wrapping around the wing. If the withdrawal were not equally exact and gentle, the hose might be pulled off and remain attached to the fighter.

Cool, steady, practiced. It went as planned, with only 20 seconds wasted at the first refueling juncture. The second was perfect. The third proved Glenn's wisdom in taking precautions. He had arranged to have two tankers in the air, in the event rendezvous with the first was not achieved. Over Indianapolis, the primary tanker was six miles off position; his rendezvous had to be with the secondary tanker, which could pump fuel at only half rate. He thereby had 1000 pounds of fuel less than planned upon for the completion of his dash. The accuracy with which Glenn figured his speed—hence consumption—for the remainder of the flight is indicated by the fact that he reached Floyd Bennett Field in New York with only enough fuel remaining to make one circle of the airport.

The flight distance of 2,445.9 miles from Los Alamitos Naval Air Station in California had been made in 3 hours, 23 minutes, and 8.4 seconds, at an average speed of 725.55 mph. Glenn was most particular that other information beyond such statistics be conveyed—for instance, that regarding the splendid cooperation this flight represented between the Navy, the Marine Corps, and the Air Force. He stressed that great credit should be given to Rear Admiral Thurston B. Clark, USN, who had supervised the operation. Photographs of the entire continent provided a unique supersonic view of the United States.

On Glenn's 36th birthday, two days after the flight, he was presented with his fifth Distinguished Flying Cross by the Honorable Thomas S. Gates, Jr., Secretary of the Navy.

When the new airport at Columbus, Ohio, was dedicated, Glenn's former Commanding Officer, "Pete" Haines—who was then retired and living in Columbus—invited him to be present and represent the Corps. His many friends were pleased to have him back for this visit, tremendously proud of the record he had made—and, most of all, happy to see that he was still the same John Glenn they had known.

Labor Day traditionally is "Potato Day" in New Concord. This celebration is wholesome Americana, rich in family tradition, and features special competitions for the school children. On this occasion an award was set up in honor of their leading citizen. The John Glenn Cup is now presented each Potato Day to the high school student who excels in mathematics.

John Glenn had always radiated optimism and high spirits to his friends. For that reason Hal Vincent was concerned about a conversation that they had at a test pilots' reunion early in 1959. Vincent recalls, "John and I found a quiet corner away from the bedlam of the party and had a long talk. He was stuck at a desk in Washington and was quite discouraged. He said that he didn't have enough education to really make a go of it in the service. He felt that he was getting old, and that as much as he loved research and development work, he could not do much more of it because it would hurt his chances for promotion. He has always been so enthused and happy that it was quite a surprise to see him so down.

"I assured him that with his ability he would make it, and that I thought a break was coming in the Corps' method of selection where someone with his personal qualifications could be selected for promotion earlier. I thought to myself that here was a man who had to get ahead—it was too hard to have drive like his and not really be given the shot at something good."

Vincent was prophetic. It happened in the spring of 1959.

When Haines heard the news, he rushed home to tell his wife, Pendery, that a Marine had been chosen as one of the Astronauts! She replied, matter-of-factly, "It's John Glenn." Anyone who knew him recognized he was the obvious choice from the Corps. He had been an outstanding member of an outstanding service.

Glenn moved from one career phase to another with the Astronaut assignment, but many ties and supports have carried over. Coss points out, "Our Commandant, General Shoup, the 'old tiger,' unmistakably sits on top of this young breed of 'cats.' He can, and does, teach them a trick or two, and has given John magnificent encouragement, then moved 'out of the limelight' in John's finest hour. There also has been inspiration to every flier in the person of the man who is perhaps the greatest of all Marine Corps aviators, Colonel Marion E. Carl (now Deputy Chief of Staff of Aviation, Headquarters, USMC). His utter fearlessness and technical competence are the driving force that the younger aviators try to emulate."

There had been abundant tradition, example, and sky-blazing in the flying career that Glenn had followed. But in moving from air into space, he became the pioneer. He would "write the book." Yet he almost didn't get the chance.

Glenn had not graduated from college. He was 37 years old. These were considered two strikes against him, in the initial standards set up by the group which was screening Astronaut candidates. But even three strikes would not have downed Glenn. Obstacles merely heightened the challenge. He had worked with tremendous diligence for all of his adult life. Suddenly, within his grasp, was something for which even a much lesser man would have volunteered his life.

Space flight. Glenn recognized the feel of a technological miracle, the taste of opportunity, the sound of one of the greatest advancements of civilization. This was man breaking free from the earth—a dream suddenly reduced to a tangible concept. He said, ". . . the Wright Brothers stood at Kitty Hawk about fifty years ago, with Orville and Wilbur pitching a coin to see who was going to shove the other one off the hill down there. I think we stand on the verge of something as big and as expansive as that was fifty years ago."[1]

On April 9, 1959, in speaking to the press on the occasion of the first announcement by the National Aeronautics and Space Administration of the Astronaut selection, Glenn said: "I think we are very fortunate that we have, should we say, been blessed with the talents that have been picked for something like this. . . . Every one of us would feel guilty, I think, if we didn't make use of our talents in volunteering for something that is as important as this is to our country and the world in general right now."[1]

With the human quality that Glenn evidences when he feels that perhaps his earnestness has made it appear that he is taking himself too seriously, he quipped, "I got on this project because it probably would be the nearest to Heaven I will ever get, and I wanted to make the most of it."[1]

The screening process had in itself been quite an experience. These seven men had been subjected to the most rigid physiological and psychological examinations that experts could contrive.

For seven and a half days and three evenings, the Astronauts had been probed, pricked, and thumped by the expert staff of the Lovelace Clinic in Albuquerque, New Mexico. In addition to a complete medical history, examinations extended to these general areas: hematology and pathology, roentgenology, ophthalmology, otolaryngology, cardiology, neurology and myology, general internal medicine, and related laboratory studies.

The group then was taken to the Wright Air Development Center Aeromedical Laboratories, Dayton, Ohio, to continue the screening with a personality evaluation, followed by tests under conditions of stress, fatigue, accelerative forces, equilibrium, vibration, high-energy noise, low barometric pressure, and thermal stress.

Of the 110 military test pilots who were first considered, of the 32 men who underwent the extensive examinations, the crack seven emerged. They have since that time experienced the sharp glare of the limelight in their every action, their lives being veritable "open books"—with pictures! For those readers who preferred to be "lookers" and garner their space indoctrination the easy way, *Life* magazine provided a running account of the Astronauts' training, their thoughts, their wives, their children, their parents.

The Project was given the name of *Mercury*. In Roman mythology Mercury was the herald and messenger of the gods. In modern parlance, it has been the prime activity of the Space Task Group. When this Group was created in October, 1958, Robert R. Gilruth was named Project Director. Gilruth possessed a background in aeronautical engineering which represented some of the finest work to be produced by the predecessor to NASA, the NACA (National Advisory Committee for Aeronautics). Since before the existence of the Space Task Group, Gilruth and some highly skilled associates had been working on plans for a manned space-flight program.

The Group headquartered at the Langley Research Center in Virginia, starting with a nucleus of less than 50 men. Their aim: to create the equipment and train the men for successful space flight! Not only were top civilian personnel involved, but medical and technical men from the military services also were included. Every progressive phase of the program has been critical; but without the solid and technically feasible foundation which these men first laid, the entire mission would have ended as ashes upon a smoldering launching pad.

In aviation's early period the pilots' general attitude toward the engineers was, "You build 'em, we'll fly 'em." The fallacy was soon recognized, for the man who best knows the problems is the man in the cockpit. However, integration of the pilot and the craft had never before been as complete as in *Project Mercury.*

Each Astronaut was assigned a special area of responsibility: Carpenter, communications and navigation; Cooper, Redstone booster; Grissom, automatic and manual attitude-control system; Schirra, environmental control system and pressure suit; Shepard, range, tracking, and recovery operations; Slayton, Atlas booster; Glenn, crew-space layout.

Explaining his specialty in more detail, Glenn said, "This involves the pilot's working space. It is the placement of controls, switches, instrumentation, presentation of all the information in readable or workable order, and arranged in such a fashion that he can function in the best manner possible."

Glenn emphasized the latter point, "The pilot's ability to function varies greatly with the manner in which the panel is laid out. This is a direct carry-over from our work with airplanes, where we have found that there is a big difference in the efficiency with which a pilot can work from one cockpit to another. It works the same as for a housewife in the proper layout of a kitchen. Both involve the least waste motion, and the most intelligent use of space and equipment."

But however clear-cut the aim, the attainment was not simple. Glenn says: "Seven men are involved in this crew-space layout, which makes it difficult—just as if it were seven women planning a kitchen. There are inevitably as many different ideas on how it should be done as there are people involved. But these differences of opinion have gradually resolved, compromises have been effected, so that agreement has been reached as to the placement of the instruments, controls, and switches."

It was evident that even though nominally each Astronaut was assigned a different area, there was great interchange of ideas. Also, their opinions were closely correlated with the technical staff, as Glenn explains: "Now we don't maintain sole responsibility for these areas, but it is our responsibility within our group of seven to work closely with the engineers on these particular areas and then report back to our group."[7]

Throughout every phase of the development of *Project Mercury,* Glenn has stressed the cooperation, the teamwork—not just between seven men, but in the broad concept of all the hundreds and thousands who have become involved. In speaking of the focus of attention upon the Astronauts, he said, ". . . we're a little like the elephant and the mouse walking across a bridge. After they get across, the mouse looks up and says, 'We sure shook that bridge, didn't we?' Well, it's like our position. We're receiving a lot of the attention on this thing but we are only the focal point . . . It's a tremendous team effort for the country, and we want to give credit for this as much as we possibly can to all of the people who are working behind us to make this thing possible."[7]

Basic conditioning for the Astronauts was of prime importance, Glenn relates: "One of the parts of the program that was left pretty much up to the individuals when we started this, was the physical fitness part. We were asked when we started whether we wanted to have a daily calisthenics period . . . It was decided at that time that every man would be left on his own as far as keeping himself in good shape."[7]

Ever the self-disciplinarian, Glenn informed the makers of the contour couch that he would trim down from his weight when entering the program, 210 pounds, to 165 pounds, and to make the couch accordingly. With a rigorous routine that included a daily run which he gradually increased to five miles, he took his weight down to 168 pounds.

Beyond this basic good-health routine came specialized requirements. Here, just as in the categorizing of the equipment phase, the Astronauts were figuratively dissected. A training program was instigated to prepare each portion of the anatomy for the mission ahead. New senses were acquired, old sensations quelled. Whirling, rolling, spinning, floating—coordination of mind and body were practiced and perfected.

Glenn moved into bachelor quarters at Langley and went home only weekends, so that he would have more time to concentrate upon the routine. There were devices for static training, dynamic training, survival training, and mission training. The giant centrifuge at the Navy Aviation Medical Acceleration Laboratory at Johnsville, Pennsylvania, accustomed the Astronauts to coping with heavy g loads. Glenn relates, "This was very interesting, especially in the working out of some of your own body problems—of how to tense your body, or what method is best used to enable your body to take the high g loads. We found there was a definite learning curve. At the end of runs, we were able to considerably increase our ability in this field, and take higher g with a lot less strain."

A particularly vital training device was the flight-procedures trainer. This tremendously complicated device consists of a mock-up of the capsule, with all systems connected to control panels and computers. Missions can be flown, emergencies can be simulated, proficiency tested and expanded—all within the trainer.

The ALFA (Air Lubricated Free Attitude) Trainer consists of a couch so perfectly balanced on a cushion of compressed air that it is practically frictionless. Moving freely on three axes, it provides the means for important practice in keeping the capsule at the proper orbital attitude.

The most characteristic of space environments, weightlessness, can be simulated only for periods of time ranging up to about one minute while an aircraft is flying the hump in a parabolic curve. An approximation of weightlessness can be experienced underwater. Both for this sensation, and for the necessary conditioning for the capsule's water landing, the Astronauts engaged in extensive practice with SCUBA (Self-Contained Underwater Breathing Apparatus).

The opportunity for some of the underwater practice came in September, 1959, when the seven men visited the Convair Astronautics plant in San Diego, manufacturer of the *Atlas* booster. Glenn's wartime buddy, John Griffith (now an engineer with Convair), had arranged the skin-diving expedition in the Pacific. But he did not have the cooperation of the elements, as he relates: "The weather and water conditions were terrible. After a full discussion, however, the Astronauts thought they would still like to go, feeling the experience would be useful. With their escorts, they ventured into the rough ocean to swim along the bottom with no more than 2-foot visibility."

Griffith continues, "After the swim, John came up to my house to meet my four children. He was the kindest, most friendly hero they will ever meet. After his return to the east, he wrote each one of them a personal letter."

Glenn has never grown so busy or preoccupied that he fails to extend kindness and appreciation to those around him. Each man has many facets —many ways in which he is viewed by those around him. The fabric of this Astronaut stands up under inspection from any angle.

The pastor of The Little Falls Church in Arlington, Virginia, Reverend Frank A. Erwin, reminded his congregation, "We remember John speaking as one of us on Laymen Sunday two years ago. The Boy Scouts remember John as the father of one of the boys. Our young people remember him as a counselor, teacher, and water-ski instructor at our first senior-high camp-out. The people in his block know him as the fellow down the street. And his children think of him first of all as 'Dad.' At our worship services he simply occupies another seat. It is inspiring, however, to know that he occupies it so faithfully and genuinely."

This humanity and humility is indeed an important balance within the character of Glenn, important to offset a drive that otherwise would be utterly consuming.

Mrs. Tom Miller—whose basis for comparison is well grounded, considering her husband's outstanding record—has observed strong traits in Glenn over the 20-year period of the two families' friendship: "John is a real student—of anything he goes about. I'm sure John reviewed in his own mind how he would feel if he were the first American to orbit—and I don't mean that he would study just the flight routine, but everything else entailed. I'm sure he had thought a great deal about what it meant to him, and what he should say. From the beginning he even prepared his family by explaining the entire project in technical yet understandable terms. Then to keep them informed, and give them a feeling of participation, he brought home as much information as possible. John doesn't wait until an event transpires—he is always thinking way ahead."

Beyond spending the work weeks away from his family, Glenn spent countless weekends on efforts of his own devising for additional training. Hour after hour after hour he would ride the simulator, practicing again and again every detail, until reactions became as automatic as breathing. He practiced his voice reporting, repeating and repeating each thing to be said during each second of the flight. It was no happenstance that during his actual orbit his tone was sure and easy in making such reports as cabin pressure, fuel, oxygen, and voltage readings. It was the result of endless hours of tedious drill.

Glenn is convinced that these repetitive training processes had tremendous effect on the outcome of his mission, and feels this is one of the most important areas upon which future space men should concentrate. Whether he flies additional space missions will be determined by Bob Gilruth. But one thing is sure—Glenn's will be a strong voice in establishing requirements and procedures for follow-on Astronauts. In the highly selective occupation of earth orbiting, Glenn is one of the few experts.

In the Astronaut group, he was in company with six other strong and determined men. The question was repeatedly put to all of them: "Do you want to be the first? Why?"

Glenn once replied in this manner: "Any time you build up a group such as this to a big mission, of course each would like to be first. But there are going to be a number of space shots, and we certainly plan to be taking part in them, and we are sure that we will all get a chance to make space flights before we are through with the program."

On that same occasion, Schirra gave an incontrovertible reply: "The only comment I could make about being first is that this is the normal way of life for all of us in this country. If you want to come in last, I think it would be much harder to think up answers for that."[7]

If competitiveness is a tendency for most people, it is a dictate for a Marine Corps officer—one with a background of seizing challenge and refusing defeat, whatever the situation.

In this context must be considered the events that transpired during the early part of 1961. On January 31, the cocky and personable chimp, Ham, delighted the nation and reassured the *Project Mercury* crew by making a successful sub-orbital flight—despite malfunctions that gave him a momentary build-up to 18 g, and propelled him at a speed of 5800 mph instead of the programmed 4200 mph.

This signified that the moment was approaching for the first manned shot, designated MR-3 (Mercury-Redstone). When it blasted off from Launch Pad 5, which of the seven proficient men would be aboard? Guesses to this question started appearing in print. The characteristic of which the seasoned press man seems most proud is his impatience. Never content to await developments, he is ahead of the race, waiting at the finish line, predicting who will win.

From seven, the contenders were narrowed down to three on February 21, 1961, when it was officially announced that Glenn, Shepard, and Grissom would enter special training toward the final stages of preparedness at Cape Canaveral for the first flight. The attention of the world was riveted on the trio as fixedly as upon the three hats upon a magician's table. From under which would the rabbit appear?

Opinion was rife. *Space-Aviation* Editor Marvin Miles echoed the prevalent conjecture when he wrote on March 12, 1961: "Marine Stands Out as Astronaut Choice."[8] Miles' article continued, "We say this because Glenn, at 39 the eldest of the group, has always been the father of the seven-man team, a leader without appointment, an officer particularly respected among the astronauts—and apparently all others in the *Mercury* program—for his personality, his dedication, his skill and his experience."[8]

A few hours before the first MR-3 launch attempt on May 2, 1960, the formal announcement came. Commander Alan B. Shepard, Jr., was designated as the first American to make a sub-orbital flight. Glenn would be his back-up.

The other six Astronauts plunged into a highly geared work routine to give all possible support to Shepard. After the late start which our space program had undergone, after the tormenting problems and delays which the perversities of such advanced technology had wrought, at last the moment had come. On May 5, 1961, Shepard soared aloft in a spectacularly successful flight! While Americans were still flushed with this triumph, plans were in motion for the second flight—a repeat of the sub-orbital.

Glenn knew that he would repeat his back-up function, and that Grissom would make the second sub-orbital flight. The press did not yet know this. So in the strange reverse-effect that sometimes occurs, some reporters who favored Glenn made it even more difficult for him by again speculating that he would be chosen.

Tom Miller, as his long-time friend and next-door neighbor in Arlington, relates, "This really hit John with a blow. He had his sights set on being the first man into space. We had talked about this many times, and we disagreed about it. He thought the first shot in space was going to be the most important, and I always felt that the first orbital would have more meaning. At the time, he couldn't see this. When he came home weekends, he wouldn't go anywhere. He didn't want to see any of his friends, because he actually felt that he had failed, personally."

Miller reflects on this strong reaction, and continues, "If there is any fault that I think John has, it is that he drives so very hard to reach a goal, then is terribly upset if he doesn't make it. I think this is characteristic of anyone who is extremely enthused and determined—it is awfully hard for them to lose."

Ken Coss, another staunch friend who was also living in Arlington, shared Miller's concern for Glenn: "I honestly believe that it was the greatest setback he ever had in his life. We all encouraged him to the utmost, but no one will ever know the mental anguish that he went through at that time. Even then, I felt he was being saved for bigger things, which would more than justify his being skipped over the first two times."

Disappointment, always, is proportional with desire. The one who never wants much never misses much. Those who strain every fiber to climb high toward a dream have far to fall in a downward plunge. But an individual's victory over rampant emotion is the hallmark of maturity. Intellectually, Glenn won the battle over the only opponent any man ever really has—himself.

After several weekends of declining the Millers' invitation to go to Quantico for some water skiing, he accepted. His smile was not quite easy, and his jokes seemed a little forced, but Glenn had come alive again. He appeared to accept what he could not understand.

Was this the final test for the man who was to be America's first man to orbit the earth? Was this last trial the climax to a lifetime of study and experience, and three years of slavish application to every phase of the *Project Mercury* training? Perhaps. And Glenn found his way out of the wilderness—in considerably less than 40 days.

On November 29, 1961, Glenn telephoned Annie to tell her the wonderful news that he had been selected for the big flight! Having shared his ordeal, her elation at this development was great. Coss points out that this tiny lady with huge eyes and a quiet manner is in herself most remarkable. "I have tried to be with Annie when I thought she might like reassurance. I can vouch for the fact that she has all the finest attributes—and is quite deserving of a place alongside some of our greatest women. It takes big words to describe my feelings toward both John and Annie. I do not believe this experience and honor could have come to a finer couple. I think you would get the same reaction if you canvassed the entire Marine Corps."

The mighty push for the orbital mission was on. First scheduled for December 20, 1961, the flight underwent ten agonizing postponements. Irresponsible unofficial statements were made about the adverse effects that the delays might be having on Glenn—and hence, the mission as well. Being human, the man would naturally have reactions to having spent hours within the *Mercury* capsule, only to have the flight scrubbed. But being John Glenn, it would take more than frustration to work negatively. He said, "All the members of the *Mercury* team have been working toward this space-flight opportunity for a long time. We have not dreaded it; we have looked forward to it. After three years we cannot be unduly concerned by a few delays."[9]

Even the youngest member of the family, Lyn, became philosophical on the day the clouds conspired to keep *Friendship 7* earthbound: "Oh, well, it was just a dry run. My dad always tells me, 'There'll always be another day.' "[10]

That "other day," February 20, 1962, started off ominously cloudy, but from the moment Glenn was awakened at 2:20 A.M. by Dr. William K. Douglas until he disappeared within the capsule, he radiated confidence. The feeling spread in all directions from Launching Pad 14, and seeped throughout the sea of 50,000 people who packed the beaches near the Cape.

Even the various "holds" did not dim the hope; the technical malfunctions were important but not critical—they included the replacement of a radar tracking device in the *Atlas* guidance system, the replacement of a broken microphone bracket in Glenn's helmet, a broken bolt on the capsule hatch, a frozen liquid-oxygen valve, and additional time for fueling the bird. A final 2-minute hold was for a check of the network computer at Bermuda.

Even these final aggravating delays served to remind the listening and watching world that they were confidants in the greatest technological feat that the United States had yet attempted. The words of Vice President Lyndon B. Johnson underscored this fact: "We have the strength to demonstrate our successes as well as our failures, and the courage to accept the risks."[11]

The Astronaut who lay strapped on a foam contour couch was calmly occupied with the intricate countdown procedure. Glenn's great composure seemed baffling to most persons. Of this he says, "People have repeatedly asked whether I was afraid before the mission. Humans always have fear of an unknown situation—this is normal. The important thing is what we do about it. If fear is permitted to become a paralyzing thing that interferes with proper action, then it is harmful. The best antidote to fear is to know all we can about a situation. It is lack of knowledge which often misleads people when they then try to imagine the feelings of an astronaut about to launch. During the years of preparation for *Project Mercury,* the unknown areas have been shrunk, we feel, to an acceptable level."[9] Proof of his conviction was to be seen on the wavy lines of a chart. They revealed that even in the blast-off, his pulse was less than 110!

The final message to Glenn from the blockhouse was not a technical reading. It was words from his fellow Astronaut and very good friend, Scott Carpenter: "May the good Lord ride with you all the way."

The *Atlas* booster carried its human cargo aloft with a fiery magnificence, spilling a white trail in the cobalt Florida sky. As eyes were turned to this rising man-made comet, Glenn's view was of the receding earth, which he was watching by means of a little window mirror. The intense vibration he felt just after lift-off reduced in about 15 seconds, then rose again at maximum *q* (maximum aerodynamic pressure), which was approximately one minute.

The muffled roar of the mighty *Atlas* engines was constant until BECO (Booster Engine Cut-Off) at 2 minutes and 9.6 seconds. His protection in event of malfunction during launch, the escape tower, jettisoned 23 seconds later. Instead of having any adverse reaction to the mounting g forces, Glenn recalled Carpenter's comment that it should feel good to go in straight-line acceleration, rather than circles as they had done on the centrifuge. Even the maximum 7.7 g which he took—rendering his body weight almost 1300 pounds—presented no difficulties. Only one unexpected experience marked this period—an oscillating, springboard effect occurred as the thin-skinned *Atlas* booster grew empty of the stabilizing fuel.

Meanwhile, back at the Cape . . .

Educated ears and eyes were following *Friendship 7*'s trajectory to a degree which could be achieved only with giant electronic brains. Data from the *Mercury* Control Center at the Cape, and from the first tracking station* at Bermuda were funneling into the Computing and Communications Center at NASA's Goddard Space Flight Center, near Greenbelt, Maryland. Through information being received regarding the velocity which *Friendship 7* had attained, a vital decision had to be rendered within a 30-second time span: were all conditions "go" to insert it into orbit? Glenn heard the decision at 5 minutes and 30 seconds: "You have a 'go,' at least seven orbits!"[9]

Other data, also, had been computed. Though Glenn had just been put into orbit, Bermuda was able to give him the time at which the retrorockets would have to be fired in order to get down out of orbit and land in the mid-Atlantic recovery area. Astronaut Gus Grissom, capsule communicator from Bermuda, relayed the message: "End of mission is 04:32:47."[9] (The data which the computers at Goddard supplied were so incredibly accurate that the time of firing the retrorockets was corrected by only 2 seconds during the entire mission.)

* Sixteen ground stations comprised the *Mercury* Tracking Network. They were: Atlantic Missile Range (Cape Canaveral); Bermuda; Mid-Atlantic Ship; Canary Islands; Kano, Nigeria; Zanzibar; Indian Ocean Ship; Muchea, Australia; Woomera, Australia; Canton Island; Hawaii; Southern California; Guaymas, Mexico; White Sands, New Mexico; Corpus Christi, Texas; and Eglin, Florida.

Grissom then reminded Glenn to begin a check of his attitude-control system; unless the capsule were positioned exactly—with its head-shield pointed down—as it began its descent, it would incinerate in seconds. Glenn reported: "Working just like clockwork on the control check, and it went through just about like the Procedures Trainer runs."[9] The hours of drill were paying dividends. The 164 dials, meters, switches, and levers of the instrument panel were as familiar to Glenn as the palm of his hand.

At 25 minutes he performed another test—on a system that later saved the mission from disaster. Glenn tested his ability to "fly-by-wire"—to take over the manual control of his space craft from the automatic system. It was successful, as Glenn related: "Maintaining orientation was no problem, but I believe that the pilot automatically relies much more completely on vision in space than he does in an airplane, where gravity cues are available. The success with which I was able to control the space craft at all times was, to me, one of the most significant features of the flight."[9]

In all of the mission planning, the paramount consideration was the Astronaut's safety and well-being. Emergency rescue teams were stationed at Cape Canaveral, the Bahamas, Hawaii, Bermuda, and the Azores. Some of the nation's finest medical specialists were on stand-by to be rushed by jet to any spot, had an accident occurred. The Air Force had readied a force of 63 crack divers of their para-rescue team, in the event Glenn needed attention on his mid-Atlantic landing. Quantities of blood of the Astronaut's type were stored on ships in the rescue area.

The doctors who were stationed around the world keeping closest possible watch on Glenn's physical responses had the authority to terminate the flight, if instruments had given readings which indicated a serious condition to be developing. Flight Surgeon William K. Douglas, Glenn's shadow and medical mentor during his entire period of preparation, remained at *Mercury* Control at the Cape to interpret the in-flight readings.

The first medical check from a tracking station occurred at about 21 minutes after lift-off when *Friendship 7* approached Kano, Nigeria.

The sensing devices attached to Glenn's body relayed information via an oscillograph to the doctor at that station, Colonel Vance H. Marchbanks, Jr. He relates: "This was my first experience in reading an electrocardiogram under such conditions in space. I had been studying Glenn's ECG's now for over a year. I knew every pattern he had shown under stress and all of the conditions on the practice exercises. The styli on the recorder started moving and all of the complexes on both leads were normal. His respiration and heart rate were also normal. Every complex of his ECG was the same as his normal tracings."[12] Vigorous exercise, consisting of pulling on a bungee (elastic) cord, did not unduly increase his blood pressure.

Weightlessness remains one of the big question marks with regard to manned space flight. Much attention was directed to this in Glenn's flight.

In order to trace its effects on digestion easily, his first intake was a xylose pill, a white sugar pill. Later, he consumed a tube of applesauce. No difficulty was encountered in eating, and no ill effects occurred.

Cosmonaut Gherman Titov reported that he had experienced nausea while in a weightless condition. This has been a point of considerable interest to the entire bio-astronautics field, so special oculogyric checks were scheduled for Glenn to see if he, too, would undergo the experience. He moved his head about, slowly at first, then more vigorously during the periodic tests. He was asked repeatedly if he were experiencing any vertigo or nausea. He always replied in this vein: "Negative. No symptoms whatsoever. I feel fine."[9]

Glenn did not react unfavorably in any way to the unique space state. On the contrary, he said, "I found myself unconsciously taking advantage of the weightless condition, as when I would leave a camera or some other object floating in space while I attended to other matters. This was not done as a pre-planned maneuver but as a spur-of-the-moment thing when another system needed my attention. I thought later about how I had done this as naturally as if I were laying the camera on a table in a 1-g field. It pointedly illustrates how rapidly adaptable the human is, even to something as foreign as weightlessness."[9]

One mechanical problem remains, however. In a weightless state, how are objects to be secured? Glenn carried his camera, binoculars, photometer, and other pieces in a ditty bag, and each was attached by a 3-foot piece of line. These became entangled—yet he realized how necessary these lines were when he accidentally bumped a roll of film and it floated away behind the instrument panel.

Glenn considered what he "did" on this flight to be of secondary importance. It was the relating of the subjective values which he felt to be of primary importance: "It is in this type of reporting that a manned vehicle provides a great advantage over an unmanned vehicle, which is often deaf and blind to the new and the unexpected. My report, then, will stress what I heard, saw, and felt during the orbital flight."[9]

Perhaps the most difficult to formalize into words was the fantastic visual aspect of the flight. Glenn's first exclamation from space was: "Oh, that view is tremendous!"[9] In his later report, he explained, "As I looked back at the earth from space, colors and light intensities were much the same as I had observed when flying at high altitude in airplanes. . . . The colors observed when looking down at the ground appeared similar to those seen from 50,000 feet. When looking toward the horizon, however, the view is completely different, for then the blackness of space contrasts vividly with the brightness of the earth. The horizon itself is a brilliant, brilliant blue and white.

"Throughout this flight, no trouble was encountered in seeing the horizon. During the day, the earth is bright and the background of space is dark. The horizon is vividly marked."[13]

Glenn related: "Some of the most spectacular sights during the flight were sunsets. The sunsets always occurred slightly to my left, and I turned the space craft to get a better view. The sunlight coming in the window was very brilliant, with an intense clear white light that reminded me of the arc lights while the space craft was on the launching pad.

"As the sun moves toward the horizon, darkness moves across the earth until the whole surface, except for the bright band at the horizon, is dark.

"The sun is perfectly round as it approaches the horizon. It retains most of its symmetry until just the last sliver is visible. The horizon on each side of the sun is extremely bright, and when the sun has gone down to the level of this bright band of the horizon, it seems to spread out to each side of the point where it is setting. With the camera, I caught the flattening of the sun just before it set. This is a phenomenon of some interest to the astronomers.

"This band is extremely bright just as the sun sets, but as time passes, the bottom layer becomes a bright orange and fades into reds, then on into the darker colors, and finally, off into the blues and blacks, as you get farther toward space."[13] Considering that the sun sets 18 times faster in space than on earth, it is surprising that Glenn's report indicated that the orbital twilight lasted for 4 to 5 minutes.

At 54 minutes and 39 seconds, Glenn reported: "Just to my right I can see a big pattern of lights apparently right on the coast. I can see the outline of a town and a very bright light just to the south of it." He was told by Astronaut Gordon Cooper, who was in Muchea, Australia, performing as capsule communicator, "Perth and Rockingham you're seeing there."[9] Glenn was pleased at their gesture, and responded, "The lights show up very well and thank everybody for turning them on, will you?"[9]

The most surprising and as-yet-unexplained sight of the entire flight is what has been named the Glenn Effect, which appeared with the first sunrise. Glenn exclaimed, "I am in a big mass of some very small particles, that are brilliantly lit up like they're luminescent. I never saw anything like it . . . they look like little stars. . . . They probably average maybe 7 or 8 feet apart, but I can see them all down below me, also. They do have a different motion, though, from me, because they swirl around the capsule and then depart back the way I am looking.

"Are you receiving? Over. There are literally thousands of them. This is *Friendship 7*. Am I in contact with anyone? . . . This is *Friendship 7,* broadcasting in the blind."[9] At that moment of great discovery, Glenn was utterly alone in space. There was not even a voice from the ground to share his excitement. He observed the yellowish green particles on successive sunrises in space, also.

One of the "sights" from space gave Texans one more thing to boast about: "The best view of any land area during the flight was the clear desert region around El Paso on the second pass across the United States, where I could see the colors of the desert and the irrigated area north of El Paso."[13] It is a common belief that little can be seen from orbital altitude. Glenn says this is not the case: "In clear desert air, it is common to see a mountain range 100 miles or so away very clearly, and all that vision is through atmosphere."[9]

But weather conditions do not usually permit this view. "It is surprising how much of the earth's surface was covered by clouds," he explains, then adds a statement significant to meteorologists: "There is little problem identifying them or in seeing the weather patterns."[9]

Glenn's report provided reassurance to the United States Weather Bureau, which is concerned with improving the optical equipment on its *Tiros* and *Nimbus* weather satellites. Our nation has scored history-making "firsts" in the applications of space—such as weather, communications, and navigation. They will be decisive factors in reaping space's benefits in our earthly endeavors.

Beyond the identifying of cloud heights from orbital altitude, Glenn was a witness to a most spectacular sight. In his third orbit, he reported to the station at Zanzibar: "There's quite a big storm area under me. . . . I see lightning flashes . . . 'way off on the horizon to the right. I also have them almost directly under me here. They show up very brilliantly here on the dark side at night. They're just like firecrackers going off."[9]

In addition to the "firecracker" sight, the flight had several aspects resembling a Fourth of July celebration. It expanded the broad American concept of freedom to a new dimension. It also had certain features of another holiday—Labor Day!

On the third orbit, as the elapsed time ticked up to 3 hours, 59 minutes, 23 seconds, Glenn called out to the capsule communicator, Gordon Cooper, at Muchea, Australia:

"I want you to send a message to . . . the Commandant, United States Marine Corps, Washington. Tell him I have my 4 hours required flight time in for the month and request flight chit be established for me."[9] Cooper responded, "Is this flying time or rocket time?"[9] Not to be topped, Glenn quipped, "Lighter than air, buddy."[9]

Not only was it noteworthy that Glenn could retain his ready sense of humor while orbiting, but he could do it in the face of trouble. The difficulty first appeared over Guaymas, Mexico before he had completed even the first orbit. He reported to the capsule communicator in California, "Yaw drifted out of limits about 20 degrees to the right. I'm bringing it back in manually at present time."[10]

The space craft had four control arrangements, set up on two independent systems to give back-up: System A consisted of ASCS, and FBW; System B consisted of MP and RSCS. The ASCS (Automatic Stabilization and Control System) was designed to fly the entire mission without any help from the Astronaut. (This is the system utilized in unmanned missions.) When the 1-pound left yaw thruster malfunctioned, a larger thruster took over to correct the attitude. However, Glenn could hear an ominous hissing—indicating that precious hydrogen peroxide fuel was being wasted by this high thrust jet performing the fine controlling. He then took over control on FBW (Fly By Wire). This has been likened to power steering on an automobile; the Astronaut's control stick operated the solenoid control valves electrically. It controlled the same jets, but was the means of reducing the excess fuel consumption.

Reassuringly, there existed the further back-up of System B, with two arrangements: MP (Manual Proportional system), and RSCS (Rate Stabilization Control System). The reason for such elaborate insurance for the space craft's being properly controlled seems poignantly understated in the technical language of Kenneth S. Kleinknecht's report on the space craft's systems: "Without such control, an orbital mission would very probably suffer mission failure."[9]

Over the Atlantic Ocean, Glenn reported that the drifting of the capsule reversed: "At one time I had no left low thrust in yaw; now that one is working, and I have no low right thrust in yaw."[9] By the time he had reached Australia, he stated: "I am getting some erratic indications in all axes. When I align everything on orbit attitude by the instruments, I am considerably off where I should be."[9]

Thus had new trouble developed—this time with the instruments. Over Africa, Glenn had performed the planned maneuver of turning his space craft 180 degrees in order to test his ability to control, as well as to see the earth and horizon from this direction. (He much preferred this forward-facing position, which he assumed three times during the mission.) But following this rotation, the gyro-reference system was not functioning properly—the readings Glenn saw on his instruments did not agree with his visual reference. He relied on the latter, and reported: "A number of questions have been raised over the ability of a man to use the earth's horizon as a reference for controlling the attitude of the space vehicle. Throughout this flight no trouble in seeing the horizon was encountered."[9]

It was subsequently determined that it was the turn-around maneuver of *Friendship 7* which caused the malfunction of the horizon scanners. (This same system was blamed for part of the difficulty which caused Astronaut M. Scott Carpenter to overshoot the landing area when he became the second American to orbit the earth.)

Glenn's problems had not ended. There was an increase in inverter temperatures.* At 20 minutes after blast-off, the temperatures reported on the two inverters were 175 degrees on the 150-volt-amp and 150 degrees on the 250-volt-amp. At 3 hours, at the end of the second orbit, they had risen to 215 degrees and 198 degrees. The cooling system for the inverters was not functioning. However, part of the years of preparation for this cardinal manned orbital mission was the determining of limits—for the man and for every system and component of his space craft. The thorough tests of the inverters indicated they could withstand the current and even higher temperatures. In addition, there was the "insurance"—the back-up inverter ready for activation in the event one should fail.

These and other contingencies had to be carefully weighed, individually and collectively, at *Mercury* Control Center; it had to be determined rapidly if the speeding space craft were to be fired out of orbit after its second circle of the globe, or be permitted to continue for the third.

Three key people were giving this matter most careful consideration. The man of top responsibility for the over-all *Project Mercury* assignment was the Director, Robert R. Gilruth; his keen ability is matched by a deep consciousness for every phase of the program. During time of launch, final decisions rested with the Associate Director and Operations Director, Walter C. Williams, Jr.—a dynamic engineer who has had long association with flight-test programs. The third key man involved in this stage of the program was the Flight Director, Christopher C. Kraft, Jr. Rapid and clear thinking had become his trademark.

Kraft related, "As the go-no-go point at the end of the second and beginning of the third orbit approached, it was determined that although some space craft malfunctions occurred, the Astronaut continued to be in excellent condition and had complete control of the space craft. He was told by the Hawaiian site that the *Mercury* Control Center had made the decision to continue into the third orbit."[9]

Glenn concurred: "I am 'Go' for the next orbit!"[9] His attitude clearly indicated that malfunction was not something over which to be concerned. In this instance, it was even the means for making unplanned determinations, as he later reported: "Of major significance is the probability that much more dependence can be placed on the man as a reliably operating portion of the man–space craft combination. In many areas his safe return can be made dependent on his own intelligent actions. . . . Even where automatic systems are still necessary, mission *reliability* is tremendously increased by having the man as a back-up. The flight of *Friendship 7* is a good example. This mission would almost certainly not have completed its three orbits, and might not have come back at all, if a man had not been aboard."[9]

* An inverter is a device to convert storage battery d-c into a-c electrical current.

The attention Glenn was required to give to controlling his capsule did have one disappointing result—it limited the time he could spend in conducting experiments, and therefore precluded his making many observations that had been planned on weather and astronomy.

Glenn began his third orbit in high spirits, commenting to Gus Grissom in Bermuda that he could see the entire state of Florida, and that his view stretched back to the Mississippi Delta. He also observed that the weather looked good in Area Hotel (the designation given the recovery area, where more than 20 ships were patrolling, awaiting the moment when one would pluck him from the sea).

His buoyant spirits were not matched among the ground controllers, however, for they had received an indication of still more trouble—far more serious than any of which Glenn was aware. A graph indicated the grave warning that *Friendship* 7's heat shield was loose!

The function of the heat shield was vital, for on re-entry, the blunt earth-facing portion of the capsule would have to withstand heat from the shock wave a foot away which rises to 8,000° F—about three fourths as great as that on the surface of the sun!

Structurally, the *Mercury* capsule is ingenious in its design. Between the capsule skin and the heat shield is a rubberized landing bag, for deployment just before impact with the water; it fills with air to help absorb the shock. While in flight, the bag is properly held firm against the capsule, secured by the heat shield. The warning which appeared indicated that the landing bag had prematurely deployed in flight, thereby rendering the heat shield loose.

In his routine, planned checks of all the space craft control modes, Glenn reported at 6 minutes; 34 minutes; 1 hour 37 minutes; and 2 hours 5 minutes: "Landing Bag off."[9] This meant that the switch which would activate this device to aid in the landing was in off position. Yet, only 15 minutes after his fourth check, the status of this system was questioned. The capsule communicator aboard the Indian Ocean Ship said: "We have message from MCC (*Mercury* Control Center) for you to keep your Landing Bag switch in off position."[9] Glenn again affirmed that it was.

From Muchea, Australia, 6 minutes later, came another query, "Will you confirm the Landing Bag switch is in the off position? . . . You haven't had any banging noises or anything of this type at higher rates?" The reply: "Negative."[9]

Glenn was puzzled. The explanation to him did not come until 20 minutes later, as he passed over Hawaii in the third orbit: *"Friendship 7,* we have been reading an indication on the ground of segment 51, which is Landing Bag Deploy. We suspect this is an erroneous signal. However, Cape would like you to check this by putting the Landing Bag switch in auto position, and see if you get a light." He checked, and found that his reading did not indicate that it had deployed.

Present space missions are pushing the very limits of knowledge and capability. Such straining, everyone knew, inevitably causes some failures. Just where this is most apt to occur, and what can be done about it, consumed a proportionate share of the planning for *Project Mercury*. It was considered an absolute necessity to formulate "Mission Rules"—an exhaustive "thinking and planning through" of just what to do in the eventuality of scores of different malfunctions.

Kraft's report stated: "The mission rules were established in an effort to take into account every conceivable situation which could occur onboard a space craft . . . if most of the contingencies have been anticipated along with the procedures to handle these situations, the time available can be used to concentrate on the unexpected. . . . Of course, it is impossible to think of everything that can happen . . . The occurrence of the heat shield deploy signal in this flight is an example of one of these unforeseen circumstances."[9]

At *Mercury* Control Center, a quiet and intense conference took place. The greatest calm outwardly prevailed as these highly skilled men tried to determine what procedure stood the greatest chance of success.

Throughout the world, millions of people were in a state of high emotion over the safety of this Astronaut who was but a name and an image to them. What must the feeling have been, then, among those who were his friends, and felt the responsibility for the mission?

John Yardley, as Project Engineer for Spacecraft Design of McDonnell Aircraft Corporation, was among those deeply involved in the discussion. He had largely conceived the design for the remarkable *Mercury* capsules, and had worked long and closely with Glenn in their development.

While some solution to the difficulty was being sought, word of the indicated malfunction was not transmitted to Glenn. It is not easy to tell a friend, even in technical language, that it appears he faces incineration upon return to the earth. However, Glenn, in his later report, expressed a valid reason for feeling that such a situation should be handled differently in future:

". . . I feel it more advisable in the event of suspected malfunctions, such as the heat-shield-retropack difficulties, that require extensive discussion among ground personnel, to keep the pilot updated on each bit of information rather than waiting for a final clear-cut recommendation from the ground. This keeps the pilot fully informed if there would happen to be any communication difficulty, and it became necessary for him to make all decisions from onboard information."[9]

Alternative assumptions could be made: (1) either assume that the heat shield was still firmly in place (as was indicated by the reading on the capsule's own instrument panel) and proceed with a normal re-entry, or (2) assume that the reading being given by instruments at *Mercury* Control Center were correct, and that the heat shield was loose. Since there was no way of further checking, the latter assumption had to be followed, and to this problem there was no good solution. But some means had to be taken to try to save *Friendship* 7 and its occupant from a flaming demise.

Although there was not unanimity of decision among the conferees, Yardley and some others felt that the retrorocket pack—which was strapped on beyond the heat shield much as a spare tire might be—should be retained rather than jettisoned after the retrorockets were fired. Hopefully, this would be sufficient to hold the heat shield in place if it were loose. Others at *Mercury* Control Center considered this untried procedure terribly risky, fearing that by thus altering the configuration of the capsule, it would lose stability and swing out of control, to the extent that the heat shield would not stay correctly positioned to accept the brunt of the searing on re-entry. But this appeared to be the best solution.

Just before the firing of the retrorockets which would slow his speed and bring him into descent for landing, instructions were relayed to Glenn by the capsule communicator in California, Walter Schirra: "John, leave your retropack on through your pass over Texas."[9] The rockets fired with such walloping force that Glenn felt he was being sent back to Hawaii. Over Texas, capsule communicator George Guthrie repeated: "We are recommending that you leave the retropackage on through the entire re-entry. This means you will have to override the .05 g switch. This also means that you will have to manually retract the 'scope."[9] (The .05 g switch senses the beginning of air resistance on entering the atmosphere, and initiates the automatic re-entry operations. The periscope can be withdrawn by means of a hand pump.)

Glenn performed those added tasks, and also exercised manual control along with the automatic attitude control. As a result of this duplicate effort, the attitude during retrofire was held to within 3 degrees of nominal —but as penalty, a large amount of fuel was wasted, causing him later, in the re-entry, to run out of fuel at a most critical moment.

As *Friendship* 7 hurtled to within the area of Cape communications, Shepard explained to Glenn: "We feel it is possible to re-enter with the retropackage on. We see no difficulty at this time in that type of reentry."[9] As much conviction as possible was put into the words. Still, with the hundreds of thousands of hours of testing that had gone into preparation of the mission, it was ironical that this most critical maneuver had to be tested with an Astronaut's life at stake.

"*Friendship* 7, this is Cape. Over."

Glenn urged Shepard, "Go ahead, Cape . . . you are going out."

"We recommend that you . . ."[9] Shepard's voice faded out.

Silence. Glenn could not hear those final instructions.

For the next 4½ minutes, there was no communication between the capsule and the ground. This was expected. The fearsome temperatures on re-entry caused the atmosphere around the capsule to ionize (become electrically charged) and block radio communication* At *Mercury* Control Center, it was a period of agony. The men who had planned, prepared, and cooperated in the execution of the flight stood rigidly, straining to hear over their earphones words from Glenn—words that were not coming through.

Within the capsule, Glenn heard a loud snapping noise and one of the steel straps that had held the retropackage swung in front of the window. He saw an orange glow and pieces of flaming debris flash past the window. At that instant, the Astronaut thought the pack had already burned off, and that the chunks were a break-up of the heat shield. He uttered words that he must have felt might be his last: "A real fireball outside." No one even heard. Silence. "Hello, Cape. *Friendship* 7. Over." Silence. "Hello Cape. *Friendship* 7. Over."[9] Glenn was alone at that moment, facing the supreme test of the mission under the most terrifying of conditions.

Seconds ticked on. G forces of deceleration mounted until they matched that of launch, 7.7. Then Shepard's voice faded in: ". . . How do you read?" Glenn responded, "Loud and clear. How me?"[9] This contact of the voices of two friends signified the end of an awful, suspenseful crisis.

Events which followed, that otherwise might have seemed serious, were taken in stride. At an altitude of 80,000 feet, the intense re-entry heat had begun to penetrate the capsule. At 45,000 feet, extreme oscillations were of concern: "I kept them under control on the manual and fly-by-wire systems until I ran out of manual fuel. After that point, I was unknowingly left with only the fly-by-wire system and the oscillations increased; so I switched to auxiliary damping, which controlled the space craft until the automatic fuel was also expended. I was reaching for the switch to deploy the drogue parachute early in order to reduce these re-entry oscillations, when it was deployed automatically. The drogue parachute stabilized the space craft rapidly," Glenn later reported.[9]

When the main parachute opened at 10,800 feet, he said, " 'Chute looks good. . . . 'Chute looks very good."[9] Only the great heat inside the capsule was of concern then. But it would not have to be endured for long. Even before Glenn impacted, Steelhead (the code name for the United States Navy destroyer, *Noa*) sent the message, "Be advised, I got your chaff on my radar and I'm heading out for you now."[9] The Cape recom-

* This is also referred to as a "communications blackout." There was a misinterpretation of the term "blackout" by some people, who erroneusly believed it referred to a "blackout" or losing consciousness on the part of the Astronaut.

mended that Glenn remain in his capsule, unless he had an overriding reason to get out.

In the 4 hours, 55 minutes and 24 seconds since his launch, Glenn had traveled about 81,000 miles, at speeds which reached 17,545 mph, completing each orbit in 88 minutes, 29 seconds. Yet the capsule which performed this mission was but a tiny speck bobbing in a splotch of sea stained green by a dye marker. Less than 9 minutes later, the *Noa* was alongside, hoisting *Friendship* 7 onto its deck by means of a lifeboat davit.

Glenn had planned egress through the top opening of the capsule. But difficulty plus the high temperature which had by this time developed inside the capsule prompted him to change his plan. After verifying that the area around the side hatch was clear, he blew off the cover—and in the process sustained his only injury of the day—some skinned knuckles.

There emerged amid the crew's wild cheers a very hot man; still perhaps a great part of his flush came from exhilaration at having proved what Dr. Wernher von Braun long ago said of space travel: "Man belongs whereever he wants to go—and he'll do plenty well when he gets there."[14]

The carrier, *USS Randolph,* had been designated the main rescue ship. The *Noa,* therefore, considered itself doubly lucky to have effected the rescue. The Astronaut's footsteps were painted in white upon its deck, as both tribute to and reminder of the greatness of the event in which the destroyer had taken part.

Glenn's stay aboard the *Noa,* was brief, but busy. His first act was to cool off with a glass of iced tea. A shower, a quick medical check, and a telephone conversation with President Kennedy followed. He then secluded himself on a portion of the deck to dictate into a tape recorder his recollections of the flight while events were still fresh in his mind.

Soon, a helicopter plucked Glenn off the deck of the *Noa* and took him to the *Randolph.* From there, he was "launched" by airplane to Grand Turk Island, where teams of the *Project Mercury* crew were converging, and where he would undergo a most exhaustive debriefing session and extensive medical examinations. With this activity, as much as with any phase of the operation, the stated missions of the flight could be furthered. Aims were: (1) to evaluate the performance of the space craft, (2) to evaluate the effects of space flight on the Astronaut, and (3) to garner the Astronaut's opinions on the space craft and its supporting systems.

During these concentrated sessions, Glenn earnestly described the amazing yellow-green particles he had encountered in space. George Rupp, the psychiatrist on the team, asked, just as earnestly, "What did they say, John?"[15] Glenn's great laughter filled the room.

The escort which the Astronaut had from Grand Turk back to Cape Canaveral was Vice President Lyndon B. Johnson. Glenn's wife and children, his parents and his wife's parents also had a distinguished escort from Washington, D.C. to Florida—in the person of President John F. Kennedy. The reception that greeted the returning hero was more deafening than the roar of the rockets that had put him into space three days before.

When he reached the tight security area of the Missile Test Center on the Cape from which he had blasted off, Glenn dutifully presented his pass to the gateman. He showed President Kennedy and the proud members of his family around various areas, including the *Mercury* Control Center. At a ceremony which followed, the President bestowed upon Glenn the Distinguished Service Medal of the National Aeronautics and Space Administration. The President said in part:

"Seventeen years ago today, a group of Marines put the American flag on Mt. Suribachi. So it's very appropriate that today we decorate Colonel Glenn of the United States Marine Corps. And we also realize that in the not too distant future a Marine or a Naval Man or an Air Force Man will put the American flag on the Moon."

Glenn had brought this eventuality considerably closer, though his response to the tribute was to turn the credit to his fellow Astronauts and others. "I can't express my appreciation adequately to be here accepting this when I know how many thousands of people all over the country were involved in helping accomplish what we did last Tuesday . . . We have stressed the team effort in *Project Mercury*. . . . It goes across the board, I think—sort of a cross-cut of Americana, of industry and military and civil service, Government work, contractors . . . thousands and thousands of people have contributed certainly as much or more than I have to the Project."*

Glenn applauded the loudest of anyone present when the President gave a Distinguished Service Medal to Robert R. Gilruth, the Director of *Project Mercury*. The President said that Gilruth ". . . represents the kind of American genius for organization, particularly in the scientific field, one in which we put so much of our hopes."

The President, certainly an authority on the subject, warned Glenn that the hazards had only begun when he was launched into public orbit! The Astronaut had cause to heed those words during the whirlwind that followed. All heroes soon learn that all personal privacy vanishes with the "doing of their deed." This was one occurrence for which there was no "simulator," or means of advanced training—yet Glenn's responses were utterly natural and always completely fitting.

He was abashed only by a question put to him by a lady—a very young one by the name of Caroline Kennedy. Glenn laughingly related, "I think Caroline really cut us down to size and put us back in our proper position, though, when after being introduced she looked up and said, 'Where's the

* It is estimated that about 35,000 people made substantial contributions to the flight.

monkey?' "[16] The Astronaut had little choice but to accept the youngster's greater interest in Enos, the chimpanzee which orbited.

Weather had grounded many a launch, but it didn't stop the parade, nor did it deter throngs from welcoming Glenn and Annie on their return to Washington, D.C. They rode in an open limousine to Capitol Hill, where Glenn had the singular honor of addressing Congress. After a thunderous 2-minute ovation, he opened his powerful speech with words so simple yet so heartfelt: "I still get a hard-to-define feeling inside when the Flag goes by and I know you do too. . . . Let us hope that none of us ever loses that feeling."

Such words were meaningful, coming from Glenn. His friend, Haines, said on this topic: "Americanism . . . young boys and girls want to know just what it is. All you have to do is look at John, and his way of life, and what he stands for—that's what we stand for in this country."[2]

Glenn epitomizes the ideal American, yet his influence is beyond nationality. Here is the image of hope incarnate. Not only our country but men everywhere were raised a step higher by what Glenn did, and how he did it—*in full view of the world*—for all to see, whether the outcome were triumph or failure.

In an editorial, Max Ascoli writes, "There is no possible comparison between the Russian conquests in orbit and ours. Gagarin and Titov may be as brave and as skillful as our John Glenn, just as the human qualities of the Russian people are as good as ours. But there is no possible comparison between the two systems of doing things. The way our system operated in the case of John Glenn's flight is even more important than the results of that flight."[17]

He continues, stressing a significant point of the tremendous press coverage of the event—something which we automatically take for granted and tend not to fully appreciate, "From what was given us during that time, and for what we felt inside, we owe an enormous debt of gratitude to our radio and TV networks, to our free institutions."[17]

This openness in conducting the event received extensive world-wide notice. The comment that appeared in the British magazine, *Nature,* characterized much of the reaction: "The United States has kept the world informed not only of her successes but also of her failures or setbacks. One learns from the latter as well as from the former; and science owes it to the world to be the universal teacher. It should never be the catspaw of nationalism."[18]

Glenn visited the United Nations, at the invitation of Secretary-General U Thant, and met informally with members of the United Nations Committee on the Peaceful Uses of Outer Space. Referring to the world-wide chain of tracking stations, Glenn said, "The flights in which we have been taking part are not only a national team effort but international as well."[19]

He continued, reflecting a truth all too often forgotten: "In a little broader sense, of course, the entire effort to explore outer space rests on many scientific disciplines whose growth over the years has been entirely international. As space science and space technology grow still further and our projects become more and more ambitious, we will be relying more and more on international teamwork. . . . We have an infinite amount to learn both from nature and from each other. We devoutly hope that we will be able to learn together and work together in peace."[19]

The transcending earthly unification that occurred with those three orbits of the *Mercury* capsule—whose very name, *Friendship 7,* keynoted the spirit—was unprecedented. Writes David Lawrence, "The event was historic, not merely because of the conquest of space by an American astronaut, but because of the world-wide manifestation of an impulse that came from the hearts of millions of human beings everywhere. It was probably the most universal expression of the spiritual feeling of mankind that we have witnessed in our time. . . . In those few minutes, more people prayed together for the same objective than at any time in history."[20]

Messages which poured in from all over the world were filled with superlatives. From Prime Minister Harold Macmillan, Chancellor Konrad Adenauer, and from other heads of states and from citizens, there were both pride and kinship: "Well done! We are proud for you! A step in human progress!"

Through it all—whether he was riding through the streets in the greatest hero's welcome that New York City had ever accorded, or walking down the road in New Concord—Glenn was at ease, appreciative, responsive. Says his close friend, Tom Miller: "If you could possibly say that this has had any effect upon John, it is to make him more humble. The reaction of people went beyond anything that he—and probably most of us—could ever have imagined.

"He has received absolutely unbelievable amounts of mail, but he has steadfastly refused to allow anyone to duplicate his signature on a photograph; he personally signs every one of the thousands and thousands that are sent. On the first Sunday he returned home to Arlington from all of the big celebrations, he started trying to wade through the hundreds of telegrams and sacks of mail. But he soon was interrupted in this activity; we heard a commotion, and realized that about 200 people had gathered on the sidewalk and street in front of his house. It was freezing cold outside, but they stood—children, old people, every kind of person—just hoping to get a glimpse of John. He went out many times, as one crowd left and another gathered. A smile and a handshake from him and they were filled with a kind of elation that I honestly believe would linger with them for a long while."

Later that same Sunday, after Tom Miller had returned to his own home, the phone rang and Hal Vincent was on the line, calling via long distance. Vincent relates, "The Washington, D.C. telephone information girl told me John had no phone, and Tom explained that he had had to have it taken out. I wanted to talk with John for two reasons: to congratulate him, of course, and also to ask him some advice about the next Astronaut selection, in which I was included.* Tom sent his daughter next door to see if 'Uncle Johnny' wanted to talk with me. He came back with her, fighting his way through the throngs of people who were around his house; he did this just to give me the information that I wanted. This is a prime example of John's extreme thoughtfulness. He will always be the same person, completely unaffected by his fame."

The Commandant of the Marine Corps said it concisely in his message of congratulations to Glenn: "You have joined the company of heroes of your country and the Corps."

The image was firmly created. "In his silver space suit, the armour of the middle of the twentieth century, Colonel Glenn on February 20, 1962, crossed the soundless barrier between the past and the future, the familiar and the uncharted . . ."[21] *Vogue* magazine, in that tribute, temporarily changed focus from style to substance.

Though Glenn's accomplishment has tended to remove him from the realm of "average people," he retains the common touch that evokes self-identification: "This very quality of imitability is a precious asset in a society that needs authentic models, yet has seen few of universal popular appeal since Lindy's day in 1927. . . . How many John Glenns are hiding in the United States? Lots of them, we think, but not too many for the challenges that lie in the heavens, beyond the seas and on the hills of home."[22] So was it stated in *America* magazine.

The pattern of progress is not a new one. We are reminded: "The tradition is that humanity advances by great forward thrusts by pioneers. Then come the slack periods when society slowly, all too slowly, catches up."[23]

From Glenn it has been learned that there are dimensions to succeeding. He capped scientific triumph with a personal victory—which stemmed not from what he did, but from what he is. His ideas have a stinging stimulation: "We are just probing the surface of the greatest advancement of man's knowledge of his surroundings that has even been made."[15]

The latent desire to emulate a hero stirs within men everywhere when this Astronaut wisely says, "Knowledge begets knowledge. The more I see, the more impressed I am—not with how much we know—but with how tremendous the areas are that are as yet unexplored."[15]

There are other "firsts" to be scored and other feats to be performed.

* Vincent was later withdrawn from the Astronaut selection, because the Marine Corps would not release him from his important military duties.

And the remarkable part of achievement is that John H. Glenn's spirit and example will continue to be a part of every phase of this unfolding space story!

REFERENCES

1. *Press Conference, Mercury Astronaut Team,* Washington, D.C., April 9, 1959.
2. *WBNS Radio Forum,* January 26, 1962.
3. *Reader's Digest,* 81:484:61–3, August, 1962.
4. Stapp, John Paul: *Civilization,* 1956.
5. Adams, Franklin Pierce: *FPA Book of Quotations,* New York, Funk & Wagnalls, 1952.
6. *Time,* LXXIX, 9:11–18, March 2, 1962.
7. *Astronaut Press Conference,* Cape Canaveral, Florida, September 16, 1960.
8. *Los Angeles Times,* Los Angeles, California, March 12, 1961.
9. *Results of the First United States Manned Orbital Space Flight,* Manned Spacecraft Center, National Aeronautics and Space Administration, Virginia, February 20, 1962.
10. *Los Angeles Herald Examiner,* Los Angeles, California, January 28, 1962.
11. *Aviation Week,* 76:30, April 16, 1962.
12. *Ebony,* 17:35–36+, April, 1962.
13. Glenn, John H., Jr.: *Summary Results of the First United States Manned Orbital Space Flight,* paper for Third International Space Science Symposium COSPAR, Washington, D.C., April 30–May 9, 1962.
14. *Time,* 71:21–5, February 17, 1958.
15. *Orbital Flight of John H. Glenn, Jr.,* Hearing before the United States Senate Committee, February 28, 1962.
16. Glenn, John H., Jr.: *Address,* before Joint Meeting of United States Congress, Washington, D.C., February 26, 1962.
17. *The Reporter,* 21:16, March 15, 1962.
18. *Nature,* 193:4818:807, March 3, 1962.
19. *United Nation's Review,* 9:25–6, March, 1962.
20. *U.S. News and World Report,* 52:108, March 5, 1962.
21. *Vogue,* 139:116–17, April 1, 1962.
22. *America,* 106:791, March 17, 1962.
23. *The Christian Science Monitor,* February 24, 1962.

Imaginative young physicist who is concentrating on the interrelationship between physical science and political science

ALBERT R. HIBBS

"The pursuit of science is a human operation, not a mechanical operation in the sense of putting in a question, turning the scientific crank and grinding out an answer. The experience of discovery is an emotional experience, and it is this personal reward that keeps scientists working at their profession. There is a thrill to discovering something new."

Al Hibbs's words pour forth with meaning and deep sincerity, as he displays an unusually articulate quality: "When I talk with students, I try to convey what science is like. It is not the dry, textbook approach to the world. The real scientist is often working in an area where there is no book—perhaps some day he will be the one to write it. Meanwhile, he will go to the library and read what others have previously done around the edges of this particular specialty. Whatever he does is completely his own, out of his own imagination. If he can get some new ideas, it is tremendously exciting!"

Hibbs admits that these "new ideas" may not always hold up with closer scrutiny—someone else already may have made the discovery—but that does not lessen the experience at the moment the scientist believes he is realizing something new.

If a scientist finds indications that his idea is right, he must continue to

PORTFOLIO OF ILLUSTRATIONS

JOHN H. GLENN, JR.
ALBERT HIBBS
RICHARD B. KERSHNER
HOMER E. NEWELL
L. EUGENE ROOT
ROBERT C. SEAMANS, JR.
CHARLES H. TOWNES
ROGER S. WARNER, JR.

President John F. Kennedy (*left*) awards the NASA Distinguished Service Medal to Astronaut John H. Glenn, Jr. (*right*). NASA Administrator James E. Webb watches the proceedings in the background.

Astronaut John H. Glenn, Jr., in a weightless state and traveling at 17,500 mph, marvels at the fantastic sight of the earth, the sun, and the stars during his orbit.

Dr. Albert R. Hibbs ponders the weighty problem of the role of space in disarmament.

Dr. Homer E. Newell pauses but rarely from his demanding duties of overseeing the nation's space science program.

Dr. Richard B. Kershner (*left*) inspects the end result of his team's effort, the *Transit* satellite. Captain Robert F. Freitag, USN (*right*), can fully appreciate the value of this navigational aid.

The United States has made gigantic contributions to earthly betterment by means of three specific space projects: *Telstar,* the communications satellite (*shown above*); *Tiros,* the weather satellite (*shown right*); and *Transit,* the navigation satellite (*shown opposite page*).

L. Eugene Root is a familiar figure at the podium of space science gatherings.

Although Dr. Robert C. Seamans, Jr. (*right*), has his offices in the nation's capital, his position as "general manager" of the civilian space effort occasions visits to NASA's field centers. Here he is talking with Dr. G. Allen Smith (*left*) of Ames Research Center, Moffett Field, California.

Dr. Charles H. Townes, creator of the maser, in the familiar setting of the laboratory.

The alert and determined attitude reflected by Roger S. Warner, Jr., has figured importantly in bringing many space projects to fruition.

probe—even though his concept upsets all previously accepted beliefs. It is not easy to persist with ideas which are in conflict with every so-called authority. But doubting—of the established as well as the new—must become a part of his scientific nature from early in life.

Explains Hibbs, "I don't mean rejecting just for the sake of rejecting. I'm talking about real serious questions that repeatedly keep coming up in your mind. Whenever you hear a new idea, you wonder if it is right. Whenever you think of one yourself, you will explore it, but reserve judgment. This becomes a continuing habit, and you have to learn how to get along with it."

In the beginning, it is a most difficult trait. "I remember when I first became consciously aware of the habit of doubting; it was early in adolescence, when there were already enough problems without this one. Doubting is not an acceptable form of behavior. The trait is not acceptable in the school, in the home, among your friends. Yet without it, you cannot be a scientist."

Hibbs has observed that one of two things usually happens to the young person who has this habit: "He will conclude that he had better get over it, if he wants to be popular and have friends. So he gets over it, accepts the world, and can live a happy life—but not as a scientist. The alternate reaction is that he just gets confused. He begins to have no confidence in himself, everything seems wrong, and he gets nowhere. From the standpoint of becoming a scientist I think the latter course is better. I believe it is much more possible to regain confidence than to regain the habit of doubting.

"It is typically society's viewpoint that you have to do away with doubt in order to have confidence in yourself—but that is not true. Any scientist has doubts in himself, his fellows, in everything that happens. But he has complete confidence in his ability to attack problems and to make progress. When he comes up with an answer, he will say, 'I'm 90 per cent sure that this is right.' Such appraisal is far different from blind, absolute acceptance—which is the more common approach—and it is this difference that is fundamental to eventual great scientific achievement."

Space is youth and vigor—courage and imagination. It embodies the qualities perceivable in Hibbs. Though only 33 years old when the Space Age burst upon the world, he was an accepted—and outspoken—national authority. On January 15, 1958, headlines from coast to coast related his views:

MORE U.S. ERRORS SEEN ON MISSILES—SCIENTIST RIPS "INCOMPETENTS."[1]

MISSILE LEADERSHIP BRANDED "ABSURD."[2]

MISSILE SCIENTIST FLAYS U.S. POLICY.[3]

Hibbs was deeply concerned at our country's position at that point: "This shortsighted attitude toward basic research into the problems of rocket motors is characteristic of the attitude toward all of the vital basic research programs in the whole missile field. This research requirement, fundamental to any real advance in missile design, has been carelessly brushed aside. The research effort receives the lowest priority in time, money, and manpower."[4]

At that time of crisis and turmoil, this young physicist did not hesitate to spell out the problems as he saw them, and he forcefully presented his own best thoughts toward solutions—well realizing that such expressions would probably not work to his own favor.

Though he professes a realistic view, is it possible that the deeply held image within Hibbs is partially that of the knight on horseback? He recalls that, as a boy, his choice of reading matter switched from *Ivanhoe* to *Buck Rogers* at about the fifth grade. "It is the same story actually except that Buck Rogers has a different type of armor and a different style of horse." Even with the guise thus altered, Hibbs felt the spirit of a crusade to be present.

Although importantly associated with many scientific phases of the space effort, Hibbs was not satisfied. "I always have wanted to become involved in some manner with the relations between society and technology. Having long been concerned with how they bear upon one another, I decided it was time to do more than engage my fellow scientists in conversations about how these things should work. I wanted to get into something that I could really believe was of great intrinsic sociological value. There were two agencies that seemed to me to function really importantly in such a respect—the Technical Cooperation Administration, which provides funds and personnel to assist underdeveloped areas, and the Arms Control and Disarmament Agency. I chose the latter."

To bring his wish to fulfillment, Hibbs has formulated a worthy plan, traveled thousands of miles, and talked with countless people. Such extensive effort could not have been expended without a deep and long standing conviction.

His desires were first instilled by the addresses and writings of Herman Kahn, now of the Hudson Institute, formerly of the Rand Corporation. Hibbs grew deeply interested in thoughts that Kahn projected: "It is most unlikely that the world can live with an uncontrolled arms race lasting for several decades. . . . Our problems are being increased rapidly by many things, including the mounting rate of technological progress, the 'revolution of rising expectations,' increasing nationalism, and an increasing diffusion of the newer military technologies. . . . We will need much better mechanisms than we have had for forward thinking, imaginative research into problems of strategy and foreign policy, and anticipating future developments and planning to meet them."[5]

Kahn's lectures are the more forceful because of his extraordinary ability to introduce light notes into the most serious matters. He delivered a series at the California Institute of Technology (Cal Tech). Says Hibbs, "In hearing them, I gained the idea that here was a tremendous new field—the field of the interrelation between politics and technology—wherein the point of view of a physical scientist might make a lot of headway.

"I went to Rand to see Herman, but found talking with him personally was more confusing than inspiring, because he talks very rapidly and speaks almost pure Randese, a language with which I am not too familiar. As he talked, there were many things which I didn't understand, but before I was able to frame a question to try to clarify any one of them, he was six ideas further down the stream."

A second major input to Hibbs's interest in the crossover between science and politics came from a lecture seminar on arms control sponsored by the Carnegie Foundation; it was coordinated by Dr. David Elliott, professor of history at Cal Tech. Relates Hibbs, "I was more and more intrigued by the idea that a mathematical analysis of alternate possibilities of the way in which international strategies might develop would reveal a lot of things which are overlooked in ordinary political conversation. Thoughtful analysis of strategies shows possibilities which either offer a way out of a given problem, or give the problem much more serious dimensions than might have been guessed initially. This sounds vague, but unfortunately the ideas are vague. You sit down to work on a problem in this business, and you put number one in the upper right-hand corner of the page. Then you sit and you stare at the page. There is no differential equation. There is no place to start. It is a new kind of problem."

Dr. Frank Press, head of the seismology laboratory at Cal Tech, is a member of the President's Science Advisory Council. Upon his recommendation, Hibbs became a consultant on arms control to the State Department. This association convinced him that he should seek the opportunity to expend full efforts working toward this vital aim. Even though Press and others advised him that this probably could be accomplished only by moving to Washington, D.C., Hibbs felt such an effort could become a beneficial part of the Jet Propulsion Laboratory (JPL). He discussed the possibility with Dr. William Pickering, Director of JPL. Pickering agreed that such a plan had merit: "I think it is very important that the country come up with some answers and some understanding of this whole problem and what to do about it. If it is a thing to which Al can contribute from here at the Laboratory, I'm certainly in favor of it."

Having this support, Hibbs, with help from Press, launched a campaign about a year ago to bring together the interests of our civilian space agency, the National Aeronautics and Space Administration, NASA (of which JPL is one research center), and the Arms Control and Disarmament Agency, ACDA. John J. McCloy, former adviser to the President on disarmament, writes in his article, *Balance Sheet on Disarmament,* "With the establishment of the United States Arms Control and Disarmament Agency, we now have a statutory organization, responsible both to the executive and legislative branches of the Government, which is prepared to do the work necessary for effective representation at disarmament meetings. The problems of disarmament are connected with some of the deepest interests of our national life; they also involve difficult and puzzling technicalities."[6]

Hibbs's scientific background and wide range of activities in space projects could add a dimension to the effort. Dr. Franklin A. Long, Assistant Director in charge of the Bureau of Science and Technology, which sponsors and coordinates the scientific research of ACDA,* was receptive to the suggestion, and sent a request for Hibbs's services to Dr. Robert C. Seamans, Jr., Deputy Associate Administrator of NASA. Details of budget and activities were discussed with Pickering, and the necessary authorizations were granted. After this extensive preliminary activity, Hibbs finally gained his wish by having established the Arms Control and Disarmament Study Group at JPL on May 1, 1962.

This has set a precedent for cooperation between NASA and ACDA, and takes NASA into an area which its Administrator, James Webb, feels is very much within its charter and interests—especially since NASA will be providing ACDA with information on space vehicles, space systems, future plans, and other items.

Explains Hibbs, "I felt it worthwhile, and NASA agreed, that someone who was intimately familiar with the NASA systems should also be working within the ACDA—first, to make sure that the information that was provided was properly evaluated, properly understood, and properly used; second, to insure that the studies which the ACDA undertook didn't just duplicate things already underway in NASA. These are but a few of the ways in which close contact by someone who is actually doing technical work can help both agencies work together better."

Working with Hibbs full time is a chemist, Richard Schuster. On a part-time basis are Dr. Homer Joe Stewart (one of the founders of JPL and Hibbs's first boss), Dr. Fred Eimer, Dr. Walter Brown, Dr. Rajinder Loomba, and Dr. David Elliott.

Where is the starting point for huge problems? How does one keep

* ACDA was under the Department of State until September 26, 1961, at which time it was set up as an independent agency, devoted solely to the purpose of reducing armaments and preserving peace. The Honorable William C. Foster is the Director.

from being overwhelmed with the enormousness? Just as the longest journey is a series of steps, the most gigantic issues can be broken into segments with which the mind can cope. Hibbs explains, "I have to be aware of all problems that face ACDA, but I can't work on everything. So the most I can do is learn the major stumbling blocks in the current negotiations in Geneva—What is the treaty? Where are the weak spots? Where are the Soviets raising the greatest objections? What have they proposed? Why don't we like it? What can we counter-propose?

"But in all of these questions, I apply myself only to the field with which I am familiar. I've never worked in the field of nuclear weapons, so I'll stay out of that. I can't be effective in the field of economics. But when they talk of areas that overlap with space efforts, of what can be done with missile systems, with instrumentation or with research, in these I could be effective."

The activity has a unique quality which Hibbs points out: "Disarmament is purely an academic subject. Usually it is the other way around, but here there is theory with no practice. There are institutes in disarmament, in many universities there are professorships in it, great research is being conducted, yet no one is *doing* any disarmament. It is very confusing, for it is a thing of the real world, yet it exists only in theory."

Hibbs already has been productive in ACDA. He has drafted three papers relating to his field; these papers concerned points which negotiators in Geneva felt required more clarification as talks with the Soviets progressed.

Hibbs has strong hope that broader interchange can bring together two arenas that previously have not had sufficiently strong contact—the political and the scientific. Not only is it important for him to learn what scientific concepts would not be acceptable from the view of the State Department, but there are lessons to be conveyed in the reverse.

He points out: "Diplomats often make politically acceptable proposals which are hopeless scientifically. For example, in the treaty which the United States suggested at Geneva, we proposed three stages; essentially, in each stage we decreased the armaments by one-third, so at the end of Stage Three there are no armaments. At that point we propose to maintain the status through an International Disarmament Organization. There are a number of items specified as to what countries are to be allowed to do from then on, and what their responsibilities are. One requirement is that each country is responsible for informing the International Organization about their research or technical inventions which have potential military application."

Hibbs analyzes this from the scientist's point of view: "This is so broad that it is ridiculous. Every line of research has potential military applications. You can't identify things in that kind of category, so in that line the proposed treaty is hopeless to enforce. There is no way of writing a codicil which will clarify what is meant by research with military significance."

At the time of the Treaty of Versailles, it didn't occur to those who drafted the document that rocketry would prove to be a threat. Hence, it did not specify that rocket research was forbidden. This oversight allowed the Germans to produce the mighty V-2. Reminiscent of this fact, Hibbs states an obvious truth: "Long before this presently proposed disarmament treaty would come to the point of enforcement, I'm sure there will be several new weapons which no one has even thought of yet. By the time Stage Three is reached—nine years later—there will have been developed whole systems that are beyond our present imagination. There will continue to be more and more, because technology cannot be turned off."

In Hibbs's estimation, there is a still more important lesson to be learned from the Treaty of Versailles: "When the terms were violated, nobody did anything. That brings up the matter of how to build into a treaty an automatic compensation for violation. How do you specify a genuine violation, against which you will take counter-measures? After Hitler began rearming, we got into a trap, saying, 'We'll let him do this little bit—it isn't worth going to war over that.' We must find a way to arrest development of a set of conditions that would permit a repetition of this kind of history. We must identify the violation, and have planned measures that would be set into operation automatically and would compensate for the action at the correct time and prevent war."

Systems already in existence might be of value in this connection. Hibbs states, "Certain related studies will be done on *Samos,* the reconnaissance satellite, or on a similar satellite, to see if they could be useful for inspection in the disarmament situation. We will try to determine, for instance, if they could help to locate any possible secret production of nuclear material for bombs. To answer a question such as this, somebody has to take the time to really concentrate and work through the problem. Up to now there has been principally hand waving—'Oh, yes, we can do that.' Maybe they are right, that it is a minor problem. If so, we will soon find out and stop the study. But if it turns out to be a major problem, we should know it and be putting more effort into it."

Those in ACDA and others at high level well realize that convenient and contrived lines of separation cannot exist if success is to be achieved in this venture. Disarmament is not one agency's business—it is everyone's hope. In this nation, there is not one group seeking peace and another group with opposite aims. No men are more utterly dedicated toward preserving the peace than those who wear military uniforms, and no businesses are more ready to convert their manufacture to "plowshares" than the companies which are now producing military weapons. But as the

Honorable Hubert H. Humphrey recently stated: "Our mightiest weapons serve the double purpose of deterrence and retaliation. As things stand now, we cannot do without these weapons, nor can we avoid perfecting new ones against the danger of an enemy 'breakthrough.' Yet armaments are undeniably a burden and a brake on our over-all economic development. This is what happens when a nation is caught in the vicious circle of an arms race."[7]

Senator Humphrey made a telling point when he stated on behalf of Congress: "We asked recognition of the fact, to which the present administration fully subscribes, that disarmament and national defense are not contradictory but are two equal sides of the same coin."[7] The extent to which this attitude is practiced is clearly evident by the fact that ACDA has reached out to the defense industry to augment its ceaseless efforts toward disarmament. As Hibbs explains: "It is important to involve the people who are now in the weapons design and production business for two obvious reasons—they will be affected by disarmament, and they certainly have great knowledge of equipment.

"For instance, the first research contracts which ACDA put out to major industry were with the Bendix Corporation and Raytheon. The contract with Bendix, for example, is for a study to identify all the various techniques for monitoring the production of missiles and aircraft. I am helping to the extent that I can—by commenting, and by redirecting when necessary—so that they hit the important factors of the program."

The involvement of different groups into this effort was highlighted by a meeting held from July 16 through August 24, 1962, at Woods Hole, Massachusetts, sponsored for ACDA by the Institute for Defense Analysis, IDA.* Assembled there, on the old Whitney estate, were approximately 15 scientists and engineers, and 10 individuals who were expert in political science, international law and international affairs. The weighty matter of inspection and control was their special problem for study.

The United States has been a leader toward disarmament with efforts dating back to the 1920's and continuing through the years. The Baruch Plan was laid before the United Nations in 1946, in which we, as the single nation then possessing atomic capability, offered to transfer all atomic weapons and materials to the U.N. for control. The inability to reach agreement with the U.S.S.R. has continually blocked progress.

After the tedious and trying negotiations of a three-power nuclear test ban, in what Senator Humphrey terms "one of the most discouraging developments of this decade,"[7] a group of 18 sovereign nations now comprise the disarmament negotiators. The efforts of our Chief Delegate to the Disarmament Conferences, the Honorable Arthur Dean, have been the

* IDA is an advisory group to the Department of Defense.

essence of patience and persistence. In the talks which are now continuing, the treaty proposed by the United States was lucidly explained by the President when he addressed the United Nations:

"First, signing the Test Ban Treaty, by all nations. This can be done now. Test ban negotiations need not and should not await general disarmament talks.

"Second, stopping the production of fissionable materials for use in weapons, and preventing their transfer to any nation now lacking nuclear weapons.

"Third, prohibiting the transfer of control over nuclear weapons to states that do not own them.

"Fourth, keeping nuclear weapons from seeding new battlegrounds in outer space.

"Fifth, gradually destroying existing nuclear weapons and converting their materials to peaceful uses.

"Finally, halting the unlimited testing and production of strategic nuclear delivery vehicles, and gradually destroying them as well."[8]

Nowhere can space figure more importantly than in disarmament. Individuals whose knowledge, background and experience are space oriented are of unique value to ACDA; the General Advisory Committee which has been set up by the Agency includes several men who have figured importantly in this nation's space effort—among them are General Thomas D. White, USAF (Ret.), Dr. Herbert York and Trevor Gardner.

The implements of space are impartial in their capability. They will orbit vigilantly to aid in exploring the universe, or in keeping the peace, or they will rise in a trajectory to deliver a warhead onto a target. The missions they will perform will be at the bidding of men. It is not space that is ever to be feared, but men.

Hibbs has entered an area wherein lies our hope as a civilization. President Kennedy has succinctly expressed it: "The weapons of war must be abolished before they abolish us."[8]

Strong opinions and deliberate planning are traits of long standing with Al Hibbs. At the age of 3, he decided he wanted to be an astronomer. Somewhat in apology for his limited knowledge at that time, he explains, "It really was cosmology that I was interested in, only I just didn't know it then. I had a great desire to figure out how the stars and the moon work. But I think it was a rather meaningless ambition until I was about 10; it was then that the excitement engendered by reading the *Buck Rogers* comic strips prompted me to determine that I wanted to go into rocketry. There was never any question that I would be a scientist. My mother, who was a chemist, had influenced me in this direction; the only choice was the field.

"My mother graduated from Buchtel College in Akron with the record of being one of the best chemistry students who had attended the school, but she didn't follow her profession except to encourage me. She bought me a Chem-Craft set, then scratched all the numbers off the bottles, so I would have to learn to read the names and would not go by numbers in running experiments. Her whole approach was not to supply answers, but to encourage investigation. This I strongly endorse."

After 3 years of serious illness, Mrs. Hibbs died before Al was 14. Mr. Hibbs resigned his position as head of the water works in Cincinnati, and assumed duties as head of public utilities at Chillicothe. With this move, Al did a rather astonishing thing:

"I determined that I would deliberately establish a different personality. The reason for it was this—in growing up, I never got along with my own age group. I got along with the kids who were younger, and those who were older. But I remember in high school, all the other boys in my class belonged to one or another of the Greek letter fraternities, but I was never invited to join. I have since learned that this treatment is not unusual for people who are inclined to be scholarly—and I use the word advisedly—but at the time I resented not being accepted.

"So when we moved to Chillicothe, I spent most of my time under my own direction, using my hours my own way. Since I did not do well as a member of a group, I decided I might as well be on top of them rather than underneath—be a group leader rather than a group follower. To do this, I set about establishing a reputation of being a real nut, which was easy to do, coming from a big city into a smaller one."

Hibbs solicited the friendship of older people, and set a new social pattern. "We spent quite a few evenings in local bistros. Though it seemed exciting at the time, I don't think it is possible to really be very sophisticated in a small town."

The entire episode is certainly unusual—that any boy of that age would so deliberately think through and act upon a situation. There was wisdom in Hibbs's father's handling of the period: "My father never said 'no' to me that I can remember. Though he never prevented me from doing anything, nevertheless, he seemed to manage to steer me in a reasonably productive direction. Through his encouragement, I did quite well in school during all of my 'wild' period. I got A's through those last two years." Hibbs was advanced beyond the course in chemistry, and thus spent that class period in the laboratory creating experiments for the other students.

A visit to his cousin, Frank Hibbs, Jr., who was a Cal Tech graduate, convinced Hibbs that it would help him achieve his aim to attend that school. He was drawn by the challenge of studying theoretical physics at the institution headed by Dr. Robert Millikan. Entrance examinations were administered by the local high school professor; after passing those, he went to Cincinnati to be interviewed by Ray Untereiner, an economics professor at Cal Tech who was traveling throughout the country interviewing applicants and selecting promising students for enrollment.

In a summer camp which is held in the mountains behind San Bernardino, Cal Tech freshmen are allowed a period of indoctrination, and an opportunity to meet upper classmen and the professors. A fellow freshman, Fred Eimer (who now works as Hibbs's assistant), relates that each freshman had to stand up and introduce himself. When it was Hibbs's turn, he decided that the only proper way was to stand on a table and declare, "I am Albert Hibbs, Albert the Elegant." Eimer adds, "Even without that, he was certainly one of the most spectacular class members. He walked around the campus carrying a large book on Egyptology. I used to wonder if he really read it, or just carried it for effect."

The student houses became Hibbs's home—first Dabney, then Blacker. Chemical glassware completely filled one corner of the room which he shared with Roy Walford (now Associate Professor of Pathology at UCLA). Walford recalls his first impression of Hibbs: "A witty sort of individual, and very intelligent—as are all people at Cal Tech. Al was quite given to pranks. He specialized in hazing tricks that would cause the hazed person to pull the trick on himself. I remember one, where he put a bucket of water over a man's door, but placed it so it could be seen. The man saw the bucket, very carefully took it down, and went over to his sink and poured it out. The trick was that Al had disconnected the sink, so that the water spilled all over his feet."

Walford, more the studious type, had many battles with Hibbs because of the constant stream of visitors who came to their room. Bull sessions were a part of the social activity which Hibbs relished. His problems in "getting along" with people had vanished.

Studies fascinated him—particularly those in theoretical and mathematical physics, with its unending realm of imagination. "Another thing that intrigued me was Cal Tech's biology department which was headed by Dr. Thomas Hunt Morgan. It is today probably one of the best in the world, yet was never 'advertised'; when I was there, it had almost no undergraduate students. I took a course in plant physiology from Dr. Frits Went, a Dutchman who is now in charge of a laboratory in St. Louis. At Cal Tech, he set up the Earhart Plant Research Laboratory and did important work in understanding the factors that affect plant growth."

The Navy took over the entire undergraduate school at Cal Tech in the spring of 1943. Hibbs became an apprentice seaman, and went into V-12 Officer Training. Three months before graduation, he was riding his motorcycle to the Vista del Arroyo Hotel to buy some cigarettes. "I finished my trip all right—but in an ambulance, and with a broken leg. The hotel at this time had been taken over as an Army hospital.

"I had to complete my work from the hospital. This was most difficult. You'd think, offhand, that all you do in a hospital is lie around, but I found it was quite impossible to study. I deserved to be washed out, but my teachers were very generous and got me through with C's and D's."

Graduation in the spring of 1945 brought Hibbs a commission, but he could not accept duty on a round-the-world troop transport since his leg was still in a cast. "According to the rules of the Navy, you can't be moved from one station to another unless you are fit for active duty. So I had to remain at Cal Tech. The Navy's contract with Cal Tech wouldn't allow them to pay for just my room and board—it had to include tuition. So I became the only V-12 graduate student in the country! I was not transferred, until I had finished that term of work."

It was during this semester that Hibbs had his first real contact with the professor who had been his faculty adviser during his 4 years at the Institute, William R. Smythe. "He called me into his office and said, 'Now that you have your bachelor's degree, what do you intend to do with it?' I was a little hesitant, then confessed that really what I wanted to do was to build rockets and go to the moon.

"I thought this would incite big guffaws of laughter. Instead he took a paper out of his drawer and said, 'That is a very interesting problem. Most people forget that when you are going on a round trip, most of the load you have to worry about is the fuel to get back home again.' "

Smythe continued to dumbfound Hibbs with his careful analysis: "He had worked out the problem most carefully. After that, I started asking other professors around the campus, 'Have you ever thought about rockets to the moon?' Every one of them had. In fact, I would say on this brief survey that at least half the people in the physics department at Cal Tech were studying physics because they originally had been attracted to science by a desire to go to the moon."

It was an indication of the times, however, that such topics were not discussed unless someone else opened up the topic. Lunar journeys had not then assumed any air of respectability. In fact, there were many who took occasion to demonstrate that it could never be done. Hibbs recalls one research seminar in which a professor theoretically proved that it would take a rocket as big as Mt. Everest to reach the moon. "I knew there was something wrong with that, but I didn't learn what it was until later—he had forgotten about doing it in stages."

Trips to destinations closer than the moon were also discussed during Hibbs's Cal Tech period. He and his roommate, Walford, laid plans for a round-the-world sail. Walford wanted to study tropical medicine, and Hibbs was intent upon doing some mathematical biophysics. The execution of this giant adventure awaited two elements: the proper time and the money.

Meanwhile, Hibbs went for a voyage as a guest of the U.S. Navy. He was in the one group which was sent to sea without having midshipman training, and he formed some dubious opinions about the sea during his trip to Calcutta on a troop transport. The second trip, to Yokohama, proved more rewarding. An officer friend gave him the name of a beautiful Japanese girl who lived on an estate in the hills near Yokohama.

"I enlisted the aid of the local Red Cross, showed them her address, and they wrote it in Japanese characters, then headed me in the general direction. I went to the end of the street and showed the address to an aged man in a hopi coat who was puttering in his garden; he drew a map on the ground with a stick and I continued. Next I came upon a Caucasian man and a Japanese woman who worked for Radio Tokyo—it had just been taken over by our occupation forces. They walked with me for a while, until we came into a countryside of rolling hills and terraced farms. The huge thatched roofs of the farmhouses had eaves that overhung until they almost touched the ground, and the big houses were generally made up of many little ones that had been built piece by piece over the years."

Hibbs continued his search until he came upon a farmer who understood the name he pronounced. He beckoned to his young daughter and instructed her to lead the way. Hibbs recalls, "She looked at me suspiciously, then started up the road. Soon others joined, until a whole herd of children were following me. When we at last reached the house, all just stared at me. I took a quarter out of my pocket and handed it to the little girl. Gravely she looked at it, passed it all around the group, then handed it back and thanked me. Still the children stared at me."

Later Hibbs learned what they were waiting for. "The youngsters wanted me to take off my Navy officer's hat. It is a Japanese folk tale that all Americans have red hair and they were waiting to see."

Hibbs did not see the girl for whom he was looking, but spent a remarkable evening with her family, interspersing stilted conversation with a gin rummy game, endless cigarette smoking, and meeting others who dropped in. Among the visitors was a commander of a Japanese cruiser which had been sunk; another was the conductor of the Yokohama symphony orchestra.

There are individuals in this world of whom it can be said, "They always have such interesting experiences." Is it happenstance, or is it that interesting people seek and attract unusual experiences? Hibbs's adventures started in his early years, and show no indication of abating. He has an approach to travel that has proved fruitful: "Even when I used to just hitchhike with friends, I learned that the way to really see a place, is to go there with a mission of seeing a specific object. Pick it out ahead of time—

and don't select a common tourist object—and read something about it, if possible. If you go seeking that object, you will really see the sights. If you go merely to see the sights, you end up seeing nothing. This formula has worked for me time and again."

When Hibbs returned to Japan in 1959, he put his time to good use. Although the purpose of the trip was to attend the First International Symposium on Rockets and Astronautics in Tokyo, he arranged it so that he might enrich his experience with a side trip: "I decided I wanted to see the Katsura Detached Palace, in the hills outside of Kyoto. It is considered by many to be the most beautiful piece of architecture in the world, and has within the group of buildings a tea house which I think is the most beautiful building in the world."

With friends who were also attending the Symposium, including Dr. Ernst Stuhlinger and Jack Froehlich, Hibbs flew to Osaka, then asked the driver of a limousine to take them to the train station for Kyoto.

"We rode, and we rode, and we rode, and we rode. Finally it was clear that something was wrong. The driver was not taking us to the Osaka train station. At last he slowed down the car. Our guesses were right—we were in Kyoto. He turned and said, 'Now, you want to go to train station?' "

As Hibbs entered this Japanese city, he had a strange feeling: "The simple beauty of the place, the way it was arranged, the architecture of the buildings, the atmosphere, the trees, the stream, the canal—the whole thing gave me a feeling of home, yet I'd never seen the place before. I've never experienced that feeling more acutely, even when I actually have been coming home."

Though by nature he possesses a broad adaptability and would fit into many backgrounds, Hibbs has an especial liking for the country and people of Japan. "I like their great enthusiasm for doing things, and their zest for life. They have an attitude which permits them to have beauty around them while they engage in a very active life. They don't have to withdraw from activity in order to contemplate beauty, but can enjoy it while they are working.

"Another characteristic that makes an association pleasant is their very good sense of humor. It is much more like the Americans' than the peoples' of other countries I've visited. It is not exactly an English variety, yet their humor and by-play are on a sophisticated level." Perhaps it is well that Hibbs's visits to Japan have been brief. Had he remained long enough to introduce them to his practical-jokes-with-a-twist, the entire trend of their humor might have been influenced!

The very serious purpose within this man prompted him to seek a continuation of his education. After being discharged from the Navy in 1946, he entered the department of mathematics at the University of Chicago, where his friend, Walford, was completing his studies for a medical degree.

They acquired a classic car, a 1929 Pierce-Arrow, which Hibbs managed to keep running. Their apartment was even more ancient, and not at all classic. Relates Walford, "It was a typical students' run-down apartment."

Hibbs is a little more specific: "It was a converted Brownstone, where South Chicago was then gradually turning into slums. We did our bit to help that along. The place was quite picturesque, really. The entrance was by an alley, through a fence, down a cellar trapdoor, and there were our two rooms—separated by a furnace and the clotheslines where everyone else in the apartment house hung their washing on rainy days."

Once Hibbs discovered the University theater, he spent little of his spare time in the apartment. The producer was a member of the faculty who supervised in a most unique fashion—he gave each student the opportunity of working in various capacities. Relates Hibbs, "I had a chance to act, direct, produce, stage manage, and design productions. In this democratic process, the student acting as producer could select the show to put on. I picked an old-fashioned melodrama. I reasoned that since plays of this kind originally had played for a period of years to standing-room-only audiences, they must have dramatic appeal. So we got the original script on *East Lynne,* which was first produced in the 1870's."

By rummaging, the group located the original backdrops which were still stored in an old theater supply store in Chicago. Hibbs approached the play with the thoroughness of a scientific experiment and researched the literature to learn the gestures and method of delivery which were typical of the first production. The cast "played it straight," and endeavored in every way to make it an authentic production—feeling that the very nature of the melodramatic piece would highly amuse the sophisticated Chicago audiences. To their amazement, half the audience was in tears by the end of the fifth act, when the deceived and dying wife was finally forgiven by her wronged husband.

Hibbs had one line in the play. As the police officer who apprehends the villain, he proclaimed: "Frances Levison, I arrest you! You are my prisoner." He walked to the footlights to deliver the line which was greeted by loud cheers, since it was the turning point in the drama.

His friends still recall that era in the scientist's life, "Hibbs was a real light in the theater—which many critics considered superior to the professional theater in Chicago. He played Oswald in Ibsen's *Ghosts;* at other times he was cast as Agamemnon and Mephistopheles. There seems little doubt that he could have succeeded in an acting career, had he not been dedicated already to a scientific career."

Hibbs's present television appearances, in the NBC science series, *Science in the News,* attest to a native ability. By combining two talents, he presents science in an understandable and highly entertaining fashion.

The years of his attendance at the University of Chicago brought another diversion that occasioned a fabled chapter in his life. Hibbs's and Walford's long-planned, round-the-world scientific expedition had not yet surmounted the hurdle of financing. Then one day Hibbs recalled a story once told to a Cal Tech literature class by Professor Harvey Eagleson. It was about a Scotch engineer who figured out a system for playing roulette; with this he had stacked up huge winnings at Monte Carlo. The premise of the system was that roulette wheels, being mechanical objects, are never perfect. So if it can be determined what the imperfections are on a given wheel, bets can be placed accordingly that have a better-than-average chance of winning.

It became a challenging mathematical problem for Hibbs. "First you have to determine how to identify a bad wheel. Then you must calculate how many observations have to be taken in order to be sure that what you are observing is an imbalanced wheel. I figured out curves for all of the particular probabilities characteristics. The biggest problem was to determine how small to make the bets for a given size capital. This I solved only by a kind of mathematical experimentation which I learned since is a standard technique in applied mathematics called, rightly enough, the Monte Carlo method."

Thus armed with the theory of how to win, Hibbs collected his Master's degree in mathematics in 1947, and traveled to Reno by a somewhat circuitous route. Being one who never wastes any opportunity for an interesting project that can be slipped in along with the major activity, Hibbs traveled west via Glacier National Park in Canada. There, in passing, he helped a group of scientists measure how much some of the glaciers had been receding.

Upon arriving in the Nevada city, Hibbs and Walford spent three weeks watching a wheel in the Palace Club, making their observations on alternating 8-hour shifts, and logging the winning number each time. Their survey was interrupted when they were arrested. "We thought at first it was because we were keeping tallies on the wheels, but it turned out that we fitted exactly the description of two men wanted for burglary in San Francisco. We had a difficult time persuading the police they had the wrong men."

Returning to the tables, they completed the logging of nearly ten thousand counts, and put the carefully precalculated system of observation and statistical analysis into action. In 72 continuous hours of alternating shifts at the wheel, Hibbs and Walford transformed their original $125 into

$6000. News-wire releases related how throngs of curious spectators jammed the Club. When the management changed the wheel, they stopped.

Subsequent playing indicated a statistical average of losing two times out of three, even with all of the preparation. At Harold's Club, their second stop, winnings climbed high. The two players finally quit with $7000 and headed for Mexico to hunt decapods.

"A decapod is a kind of very small crab—the name, which means 'ten foot,' comes from the fact it has five pair of legs," Hibbs explains. "So in this trip this search served my precept of always having an objective when you travel. But there was also another reason. A friend of Walford's, a marine zoologist named Robert Menzies, was then working at Scripps Institution of Oceanography, identifying all the species of decapods in the world; he quickly became the world's leading authority on the subject."

The destructive decapods, which eat timbers and pilings, live in the roots of seaweed. Once Walford and Hibbs had reached the beach at Punta Baja, collecting the crustaceans was simple—all that was necessary to do was to dip the seaweed roots in a bottle of formaldehyde.

In addition to collecting decapods, the two men also collected some Mexican fishermen as friends. Among them was a muscular fellow with a cold, and he became Walford's first patient. The treatment sounds familiar: he was given aspirin and lemons. From him, Walford collected his first fee—two live lobsters.

A moment of difficulty arose when Hibbs and Walford reached the border to re-enter the United States. "We've been collecting crabs," they informed a dubious guard. The gallon bottle of formaldehyde to which they pointed did little to substantiate the story. The suspicious guard made a thorough search of their baggage, then waved them on—still puzzled over their unlikely story.

The $7000 in winnings from Reno would not buy the kind of boat and make the scientific expedition that Hibbs and Walford had planned. They returned to Nevada—this time to Las Vegas—where the system worked only on a slim margin. When the Pioneer Club became interested in the attendant publicity and staked them, the winnings rose sharply.

After all expenses, they had cleared $12,000 from the five months of trying to combine mathematics and luck. After a search around the East Coast, they found a 40-foot, 16-ton English Channel cutter named *Adonde* —the Spanish word meaning "to where." After years of dreaming, the voyage was at last under way!

Since their capital had been spent on the boat and equipment, they arranged to write monthly articles for *Science Illustrated* to provide an income. The Great Adventure was working out more wonderfully than they had even hoped.

"On New Year's Day, 1949, we sailed out of New York Harbor. I had always thought the pictures of the rigging on boats covered with ice to be most beautiful. But when you have this experience when you are in the boat, it is miserable. About an hour after we left the Harbor the wind hit, and the result—ice! Still we had fun sailing down the East Coast—until we got stuck on a mud bank at Georgetown, South Carolina. For two days the boat lay on its side before being able to proceed. The next stop was Charleston."

There, Hibbs had his first—and last—lesson in anatomy. "Walford had been having stomach pains, and didn't want to get out to sea without my knowing how to operate on him in case of an emergency. A professor of the Medical College of South Carolina arranged for us to have a cadaver. After Walford witnessed my dissecting, he decided he'd be better off suffering."

A very immediate threat appeared as they continued their sail. As they approached Cape Canaveral, a 50-knot gale struck. "It was a serious situation," Hibbs explains. "The nearby entrances to the inland waterway were too shallow for our boat, which drew 6½ feet. The mainsail was torn. The cooling system for the motor had been built for Lake Michigan, so the water pipes were too small for the warm water of Florida; as a result the motor overheated and stopped. All we had was a staysail, a 50-knot, on-shore wind, and the looming rocks. We finally just squeezed around the Cape, actually passing inside the buoy; the Cape at that time was a vacant beach with a few palmettos."

Cuba was their first foreign destination, and a rhombifer crocodile their objective. The adventurers had an agreement with Dr. William Mann, then director of the National Zoo in Washington, to pay them $450 if they shipped back one of the rare species which was to be found only on the island. Says Hibbs, "Cuba is a marvelous place for a naturalist. There are species there that are no place else in the world, because of being completely isolated. For instance, there is the horned, ivory-billed woodpecker; this bird's bill crosses itself and curls around so that actually the lower bill is hitting the top of the bird's head and causes some damage. They have to get their food from the side. There is also a solenodon, which is a three-toed marsupial—the species which carries its young in a pouch. It looks like a possum. And there are more species of bats than anywhere else in the world because there are limestone caves everywhere."

Hibbs and Walford met a man who was a cave explorer, a geographer, and an active political figure—so active that now he is the Minister of Agricultural Reform in the Castro regime. "His name is Antonio Nuñez Jimenez, and he acted as our mentor. He took us to the dean of Cuban naturalists, Carlos de la Torre, for help in identifying the rhombifer crocodile. This very old man was most hospitable and helpful, and advised us to employ professional crocodile hunters. Acutus, the common species which we did not want, Cubans called the *kayman*. The rare species, rhombifer, is called *cocodrillo*—the Spanish word for crocodile. We visited the zoo to try to recognize each, but it was very hard for us to tell them apart."

They sailed from Havana to the famous Bay of Pigs, and made contact with two crocodile hunters. The party poled around a lagoon in a mangrove wood boat until jabbing underneath the roots of mangrove trees bestirred a crocodile.

"The hunters clobbered it right on top of its head with their poles, but it sped across the lagoon. They poled like mad, caught up with it, and again clobbered it. We tried to convey to them that we didn't want to kill it, but our Spanish was not good enough to communicate. They kept beating it, until finally it got mad and turned and came right for the boat, its jaws wide open. The hunters were very pleased at this, for it couldn't hurt their thick mangrove hull—even though the crocodile was like an express train each time it charged."

For just such a moment, Hibbs and Walford had come prepared. They had a .45 Colt revolver in case of emergency, and a half-inch-thick nylon rope. This set the hunters into gales of laughter; they had only an old and frayed clothesline, which proved to be quite sufficient. They formed a noose, leisurely waited for the crocodile to attack again, dropped the noose over its upper jaw and hauled it out of the water. Immediately the huge reptile became rigid. The jaw, the legs, the tail—all were motionless. Only the closing muscles of the jaw are strong; the ones that act to open the jaws are very weak, so the old clothesline proved most adequate to wrap around the mighty jaws.

But it looked like no crocodile Hibbs and Walford had ever seen. They double checked: *"Cocodrillo?* Not *kayman?"* The hunters were most emphatic: *"Cocodrillo!"* It had all been so simple! They paid the hunters $10, transferred the still-rigid reptile to their yacht, lashed it to an oar and put it on top of the cabin. No sooner had they set sail for Cienfuegos, a city on Cuba's south coast, than Walford became ill with the recurring stomach pains and went below. A driving rainstorm suddenly came up and roused the crocodile; thrashing about, he soon wriggled loose from the oar and fell onto the deck.

Hibbs did not dare leave the tiller, for cliffs were but 100 yards ahead, so he shouted for Walford to come and subdue the crocodile. "Into the driving rain, feverish and wild looking and naked, Roy came up to do battle with the crocodile. It was almost mystical, like the tale of *Beowulf,* to see him get astraddle of the thrashing reptile and beat its head on the deck. He finally got a rope around its throat and choked it into submission, and then we wrapped it in canvas so it couldn't wriggle anymore."

At Cienfuegos, they got the crocodile crated, all shipping papers filed, and had paid the air freight on it. Then, as a final precaution, they asked the professor from the local technical institute to come down and see it. He peeked into the crate, and proclaimed, "Oh, an Acutus." The men were stunned! Hibbs protested, "We told the crocodile hunters *cocodrillo.*" The professor agreed, "You have a *cocodrillo.*"

Walford spoke up, "But de la Torre told us a rhombifer is called *cocodrillo?*" The professor explained, "That is true on the north coast of Cuba. But here on the south coast, the names are interchanged." Resignedly the adventurers uncrated the crocodile, loaded it aboard their yacht, and took it to the open sea and dumped it out. The experience had been sad, if enlightening. Hibbs conjectures, "Right now, that crocodile is no doubt back practicing the favorite pastime of the species, chewing on the legs of cows when they come to drink the water."

The most profitable thing that came out of the Cuban stay was meeting some other Americans who told Hibbs and Walford how they might join the Escanaba Michigan Yacht Club for $10; a membership in any registered yacht club provides a special rate for berths at any other yacht club in the world. They set sail for San Juan, hoping the letter of reply from Escanaba would reach them there.

"The trip to San Juan was a wild one. We were arrested in Haiti on suspicion of gun running, and arrested in the Dominican Republic—we never learned what for. We finally ran out of food, water, fuel, and everything else. We made it to the entrance of San Juan Harbor, then sat becalmed between the buoys for three hours with big steamers sailing past us on both sides.

"Finally, we made it in, docked and anchored at the yacht club. We walked in hungry, thirsty, unshaven, barefoot, in foul-weather gear. It was a very fancy place and we expected to get thrown out immediately. Instead they loved us—we were the saltiest things that had ever come into that club. All of their members just gave parties on their boats and never got to sea, so they thought the sight of real sailors was great."

When Hibbs and Walford were asked if they were members of any yacht club, they countered by asking if any mail had arrived. One letter had—from the Escanaba Yacht Club! They ripped it open, and handed over the membership card. At this point, gaining a cheap berth was an important item, for the men had not received any checks for the articles they had been sending in to *Science Illustrated.* As they relaxed in the lounge of the San Juan Yacht Club and perused some magazines to see what had been happening in the world, they learned why: An item in

Time magazine, headed "The End of an Experiment," described the demise of the magazine.

With the prospect of any income thus ended, Walford entered the San Juan School of Tropical Medicine. Hibbs had heard of the fellowships in rocket propulsion that had been established by the Guggenheim Foundation at Cal Tech. "I'd had it as far as sailing went. I wanted to get back into science again, so decided to return to the States and get an honest job."

The tale that Al Hibbs applied for a position at Cal Tech while wearing a T-shirt and a beard should be forever stilled. He protests, "I was quite properly dressed in a business suit." But he does admit his hair was pretty long and he had a mustache. "They said I looked like a refugee from the Pasadena Playhouse."

The information Hibbs had gotten was correct—the Guggenheim Foundation was sponsoring fellowships for graduate students. But he was asked if he would prefer a job. He would. An appointment was arranged with Dr. Homer Joe Stewart, Chief of the Research Analysis Section, at Cal Tech's Jet Propulsion Laboratory, JPL.

Hibbs recalls, "I told him my wish hadn't changed—I still wanted to go to the moon, and I thought this was a pretty good place to start. Homer Joe countered by telling me a mathematical problem. I claimed I knew how to solve it. I didn't really, but I thought I could figure it out." Hibbs must have been convincing, for he next saw the Director of JPL, Dr. Louis Dunn. Notably a man of few words, he said, "I understand Dr. Stewart has talked with you. $300 a month?"

Hibbs accepted. The interview was over and he had acquired the only job he has ever held. But there was one hitch that he feared might cause difficulty—he had to return to Puerto Rico and help Walford sail their boat to Miami. "To my surprise, the people at JPL were quite taken with the idea, didn't object at all—they merely extended the date on which I was to report to work for two months, to February, 1951."

Nothing that has occurred in Hibbs's life seems quite usual or ordinary. Even his airplane trip east was eventful. "I flew on a Constellation that was being delivered to KLM Royal Dutch Airlines. My fellow passengers were a load of live mink. They look much more beautiful than they smell."

As can be expected, the return sail was eventful. "We were becalmed in the middle of the Gulf Stream. The generator had stopped working so we couldn't get the motor to work. We had run out of water and food long since. For the first time since we'd had the boat we tried the flares; they were so waterlogged they wouldn't work. We had bought $250 worth of laboratory equipment to do various pieces of research; none of it had been used. So we set up a little still to distill sea water.

"Finally I got the motor started by cranking it. Although there wasn't enough juice in the battery to turn it with the starter, there was enough juice to operate it once I got it started. Fortunately, we had plenty of gasoline because the motor had not worked during the entire trip."

Hibbs and Walford reached Miami in the middle of the night when the customs office was closed. After explaining to the guard that they had not eaten in three days, and with the promise that they would return to their boat and go through quarantine officially the next morning, he let them through to consume two steak dinners each.

There was a moment of fond regret after the graceful *Adonde* had been sold. Although the mission planned for her voyages had never been fulfilled, sailing on her had taught Hibbs many lessons. Perhaps the most important of these was that he should change course and head into space.

Cal Tech's research into rocketry started with a handful of enthusiasts in 1936. JPL was later spun off from the main campus and established in the foothills behind Pasadena as a rocket research center. It was here that was undertaken during World War II the development of America's first jet-assist take-off, JATO. Army Ordnance requested JPL apply this knowledge toward the creation of rocket-propelled guided missiles. This ultimately produced the *Private,* the *Corporal* and the *Sergeant.* Of more importance than the actual hardware that came out of this far-looking Laboratory, perhaps, was the policy of instigating basic research in physics, chemistry, metallurgy, electronics and aerodynamics. These were the building blocks for space science. Just as JPL was expanding, so also was Hibbs, personally, undergoing quiet growth. Long before he received his Master's degree in mathematics from the University of Chicago, he had realized that his selection of field had been a mistake. "It was very dull. Perhaps it was the particular method of teaching, but to me it was not satisfying to memorize things from books and repeat them back on command. I was eager to get back into theoretical physics."

Hibbs's wish was granted with the first problem that befell him at JPL: to determine the optimum burning program for rockets which were flying horizontally. (The optimum program for the burning of fuel of rockets in vertical flight had previously been determined.)

"Fortunately," he recalls, "Homer Joe didn't tell me how difficult he considered the problem, or I probably would have had an awful time." But not being aware how much effort had been expended toward solving this long standing major problem, Hibbs had the answer and had published his findings within three months.

A short while after assuming his position at JPL, Hibbs enrolled at Cal Tech to begin work on his doctorate. It was a heavy schedule—30 hours a week at each place. The following year he got a fellowship, grading papers and teaching sophomores, and worked at JPL only during vacations. The last two years he attended school on fellowships from Cal Research Corporation, the research branch of Standard Oil Company.

Studying under Dr. Richard P. Feynman, his major was theoretical physics. "I did my thesis in oceanography. Actually, it was low-speed aerodynamics—studying how the wind makes the waves grow, and the wind flow over waves. It's a very messy problem which I don't think I adequately solved, but I produced some techniques for solving it. Most of it was based on data taken during World War II, when it was important to try to figure out what the wave conditions on beaches would be by measuring wave and weather conditions in other locations. The theory of how this happens was still quite up in the air. There had been several mistakes in mathematics in the generation of the prediction scheme that existed—some of which I found and managed to straighten out, and then continued to develop this theory of wave growth."

Although it might appear unusual to the unscientific person that a man who is interested in the air would study the water, it must be observed that these media react similarly in many conditions. For example, Dr. Theodore von Kármán's great aerodynamic Theory of Vortex Trails—which explains how alternating motions behind a moving body produce stability—was inspired by observing the flow of water around a cylinder.

Increasingly, it is being realized that nature does not write separate rule books for things that men have arbitrarily categorized. Porpoises have been studied to learn how to make submarines that will go faster. Single and generally simple concepts are tending to replace complicated and not-quite-consistent old theories.

No technological limitations existed, and no wide-ranging views on science remained unexplored by the inquiring minds of the JPL crew in the 1950's. The Laboratory in those days was a friendlier place, possibly because there were about 600 people instead of today's nearly 3000. There was a spirit in the work which later tended to be greatly sobered when space became the arena for such a grave competition. One of the projects to which Hibbs devoted much time was the *Loki,* an unguided barrage-type missile, which is now being used as a sounding rocket. Says Hibbs's friend and colleague, John Porter, "In the ballistic test program for this project, Al was responsible for the theoretical analysis of the accuracy and performance of the rocket. We made many trips together to White Sands Proving Ground, New Mexico, for test firings. In trying to develop a very accurate, high performance weapon every possible kind of problem seemed to come up and Al was outstanding in this work—as in all other things he has done—because he grasped things so fast. He would just 'take off' and accomplish the job then and there. He's a really hard worker, and very easy to get along with.

"Though at that time we were just dealing with Army contracts for small rockets, we kept looking forward to the prospect that eventually we would get into outer space. Al and I discussed many science fiction novels which we had both read. We wanted to go in the direction of space, but at that time we weren't sure if the other people—the taxpayers—would want to.

"By 1954, we began to suspect what the decade would bring in space, because of the tremendous strides in propulsion and booster technology. Our own people here at JPL had made great strides and Dr. Wernher von Braun was doing remarkable things. We became involved in the RTV (re-entry test vehicle), which was a *Redstone* with a cluster of solid rocket motors (scaled-down *Sergeants*) on top. With this, we saw that a satellite could be placed into orbit," says Porter.

Building No. 85 was the scene of this advanced activity, as Hibbs relates: "In Homer Joe's Section One, Research Analysis, we computed such problems as how big a load a multi-stage rocket could carry to the moon. With rockets that were then developed, a *Redstone* plus *Lokis,* we figured that we could put a half-empty beer can on the moon. There were many lively sessions that included Jack Froehlich, John Porter, Fred Eimer, Mort Alperin, Henry Nagamatsu, and in the early days, H. S. Tsien." When Dr. Homer Joe Stewart took over a newly formed Liquid Propulsion Division, Hibbs took over as Chief of the Research Analysis Section.

Regarding the "space status" in that year, Hibbs points out, "There was a great deal of serious talk about it, within the community of those who were working on rockets. But it must be remembered that there weren't a lot of people so occupied. Consider that the average man who is working in the missile business today has less than one year's experience; this indicates how rapidly the field has been expanding—doubling every year or two. Most of the experienced people are doing administration, not engineering."

In 1954, JPL became involved with a proposal to send up a satellite, Project *Orbiter,* a joint Army Ballistic Missile Agency–Office of Naval Research effort. In reviewing the project, JPL suggested a major change—instead of placing a spinning cluster of 37 *Loki* rockets as upper stages on a *Redstone* booster, they proposed using 15 scaled-down *Sergeant* rockets. Thereby, both reliability and payload weight could be increased.

This configuration was built, and took on the designation *Jupiter-C.* With it, the *Orbiter* satellite could have been the first into orbit, and space history could have been changed. *Jupiter-C* underwent three successful launchings, beginning in September, 1956, as a re-entry test vehicle, and Hibbs says, "Either the second or third of these could have put a satellite into orbit."

The limiting factor was not technological capability but official policy.

Project *Orbiter* was cancelled, and Project *Vanguard* was chosen to develop a capability to try to orbit the first United States satellite.

To insure that those involved in the hopeful planning of *Orbiter* no longer harbored the thought of continuing the project, Hibbs relates the rather drastic measures that were taken: "There was a story out of Huntsville that the government accounting office went to ABMA and confiscated all reports which bore the word 'satellite' in their title, and any equipment which looked like it had to do with satellites.

"At JPL, we had for several months been building the satellite for *Orbiter*. We had a difficult time continuing, and bootlegged the whole job under the title of a re-entry vehicle program. When finished, we locked up the satellite in a cabinet in a building up in solid-motor test area so it wouldn't be found."

It was a frustrating experience for those who had expended so much effort and knew the capability of *Orbiter*. Says Hibbs, "It was ready. We were ready. But we couldn't get permission to launch it. We even contemplated doing a re-entry test which would 'fail'—in that it would not re-enter but would send the payload into orbit. All that would have been needed to accomplish this was to put on the last stage that we had ready and waiting. But this never happened, because the Army had direct orders not to launch a satellite."

The situation became the more maddening because the activities and intentions of the Soviets were known. Hibbs says, "The Russians had published their intentions, so it could be anticipated almost to the month. I remember that on October 4, 1957, an engineer, Walter Downhower, came into my office on some other business; as he was leaving, he said, 'Oh, by the way, word came through that the Russians have launched their satellite.' I said, 'Oh, really?' Then I went back to work. The only thing that astounded any of us was that it could have come as a surprise to anyone in scientific or official circles."

Displaying a remarkable sense of humor about this disappointing situation, John Small, a highly respected section chief at JPL, made this pronouncement which is familiar to card players: "The winners laugh and joke and the losers yell 'deal.'" The name stuck. *Deal* became the new designation for the *Orbiter* satellite which was locked up in the cabinet. Hibbs and Pickering journeyed to Washington, D.C., feeling that at last they would encounter a receptive attitude toward proceeding with the project.

As it then stood, *Orbiter-Deal* was a satellite without any scientific experiments aboard. But the situation could be quickly rectified, as Hibbs relates: "Dr. James A. Van Allen was responsible for the cosmic ray experiments that were to be put aboard *Vanguard*. But he had seen the handwriting on the wall; because of the trouble that was being encountered with *Vanguard,* he proceeded differently from the other experimenters—instead of designing a package as a 20-inch sphere which would have fitted into *Vanguard* only, he designed a 6-inch cylinder which would also fit into the JPL satellite. He had a strong hunch that the latter would be the one to fly his experiment."

An incident occurred during the immediate post-*Sputnik* period which reminded Hibbs of the fact that science often awaits the machinations of politics and service rivalry. "A highly placed individual depreciated *Sputnik,* calling it 'a hunk of iron,' and said that our Army's desire to get a satellite into orbit was a 'boondoggle.' He contended that the *Jupiter-C* couldn't work, that there had never been any tests of the stability of the launching top; he further charged that JPL's cluster of solid-propellant rockets had low reliability, and so forth."

The group which was endeavoring to reappraise the situation and reach a decision on what should be done regarding a program to launch an American satellite insisted that the allegations must be resolved. A meeting was held in the office of the Army's top civilian scientist; to this Hibbs was summoned to give an opinion: "I was called in since I had all the calculations on the probability of orbiting a satellite with a *Jupiter-C* missile, based on all the tests that had been done so far. Pickering and Froehlich were there, and we had been rather quietly overcoming this gentleman's strong charges, when Dr. Eberhardt Rechtin (who headed Guidance Research) came in. The accuser asked Ed if he had any comment, and Ed opened up with something like, 'Sir, it is perfectly clear what your whole motivation is. All you are doing is just throwing sand in the air, hoping to get this whole decision thrown back to another committee where you felt you could stifle it and permanently sabotage the whole program. Your actions are completely un-American. You do not have the interests of your country at heart. You should be removed from your position.' "

After this blistering commentary, the superior to the man making the allegations informed Rechtin that they had not come to be insulted and abruptly terminated the meeting. However, Hibbs relates that on the way out of the office, the superior said in a quiet aside to Rechtin, "You'll go far, young man!"

Soon after, the Army received official sanction to proceed, using the *Jupiter-C* as the launch vehicle, and the satellite which JPL had long been waiting to finish with the inclusion of the selected experiment.

Before launch, the satellite was again rechristened. This time President Eisenhower chose the name *Explorer.* Had names been pounds, this satellite would surely have grown too heavy to have made it off the launch pad. In addition to the name *Deal,* which JPL chose, Maj. Gen. John B. Medaris, inspired by an earlier design shape, felt it would be appropriately called *Highball.* Secretary of the Army Wilber Brucker was faithful to the tradition of his service when he suggested the name *Top Kick*. No doubt other appellations were hatched in midnight planning sessions, but are now lost to posterity.

Al Hibbs had a good chunk of his heart and soul—and all of his scientific capability—tied up in that satellite. He had done the mathematics for the design of the upper stage cluster which would kick it (he hoped) into its orbit: "What was the probability that all the motors would ignite? It was of great concern. There were 11 motors tied together in the second stage. What was the chance that one of them would blow up? As the second stage comes out of the spinning 'tub,' on the front end of the *Redstone* booster, it tends to tip. How much will it tip? Will it bang the side of the tub? What are the dispersion effects? The dispersion problem of the high-speed solid-propellant stages, spinning and under thrust, was quite a difficult problem which I had to work through. Then I had all of the trajectory calculations, plus the data reduction of the trajectory. Also, I was one of the two experimenters on the temperature problem, putting aboard what was termed an experiment but was really more of an engineering device."

On January 31, 1958, Hibbs and three others were locked in a room in JPL's Quonset hut at Cape Canaveral. It was Hibbs's responsibility to determine, at the earliest possible instant, whether *Explorer I* had gone into orbit. Those assisting him were his deputy, Fred Eimer, Fridtjof Speer, and physicist Charles Lundquist of the von Braun team. Relates Eimer, "It wasn't done in those days like it is now with computers and such aids. We used pre-computed charts and slide rules. It was a frantic process." The remarkably unprecise and unscientific method was fraught with difficulties, since it was literally thrown together at the last moment. Only on the very day of the launching was it finally arranged with the Navy to receive teletype messages from their Minitrack stations.

Hibbs relates, "The first bit of data we were to receive was to be from the impact predictor on the Cape, which was going to be tracking the *Jupiter-C* to give us an initial point for the high-speed stage. It never worked. All they could relate was that the booster was going to come down someplace around Tampa, Florida.

"The next data was to come from Antigua. We had set up a Microlock*

* "*Microlock:* A satellite tracking system developed by Cal Tech's Jet Propulsion Laboratory for use with the U.S. Army's *Explorer* series of satellites. The tracking mechanism employs a low power, lightweight flight transmitter in conjunction with a receiving system of advanced design. The flight transmitter radiates 3 mw for three months and provides two narrow band telemetering channels in a unit having a total weight of 2 lb. The ground receiving equipment is capable of acquiring and tracking the beacon signal at a line-of-sight distance of 3000 miles and at any azimuth and elevation angle."[9]

receiver, and hooked it up to a Minitrack telemetering antenna. We had the other Microlock receiver set up at the Cape. From them, we were going to try to get a two-station Doppler to triangulate on the velocity as the satellite left the last stage. I had a hand computing method set up to compute the orbit on the basis of these two Doppler signals, with various back-up schemes, depending upon what the satellite would do. But when they threw the switch between the Minitrack telemetering trailer to our Microlock equipment, we didn't get any signal; this fairly complicated switch had corroded."

The countdown on *Explorer,* which had started at 8:30 P.M., had only 2 holds for indications of trouble—and they proved to be false alarms. The bird lifted from the launch pad with perfect performance and its fiery trail faded into the night skies. But this was only the first hurdle and did not guarantee that the upper stages would place the satellite into proper orbit. The attention of the world was focused on this scientific attempt, and U.S. prestige had suffered a sad blow December 6, 1957, when the first *Vanguard* had failed.

As word was awaited on the fate of *Explorer I,* moments mushroomed into eternities. It was up to Hibbs to give the answer and two of his sources of data had failed. "All we had to figure with was the data we got from our single Microlock station at the Cape, and this was ambiguous. It was not possible to say precisely what had happened in the launch, because there was no indication of the direction in which it had pointed. We only knew the speed.

"We waited to see when we lost the signal over the horizon. If it were going too high, we'd lose the signal later than our standard trajectory figured; if it were going too low, we'd lose the signal earlier. On the basis of this single bit of data, we took a flier and started figuring out a perigee, apogee, period of time around and even a lifetime in orbit."

General Medaris was sitting across the hall, patiently waiting for Hibbs's answer. It took 45 long minutes before it could be rendered. Hibbs recalls, "I rushed in at last, and announced—just as though I were confident—the apogee, the perigee, the period, and then he interrupted: 'All right, but just tell me—is it in orbit or not?' I said, 'General, it will be in orbit for four years!' "

Medaris grabbed the phone, relayed the word to the Secretary of the Army, then the group rushed for the theater at nearby Patrick Air Force Base which was crowded with restive members of the press. Medaris confidently strode upon the stage and made the momentous announcement that orbit had been achieved for *Explorer I!* Outwardly, Hibbs matched his air of triumph. Unobtrusively, he kept noting his watch. He knew that it was time for *Explorer* to have completed its first orbit and be coming up over the horizon of the West Coast. With as casual an air as he could muster, Hibbs telephoned back to his office asking if they had received any word via their teletype line to California. They had not. Seconds piled into minutes. Hibbs and Lundquist, who was in the back of the theater, exchanged looks. An air of anxiety began to permeate the group. It was 10 tortuous minutes later than they had calculated that California verified *Explorer* was in orbit! The fact that it had gone in a higher orbit than figured accounted for the delay and also indicated that it would remain in its path for ten years instead of four!

There were devices aboard *Explorer I* which revealed important measurements to scientists. The best known of the findings is the Van Allen Radiation Belt. But there were others. *Explorer I* carried an experiment devised by Dr. Maurice Dubin and Dr. Ed Manring of the Air Force Cambridge Research Laboratory which consisted of a small microphone mounted against the case which would pick up the noise made by subparticles hitting the case. The data sent back was analyzed by Dubin; he published his findings two months later showing the average flux of the micrometeorites and how it changed from day to day during the course of the 12-day experiment.

Dubin found no other pieces of information in the data. Hibbs, however, felt it might be worth a more thorough analysis to see not only how the micrometeorites changed from day to day but how they changed in space. His original hope was to find a ring of dust around the earth, so he was looking for a concentration of impact as the satellite crossed back and forth across the equator. He had a good trajectory, and could compute where the satellite was at the exact time it reported each hit; this was possible because it was direct telemetry. (In later experiments, micrometeorite experiments were often recorded so that it was not possible to tell when the hits occurred, but merely how many there had been during an orbit.)

Hibbs did not find what he was really expecting—a concentration of hits near the equator. But another finding was of interest—there was a sharp change in the concentration of hits with altitude. After weeks of thought as to the significance of this, Hibbs concluded that this change could be analyzed in such a way as to show the speed of the particles that were hitting. (As particles get nearer the earth they speed up and this would give more particles to be counted in the same length of time.) In carrying out the analysis, he found that the average speed was less than escape velocity, which indicated they were not falling toward the earth from outer space, but were in orbit around the earth. He concluded that more than half the particles counted were in semi-permanent earth orbit, implying that not all the particles were on their way to impact with the earth, but that there exists around the earth a permanent cloud of dust particles.

Says Hibbs, "They can't have been there very long, perhaps a few years or a few thousand years, or they would not be distributed as a cloud surrounding the earth, but would be in a ring."

Hibbs was the first to report this finding in a scientific article, in the *Journal of Geophysical Research,* February, 1961; it is noted that his manuscript was received November 22, 1960.

The astronautical literature of these past few years is dotted with "firsts." It is an era of scientific discovery which is unparalleled. The opportunity is vast, and so is the challenge. Says Dr. Pickering, "In general, there is need today for people in science and engineering with good training in breadth—because so much of the engineering and scientific work we are doing is in fields that did not even exist only a few years ago. Repeatedly, a man will be working in a field that was completely unheard of when he graduated—even though he still may be quite young. The ability then to have the fundamental training of considerable scope may be an important element in a man's ability to adapt himself to the new field.

"Al Hibbs has had an interesting variety of work in his career with his activity in aeronautics, mathematics, physics, and aerodynamics. It was important that he had capability in a variety of scientific disciplines, as well as the basic engineering experience gained in working at the Laboratory in some of our programs for a number of years. So Al has this great versatility, added to his considerable scientific curiosity. It has played to his favor, since space science is such a very broad field."

Another trait which has characterized Hibbs is a love of games. As a boy, he created a war game involving 5000 lead soldiers which he made himself by heating lead in a ladle and pouring it into molds. "Each game lasted several months—we really mounted a war. There were very complicated rules about moving, and about determining when two groups of soldiers met how many were killed and how many captured. I seldom could find anyone who was willing to stick with it until a game was finished."

The games Hibbs prefers in his adult life are no simpler. Three-handed gin rummy is a favorite, and he says, "I've never seen it played anywhere but at JPL. The scoring mechanism is so intricate that mathematicians cannot keep it—only engineers can." (*Author's Note:* Hibbs was not smiling when he said this!)

Perhaps his favorite game is one which Porter says they used to play during their lunch hour: "It is a Japanese game of strategy called 'Go,' in which you have a board with crossed lines making 19 by 19 squares. One participant has buttons made out of bone, the other has buttons of slate, and each puts down a button in turn—the object being to take as much territory as possible and surround your opponent. In Japan it is a very popular game, but here it is considered highbrow. We would eat our lunch out of a sack and play this each day—sometimes becoming so absorbed that our lunch hour was pretty long. But we could rationalize that this kind of activity helps to train a scientific mind!"

Time soon grew too precious for Hibbs to have even moments for relaxation such as that—but the rigorous routine was of his own doing.

On December 3, 1958, the newly created civilian space agency, the National Aeronautics and Space Administration, NASA, had immediate need of acquiring already-operating facilities to carry out the space programs it was formulating. It reached out to Pasadena and designated that JPL would become one of its centers. The Laboratory still would be operated by Cal Tech, just as it had been while JPL was under the jurisdiction of the Army. But the responsibility which JPL assumed underwent considerable change.

Under the Army jurisdiction, the sequence of work began with that military service making a statement of objectives for an engineering task. This was studied by members of JPL, and they countered by saying what was, and was not, feasible. Next, the two groups would compare and draft compromise objectives. After this, JPL performed as an engineering organization to develop the missile which the Army wanted, and eventually delivered it to them for use in the field.

As a NASA center, it was up to JPL personnel to specify their own objectives, as well as to develop the hardware, participate in the launch, and finally analyze and publish scientific results. This greatly extended their field of responsibility.

The initial NASA program was for exploration of space by earth satellites. Hibbs, like many other JPL engineers, was convinced that this was not far-reaching enough, and that the major objective of our national space policy should be the moon and the planets. He prepared a detailed report outlining this view, and persuasively discussed the matter with many at the top level of NASA.

Within a few months, this expanded view became the NASA policy. In July, 1959, a Space Sciences Division was created by JPL and Hibbs was named Chief. Says Pickering, "Al was responsible for the first detailed thinking and planning which was done on space science activities here at the Laboratory. He was well suited to the position, for he has good ability to analyze the situation and attack the problem, and he has initiative, which is important."

George Hobby adds, "It seems to me that what Al has been able to accomplish career-wise is due to an aggressiveness—which certainly is not an offensive aggressiveness—and to his intellect." Both were indeed required to fabricate plans and procedures from the nebulous thinking of so vast an undertaking as was the Space Sciences Division. It started with a theoretical section and an instrumentation section of 40 people. By the time Hibbs left it, he had built it up to 256 people.

But everything has its price! John Porter observes a little pensively, "Al lost some of his flamboyance when he became an administrator. He used to wear fluorescent green socks and not be too neat in his dressing." Even individualists must make certain concessions to conformity.

Since the launching of the first satellite, JPL and Hibbs have figured in the efforts to place successive ones aloft. *Explorer II* failed to orbit, *Explorer III* carried a tape recorder which stored data, *Explorer IV* was devoted entirely to cosmic ray studies, *Explorer V* failed to orbit after a successful launch because the booster and instrument compartment collided. JPL has continued to participate in similar scientific investigations.

Concurrent with these efforts, JPL was also involved in the *Pioneer* series of deep space probes. *Pioneer III* failed to reach escape velocity, but in the rewarding way that space experiments have of compensating for their "failures," it proved the existence of the second Van Allen Radiation Belt. *Pioneer IV* passed within 38,000 miles of the moon and went into orbit around the sun.

For these probes, JPL constructed the Goldstone Tracking Station, with an 85-foot diameter parabolic receiving dish; this became the center of NASA's Deep Space Instrumentation Facility, DSIF, of which other stations are located at Woomera, Australia, and Krugersdorp, South Africa. With the Goldstone facility, the world's first two-way telephone call was bounced off the moon on August 4, 1960. Thus with projects and installations, JPL has been heavily engaged in both research and engineering.

Though Hibbs's close association allows him full appreciation of the complexities involved, he is convinced that one phase of space negotiations could be changed for the better. "It appears to me that the government can defeat its own purposes by the manner in which contracts are drawn. After a company's proposal is accepted and a contract is drawn, the company is guaranteed its profit, regardless of whether it produces a success or a failure. In fact, it is possible that it can be more to the advantage of the company not to succeed too quickly but to get an extension of the contract—because thereby the profit, which is a percentage of the cost, increases. It is possible for a company to do this, rather than to simply finish a project immediately on schedule.

"This method of operating also puts a premium on proposal writing. Salesmanship is *the* thing, because once you have the proposal accepted, you get the fee. Nothing else matters, such as delivering on schedule. So the best engineers, the most qualified people are proposing, they are not designing. As soon as a contract is signed, all too often the company puts the second string on the doing of the job, and lets the first string go after the next job. Top men are writing proposals in every one of the aero/space industries."

Would companies be receptive to a change in this policy? Hibbs cites this reaction: "When we were seeking a contractor for Project *Surveyor,* we said to several companies: 'What would you think about an incentive fee? No *Surveyors* on the moon, no profit. If two or three land, you get the average 7 per cent profit. If you get anything more than that, you get more profit.' Every one of the contractors said they would love such a deal—that it was exactly as they would like to do business. We then asked the government to OK it; since it was a sub-contract from JPL to the contractors, legalities would not prevent it. But it sounded too complicated and it was too novel. It was not permitted." Incentive contracts are being more widely considered, and will doubtless be adopted in time.

After building up the Space Sciences Division, Hibbs became restive with administrative responsibility. Confides one friend, "Al is an empire builder, but not an empire operator. He likes initiating an idea and building up an idea from scratch, but being the manager of a going concern is not something he enjoys."

Since becoming affiliated with the Arms Control and Disarmament Agency, Hibbs has retained one activity of his former Division: "I'm currently the convener of the experimenters for the photography of the moon by the *Ranger* series. The others involved are Dr. Harold Urey, Dr. Gerard Kuiper, Dr. Eugene Shoemaker, Raymond Heacock and Edwin Dobies. We are the six involved in the *Ranger* TV experiment, which will come in and take close-up photographs."

A myth has grown up, Hibbs feels, about the relative positions of science and engineering. "The concept that science precedes engineering is generally not true," he states. "The principle of Nicholas Carnot* and the birth of thermodynamics came after the invention of the steam engine, and was propounded in an attempt to explain how it worked. It wasn't that the research on thermodynamics was done first and then some engineer took that and built steam engines. It was the other way around. This is quite often true, that the engineers do something because it works, and then the scientists come in and try to explain how.

"There is a great distinction between them. A scientist is judged by his peers; his work is held up to his peers to judge whether or not it is successful. But engineers are judged by society. An engineer's success depends upon whether or not what he makes is socially useful. Engineers are paid by society. Scientists are usually 'paid' by each other, sometimes by others who

* *Carnot's principle:* " . . . the efficiency of a reversible engine depends on the temperatures between which it works, is fundamental in the theory of thermodynamics."[10]

believe that their work is worthwhile, for reasons they can't quite describe."

In this interesting view, Hibbs continues by saying: "So when there's big money involved, it's usually engineering. There's big money in the space program, and it's going mostly for engineering."

This changes from a rather simple statement to an indication of disappointment from Hibbs when interpreted by the man who served as his assistant in the Space Sciences Division, Dr. Fred Eimer: "The Division, under Al's leadership, took on the task of finding out what's on the moon, the planets, and in outer planetary space. But there is still a great deal of work to be done in convincing and selling people on the idea that the scientific aspects of space exploration are indeed an important part—or maybe *the* most important part—of the entire program. The people who are concerned with the technology like to think of that as an end in itself. But this engineering aspect of the spacecraft and the booster rocket—though undeniably important—is not the eventual aim. It is merely the means of getting into space.

"Both the manned spaceflight people, and our unmanned space sciences effort are faced with providing a real reason for going into space—and that is to do something once you get out there. To go to the moon once, and to be the first there, is important. But you don't go the second time just to go—there must be more reason. Yet there is still not wide acceptance of the importance of any scientific measurements, or the testing of new concepts or systems. Though Al has been quite effective in trying to put across recognition of this, he wished that he could have accomplished more."

The man of imagination and capability will always strain against the slow pace of change, or progress, and of understanding. Hibbs quotes two descriptions of the moon: "The prominences there are mainly very similar to our most rugged and steepest mountains, and some of them are seen to be drawn out in long tracts of hundreds of miles. . . . In the middle of many of these there is a mountain in sharp relief and some few are filled with a rather dark substance similar to that of the large spots that are seen with the naked eye; these are the largest ones, and there are a very great number of smaller ones, almost all of them circular."[11]

The second description relates: "The most striking formations on the moon are the craters, which are of all sizes up to a hundred miles or more in diameter and are scattered over the surface with a great profusion, frequently overlapping. . . . The darker areas which are not so much covered by craters have been considered to be seas of lava which have spread over the moon's surface at a later date than that of the formation of most of the craters."[11]

Hibbs makes the interesting observation that the first description was that of Galileo in the early 1600's. The second is from the *Encyclopaedia Britannica,* written 300 years later. Says Hibbs, "As you can see, there is very little difference in the two descriptions, which is not surprising since neither the moon nor our observational techniques have changed much during the intervening 300 years. . . . The one outstanding difference in the two descriptions is that the *Encyclopaedia Britannica* indulges in a little speculation, whereas Galileo restricted himself to the things he could see."[11]

Soon men will not have to content themselves with far-away observations. The moon can be studied from its very surface. But the means by which this and other space exploration shall be best carried out is open to vociferous controversy. Shall the eyes of men do the observing, or shall the electronic eyes of machines report back their findings? With effort toward impartial openmindedness on the question, Hibbs states the argument on the side of sending men aloft:

"The point is often made that no matter how adaptive and creative automatic machinery is made it can never surpass in creativity and adaptivity the abilities of its makers. Certainly, in this new and completely unexplored environment, on the surface of an only partially known planet, the unexpected will be routine. Only a man on the spot will be able to adapt sufficiently well to preserve the usefulness of the mission."[12]

In the rebuttal, Hibbs quotes two points customarily made: "First there is the point that automatic machinery can make all of the necessary measurements required in planetary exploration. Furthermore, they can be made somewhat adaptive to their environment and can certainly respond to command from earth to change routines in the face of unexpected developments. Machines generally demand much less complexity of their carrying spacecraft and launching rockets as well as less auxiliary equipment to maintain them in functioning condition."[12]

Just when the balance of the argument appears to be tipping to the greater use of machines, Hibbs impishly confuses any clear-cut decision: "For all our vaunted capacities in the field of automation, there is still no complex automatic piece of equipment which does not at least have a 'red light' which turns on to call in the human repairman. Most automatic equipment requires at least one human operator a large fraction of the time. Such automatic equipment as we do have is seldom found in a scientific laboratory. There is still plenty left for the man to do in the experimental process, and, from all appearances, there will be for many years to come."[12]

In actuality, these are but techniques toward the solving of a basic issue of how to explore the universe in the best manner possible. There are other issues removed from technology or method that are of more profound concern to many men who contemplate the less obvious ramification of the space adventure. We are somewhat like innocent children who have suddenly found the key that opens the door to a world we have longed to see. The opening of the door is an accomplishment, but it is in itself no guarantee that there exists a degree of sophistication sufficient to cope with all contingencies.

We cannot be dismayed by not having all the answers, for the greatest questions may be still unposed. Project *Ozma* pricked up its electronic ears, and listened for any indication of intelligent communication from other worlds. Projects could continue such efforts for a decade, a century, and yet the lack of results would not refute the possibility.

The brilliant British writer and scientist who first predicted world-wide communication via space satellites, Arthur C. Clarke, has written in a thought-provoking manner: "A man may walk the length of a beach in a few minutes—but how long would it take him to examine every grain of sand upon it? For all we know, there may be fleets of survey ships diligently charting and re-charting the Universe. Even making the most optimistic assumptions, it is hardly likely that our world (which lies, it will be remembered, in the thinly populated frontier regions of the Galaxy) would have been visited in the few thousand years of recorded history."[13]

On a speculative note, Hibbs writes of the possibility of extra-terrestrial life and its implication for mankind. It is an area where the opinion of any man may be regarded as "expert," for no one knows any answers. It is only intriguing that some are considering the problem.

It is interesting that a mind which can ponder such a vast issue still has the capacity for great consideration toward each individual. George Hobby relates, "When Al first became Division Chief, he had a very incompetent person working for him. He waited and waited and waited—just couldn't bring himself to discharge this person. Finally his duties became so enormous and he was getting so little help that something had to be done. He got the person transferred to another less demanding position."

Outwardly, no one could say that Hibbs appears soft. Yet friends suspect that beneath the veneer is a sentimental nature. It appears to be borne out in the instance where he could not discharge an incompetent person—feeling the person was defenseless. In business dealings with those whom he feels can "fight him on his own level," he is a determined opponent. Says Hobby, "Though we have known one another since we attended the University of Chicago, he has been quite distant in our working relationship since he invited me to join JPL in 1959. This is good. He can be perfectly objective about decisions."

Associates feel Hibbs to be a good judge of people. Yet he candidly says, "The places in my life where I feel the most uncertain are not in work, but more in my social contacts. I don't quite know how to approach people in a particular situation when I don't understand their desires and their motives. I am sure people always have motives, though perhaps I'm being too logical in wanting to understand them.

"I often admire the people who can work quite successfully with a deep intuitive feeling for others. My wife, Florence,* for instance, has a very quick intuition. It allows her to operate with other people much more effectively than I can." Hibbs acknowledges periods of uncertainty in his work, also: "When I am going into a new field, or attacking a new problem that I don't know much about, I am usually quite hesitant and uncertain. But I simply keep working at it and trying to learn a little about it until the ground is a little steadier."

This comment separates "people" and "work"—which, of course, isn't too realistic. Hibbs is generally very well liked, and highly respected for his great capability. But as might well be expected with anyone of intellect, and anyone who has accomplished a great deal, there are those who are bothered by it. Although a JPL man says, "No one around here feels anything but pride in Al's work. Still there is an element who feel envy. I sometimes hear that 'they'—whoever 'they' are—are most upset by his excellent ability to communicate. If it is in giving papers or addresses, with the press, or on TV, Al can really put it across."

Part of this ability doubtless stems from the theatrical training of his college days. (He still bursts forth with speeches from Ibsen or Shakespeare when he is in a friendly gathering.) Cal Tech has now become so aware of the importance of training scientists in the art of communication that there has been instituted a course in speech, being conducted by Herbert Booth.

This is but one added demand which has been placed upon today's scientists. Space, so all-encompassing by its very nature, has brought together the widest range of scientific talent. The revered holders of Nobel Prizes are working with just-graduated holders of Ph.D.'s who appear too young to have been using a razor for very long. Even many of the recognized space scientists are still under 30, for this is a young man's game. Cogitates one of them, "We are involved with so many outstanding people that it is difficult, for instance, to assess how men like Dr. Harold Urey, Dr. Joshua Lederberg or Dr. John Simpson really feel about us. We deal with them very well, but I'm not sure if these brilliant scientists just accept us because of the role we play in the space program, or if they can actually feel that there has been a worthwhile exchange of technical knowledge."

Nowhere is the youthful spirit of space science more evident than at JPL. "Everyone around here is about the same age," comments Eimer.

* Hibbs and the former Florence Pavin were married on September 8, 1950.

"Bob Parks, who is in the Planetary Program Office, was a junior when Al and I were freshmen at Cal Tech. Cliff Cummings, who heads the Lunar Program, was also a junior. Jim Burke, who is the Deputy Lunar Program Director, was in our freshman class, as was Harris 'Bud' Schurmeier, who heads the Systems Division. This provides us with quite a long period of association and understanding."

If any "leveling" influence were needed, this may have provided it. Hibbs is known as a well-adjusted, down-to-earth person, who has not succumbed to an overly inflated ego. Being surrounded by associates of 15 years standing is a bulwark to keep one level headed.

A trait from early days which still persists is that of multiple interests. Porter relates, "Al dabbles in a dozen different things at the same time. Yet his mind is very well organized and he correlates them all. It in no way leads to confusion. He sets out and picks objectives. Usually it is the toughest objectives first. He plunges into work, and I have yet to see him not come up with the solution."

A matter on which Hibbs feels so strongly that it has almost become a crusade is that of science education. In his addresses to teachers, he produces surprise and sometimes consternation by his views: "Technical mistakes are completely compatible with modern science. Boredom is not. . . . Science thrives in an environment of ignorance. In a field where all things are understood, there is no science."[14]

Such a startling approach requires an explanation in order to be understood: "In my talks to teachers, I have tried to impress upon them that a working scientist who is practicing his profession is not motivated by the desire to record facts. In a sense, the process of science is not to produce a book of answers. This comes out of it along the way, but the real importance is to discover deeper understandings of how the world works.

"The teaching of scientific answers is not important. It is the teaching of scientific methods that is important. If at the end of an investigation a student comes up with an answer that disagrees with the textbook, that is not wrong. The student could be right and the book could be wrong—that's the first thing to remember. The second thing is that the student was not after the answer in the first place. The objective was to teach him how to learn."

Hibbs feels it is only with the help of his own daughter and son, Tory, 8, and Bart, 6, that he has been able to understand some of the problems of education, and to formulate the ideas which he now holds. He further explains them by saying: "About a year ago at a meeting of the Council for Elementary Science International, I made the point that in teaching elementary students, facts have no purpose at all. All the facts that you can teach him in 6 years of science he can learn equally well in one week in college. Furthermore, by that time it will be 5 or 10 years from now, and science will have advanced so much that the facts will be different anyway.

"Generally the reaction from teachers is, 'You have to get across some facts, though, don't you?' My answer is always no. There are no facts to get across in the elementary grades. The important thing is that the students do their own experiments and reach their own conclusions. The teacher's evaluation of the conclusion should be based on how good was the student's process which led to it—not on whether it agrees with a textbook. The one and only important thing is that the student reach his conclusions by following through a legitimate process of observation and learning."

Having rejected the accepted formal teaching of science, Hibbs has alternative suggestions—4 items which he feels must be learned if the student is to become a productive member of society: "Reading, writing, mathematics, and a scholarly attitude." The last item, he admits, is the most difficult to define: "It includes curiosity—so dominant in a pre-school child and so mysteriously lacking in a typical high-school graduate, in spite of (or because of?) the educational process which has transpired between these states."[14] Hibbs sums up his thoughts by saying: "It does not matter whether the student learns any particular set of facts, but it does matter whether he learns how much fun it is to learn. . . ."[14]

Hibbs also has learned the great excitement to be derived from "far out" thinking. "In the very distant future we'll undoubtedly have very thorough explorations of all the planets of the solar system, and will undoubtedly have at least some permanent establishments. They will not be family-type colonies in that sense, but at least expeditionary-type, permanent establishments on the moon and on Mars.

"The possibility of modifying the weather on Mars or of introducing an atmosphere on the moon—both of these are possibilities for a very long-range future which would make economically and socially desirable colonization more realistic. The flight to distant stars—distant in the sense of the solar system, but close by in the sense of the stars—will be limited only by the time it takes to get there and back again at the speed of light."

In considering these stellar voyages, Hibbs points out, "The trip out and back, from the crew's point of view, would not take too long, if they achieve near the speed of light. To them it might be 10 or 20 years, for example, to a star 50 light years away, but from the point of view of the people back here on earth it might be more than a century before they return. So the culture here on earth will have fairly long jumps in reaping the benefits of this kind of travel, whereby they can bring back their findings and teach the next crew to go out on the following voyage."

Quite matter-of-factly Hibbs outlines the expansion of space exploration for the next few hundreds of years. But even his rich perception is bogged down by the really long-range view: "What happens in a few thousands of years? In a few millenniums? You can't take present technology and sensibly go that far." Whether it can be laid to a hunch, or to Hibbs's scientific doubting, he projects the possibility that a magnitudinous discovery will be made. "The reason that I have a feeling this will happen is because of the difficulty we have in visualizing the real physical nature of atomic particles; this has caused us a great deal of difficulty in describing their behavior.

"The current descriptions of theoretical physics, although they are working pretty well, I think are unnecessarily cumbersome. This is just a vague hope. I have nothing on which to base it, except the realization of how difficult some parts are, such as visualizing a wave and a particle both at the same time.

"We know that an electron, for example, behaves as a wave when we do wave experiments, and it behaves as a particle when we do particle experiments. It can do either one equally well, and is both and yet neither one. Intuitive grasp of what these particles are, if we could get it, would help to make much more rapid advances in our understanding of physics. I'm not saying that our understanding now is wrong—I'm just saying that it is awkward."

Although taking a journey into space appears the greatest of possible experiences, Hibbs has another personal desire: "There are many adventures in which I want to take part. Most of these are done within the head, rather than by going someplace. The political technology that I am involved in now is a specific example. There are many others, for technology affects society now very greatly. It has a very positive effect, but to me the disconcerting thing is that it's not a planned effect. You don't know ahead of time what a technical innovation is going to do.

"Another problem is that with all the wealth of science and our understanding of the interrelations of systems and organisms, the interrelations of people still go far beyond the understanding that we now possess. I would like to figure out if there is any way of applying technology to try to understand the growth of society. The development of such ideas is to me more exciting than going someplace."

Al Hibbs—the doubter, the doer, the dreamer. They are one man, yet all men. The mysteries of nature and the foibles of men have been unraveled by such characteristics as he possesses. His training and great talent belong to the Space Age, but his spirit has existed since man first asked "Why?" and set out to learn.

REFERENCES

1. *Chicago Daily Sun Times,* Chicago, Illinois, January 15, 1958.
2. *Mirror-News,* Los Angeles, California, January 15, 1958.
3. *Los Angeles Examiner,* Los Angeles, California, January 15, 1958.
4. Hibbs, A. R., *Science, Satellites and National Defense,* Address at Pasadena City College, January 14, 1958.
5. Kahn, Herman, *The Nature and Feasibility of War and Deterrence,* Santa Monica, California, The Rand Corporation, 1959.
6. *Foreign Affairs,* 40:3:339–359, April, 1962.
7. *Review of Operation of the Arms Control and Disarmament Agency,* Hearing before a Subcommittee of the Committee on Foreign Relations, U.S. Senate, 87th Congress, 2nd session, March 8, 1962.
8. Kennedy, John F., Address to the United Nations, New York, September 25, 1961.
9. Merrill, Grayson, Ed., *Dictionary of Guided Missiles and Space Flight,* Princeton, Van Nostrand, 1959.
10. *Encyclopaedia Britannica,* Chicago, Benton, 1957.
11. *Engineering and Science,* 23:9:7–12, June, 1960.
12. Hibbs, A. R., *Space Man vs. Space Machine.*
13. Clarke, Arthur C., *The Exploration of Space,* New York, Pocket Books, 1954.
14. *Teachers College Record,* 63:2:136–142, November, 1961.

Leading scientist in the development of Transit, *the navigation satellite*

RICHARD B. KERSHNER

As a small boy, Dick Kershner hid behind the door to listen to discussions he was not supposed to hear. He wasn't supposed to hear, because he wasn't supposed to be able to understand algebra at that young age. But he still recalls the great delight he experienced in eavesdropping on his father's tutoring sessions. From that early memory to the present, his thoughts have been immersed, absorbed and consumed with science and engineering.

It is reflected in his utter zest for work, in his passion for tackling a difficult task. "The greatest fun I can get from living is the enormous satisfaction of finding a really challenging job, then trying to do it properly. If I could not feel that way, and could not spend day-to-day doing what I like most to do, I would feel I had failed.

"I think anyone who separates work from pleasure, who does his job with the anticipation that he can once a year take two weeks to vacation and enjoy himself, has entirely the wrong approach. Everyone should find a way to manage to spend most of his time doing what he loves to do—and that's where I have been very fortunate. I get paid for doing what I most like and want to do!"

From the aspect of one scientist viewing another, the outstanding Technical Director of the Navy's Special Projects Office, Rear Admiral Levering Smith, says of Kershner, "He has the capacity to become completely involved with every project that he undertakes—to such an extent that his enthusiasm transfers into a powerful drive.

"Kershner has another capability which is, I think, common to the very best of our scientists—and that is the ability to clearly convey the basic points of a development. The top ranking ones are always the best at explaining the fundamentals and broad purposes of a project. I think this characteristic is a manifestation of their firm grasp of the real principles involved—and it is this same grasp that permits them to see the path through to the successful culmination of a project."

The completion of the development stage of *Project Transit* is in sight, and the greater part of the scientific responsibility has been Kershner's. *Transit* is startling in its concept, and limitless in its application as a navigational aid. It can be singled out as a prime example of the kind of benefit that can be reaped from the pursuit of pure research—research without an objective in the way of an end product. The application of the principle was effected by Kershner, but there is a story about its origin.

At the Johns Hopkins Applied Physics Laboratory, APL, is a small Research Center, a division that comprises no more than 10 per cent of the total effort. The Navy exhibits a very enlightened attitude in supporting this Center's basic research program, at the same time permitting investigation of areas without any specific Naval application in mind. Thus it was that two young physicists were enabled to lay the groundwork for one of the most valuable applications to come out of the space effort.

Dr. William H. Guier and Dr. G. C. Weiffenbach wanted to tune in on *Sputnik I* as it began its orbiting on October 4, 1957. They had no specific purpose in mind, but merely were fascinated by its existence, were curious to know what it sounded like, and wondered if they could receive its signals. They quickly assembled equipment—some from the Laboratory and some borrowed from their own home hi-fi sets and tape recorders—and with this impromptu gear they picked up the signal from *Sputnik I*.

Says Kershner, "The men then proceeded to make extremely subtle and enlightened use of the information. In doing this they applied the Doppler principle, which is illustrated by the sound of a whistle from a passing train. Because of the alternate piling up and stretching out of the sound waves from the motion of the object relative to the listener, the sound has a higher pitch as the source of the sound approaches. This phenomenon derives its name from the Austrian physicist, Christian Johann Doppler, who stated the principle quite carefully in the mid-19th century."

Kershner continues his explanatory narrative, saying, "The Doppler effect occurs for radio waves just as it occurs for sound waves, although it is not generally recognized. This is because movement must be very fast to create the effect. In the case of radio waves, the movement has to be fast relative to the speed of light; in the case of normal sound the movement required is fast relative to the much slower speed of sound. So it is easy to understand why the effect is more readily noticed in sound phenomenon."

But *Sputnik I* was an object which did attain speeds sufficient to exhibit the effect with radio waves. The signal from the satellite shifted with respect to the receiving equipment. As it approached, the signal was piled up, pushed together, and was heard at a higher frequency than was actually being transmitted. As the satellite was overhead, approximately at right angles to the receiver, the true frequency was heard for the first time. As it went away, the signals were stretched out so that they were heard more slowly.

"By employing this Doppler shift in only one pass of *Sputnik,* from the one receiving station," says Kershner, "Guier and Weiffenbach were able to compute the satellite's orbit! The feat is even more incredible when you consider that the analysis was completed before publication of orbit determinations by the British and the American groups; each of these employed data gathered over a period of weeks from points all over the world, and yet their two calculated orbits varied slightly. The orbit plotted by Guier and Weiffenbach rested right between the two."

Science is like a giant relay race. A development is carried to one point, then it is snatched up and taken still farther by someone else. Such was the case with amazing results from the data of Guier and Weiffenbach. The Chairman of the Research Center, Dr. Frank T. McClure, saw in their work a tremendous potential. Kershner reconstructs the thinking, "McClure made the most interesting suggestion of reversing the problem. Instead of trying to locate a satellite from a given position on earth, let the inverse be the case—from a known exact position of the satellite determine where you are on earth! Actually, working out this inverse problem was far simpler than the original one that Guier and Weiffenbach had tackled. In determining where *Sputnik* was there were six parameters to ascertain, but the upside down problem reduced the parameters to only two—longitude and latitude. McClure had a brilliantly simple concept, and one in which the Doppler data could be used to give a fix in a revolutionary navigational scheme."*

* The first NASA Inventions and Contributions Award was presented to Dr. Frank T. McClure on January 17, 1961, for the Satellite Doppler Navigation System Concept (which became the basis for the Navy's *Project Transit*). It carried with it a cash award of $3000.

"Ideas are, in truth, forces,"[1] said Henry James. Conversely, forces are required to transform ideas into operation. Kershner recalls some of the immediate questions that begged answers: "How stable is a satellite's orbit? How far in advance can its orbit be predicted? If you can predict it for a short period of time only, how can you convey new information to the user each day?" To analyze these and other questions to determine if a practical system could be worked out, a study group was formed under Kershner's strong leadership.

Organized in the spring of 1958, this highly competent group required but a month to generate sufficient answers to know that there were ways of surmounting the obstacles to the concept. Kershner says, "We concluded that it should be possible to determine the orbit, using the same technique that Guier and Weiffenbach had used, but employing more than a single observation at a single place. By setting up a network of stations—we estimated that four locations would be required—and by using a number of passes from each station, then it should be possible to determine a good orbit and predict it quite accurately for at least twelve hours."

Even with the leeway, the matter of conveying information as to the satellite's position relative to a ship at sea could be a major obstacle. The study group produced an ingenious solution: "Let the satellite tell where it is!" The steps in operation that were devised and suggested were these: (1) from ground stations, determine the satellite's orbit; (2) send up information to the satellite as to its position—this would be twice a day if it were necessary to make corrections; (3) the satellite would record this information as to its position; (4) it would retransmit these data to ships at sea, at intervals as frequent as once a minute.

Kershner further explains the function of the satellite, "It becomes a communication link for this one special purpose. By no means is it a communications satellite which is large and has the capability of carrying tremendous amounts of information. The navigation satellite has just a tiny fraction of the requirements, for it conveys only one little piece of information concerning where it is."

It is the Heaviside layer that makes possible the phenomenon of long-distance radio transmission. Named for the British physicist, Dr. Oliver Heaviside, it acts as a reflector to bounce back low-frequency transmission signals. The name has now become rather archaic, and the layer of ionized atmospheric gases, ranging from 30 to 250 miles altitude, is now commonly termed the ionosphere.

Says Kershner, "This ionosphere is a bit of a nuisance in that it also causes a shift in frequency which you may misinterpret as being due to the Doppler effect, unless a way is found to compensate for it. The transmission path from the satellite to the earth is not the straight line joining the two, but is a longer curved (or bent) path, caused by the refraction of the ionosphere. Although the refraction can be made negligible by going to a sufficiently high frequency (microwave and above), this was not a practical solution for transmission from the navigation satellite since it would require either large antennas for reception, or high power for transmission.

"The second solution we considered has proved workable—the satellite transmits on two harmonically related frequencies; by comparing these two signals, each of which is bent a different amount, it is possible to determine with great accuracy the refraction effect. By this described means there can be determined a so-called refraction corrected Doppler, or vacuum Doppler—that is, as it would have been received if there were no ionosphere. And it is only at upper latitudes during periods of high auroral activity that the degree of accuracy of this method requires further investigation."

A third problem appeared to be present: "That was the matter of building an oscillator that would hold its frequency very, very steadily in the satellite environment. It doesn't often happen in the practical engineering of a project that something turns out to be less of a problem than expected, but such was the case in this instance. We never had any serious difficulty, for the present oscillators have quite remarkable stability—to the degree that if you think of them as a clock, they will gain a second's time in a hundred centuries!"

In his Progress Report, Kershner further details the capability of the oscillator: "A rather elaborate temperature isolation of the crystal from external heat sources, taking advantage of the superb vacuum available in the operating environment, has kept the rate of change of frequency due to temperature change at the crystal within acceptable limits, and careful circuit design has minimized other sources of frequency change."[2]

This matter of frequency stability becomes most important to determine accurately the Doppler shift, he points out: "Although there is no simple relationship between an error in Doppler measurement and the corresponding position error, a crude rule-of-thumb relationship, usually valid within an order of magnitude (ten times), is given by the statement that an error of 1 cps in Doppler gives an error of 1 mile in position if the transmitter frequency is 100 mcps. . . . it is clear that a frequency drift of only 1 part in 10^8 during the time of a pass can result in a serious error in position determination."[2]

The oscillator, in addition to sending out a signal, also controls a satellite clock which determines when the information giving the position is transmitted to the ground. To use for time synchronization between the two points, and to mark the beginning of each transmission, the "Barker" code word is transmitted. It is expected that the satellite clock will have precision of 100 microseconds—making it far more accurate on a world-wide basis than any other time source, such as the reception of WWV* radio signals at a distant point.

After but a month's concerted consideration of all aspects of the concept, the members of Kershner's group had satisfied their natural scientific skepticism. They concluded this was an approach to navigation worthy of Space Age dimensions. It had the imaginative flair of a fiction writer's dream, and technological demands that were formidable—but it appeared they could be met. It was bold and dramatic, to put a point of reference 500 miles high in the sky, speeding thousands of miles per hour in its orbit. But this is an era of learning, and man's most vital lesson is to remove from his thinking the restriction that anything is impossible. The navigation satellite idea still rested within a cocoon of theory. Only when this protection was stripped away and the stringency of performance was demanded would the final verdict be rendered—but the outcome which seemed most probable was that this would be the solution to a problem that has plagued seafaring men since earliest days.

Captain Robert F. Freitag, the highly respected Astronautics Officer of the Bureau of Naval Weapons, recounts: "The earliest form of navigation was 'piloting.' Piloting is navigation by observing visually the relative location of the navigator and known landmarks. Piloting techniques were improved by 'dead reckoning,' a corrupted abbreviation of 'deduced reckoning.' This can be described as an educated guess as to where you are or will be, based upon an extrapolation of a previous position with estimates of course, speed, winds, currents, etc.

"Thus, in the above navigation procedures, the ancient mariner faced the same basic problems we face today in modern navigation though today's technology has severely increased the requirements for navigation. The advent of the nuclear submarine with long underwater and under-ice cruises, the Fleet Ballistic Missile with its need for precise absolute reference between open seas and the heartland of the continents, and the dynamic swiftness and speed of modern warfare which requires precise navigation data without always the ability of selecting weather or convenient landmarks all contribute to intensifying the navigator's task."[3]

The Fleet Ballistic Missile, *Polaris,* was the product of the Special Projects Office. Vice Admiral William F. "Red" Raborn had developed this deterrent weapon in an unprecedented manner—taken from the standpoint of time and of required technological advances. The formula was evident if not simple: hard-driving Raborn had employed altruism

* *WWV* are the call letters of the radio transmitter at Beltsville, Maryland, which is operated by the U.S. Department of Commerce, National Bureau of Standards.

and alchemy by gathering superb people and expecting fantastic results. He got them!

But long after other barriers had yielded to scientific acumen, the grave matter of an adequate navigational aid still plagued them. Rear Admiral Levering Smith is a perfectionist. He knew the strengths of the *Polaris* development, and he knew its weaknesses were attributable to their straining the state of the art to breaking limits. And still, solutions had to be snatched through talent and tireless effort. He sought the best assistance available:

"We asked the Applied Physics Laboratory to review and constructively criticize various parts of the system; one of the more difficult of these areas was the navigation system. This well prepared APL for the bigger job of assisting in the final over-all testing and evaluation of the missile, which we had asked them to undertake.

"In these efforts, many people of APL became involved—among them, Dr. Frank McClure, who had our navigational needs in mind when he proposed his concept for the navigational satellite. From the first hearing, I thought the idea was sound, but I asked our navigation development group to review it. Quite properly, they started to think of all the possible ideas that could shoot it down. Though they questioned the vulnerable areas, it withstood the barrage."

The support needed to proceed with the study was forthcoming from the Special Projects Office. It came, as Kershner recalls, "with unprecedented speed." This was, however, only an interim measure until action could be taken by the group which is designated to sponsor projects in this category, the Advanced Research Projects Agency, ARPA. There, fortunately, it came to the attention of Roger S. Warner, Jr.—another name for a dynamo. The Applied Physics Laboratory had the idea, the Special Projects Office had the need, and ARPA had the money. Warner was the catalyst to intermingle it all into *Project Transit*.

"After Roger Warner had picked up the ball and put through a program that got the appropriate support from the Department of Defense, then came the real job—the demonstration of the feasibility of what had to that time been a concept," says Kershner, the man who directed the scientific development of *Transit*. "We immediately started gathering an organization, assigning people to this task, and getting equipment facilities. It is quite an operation to pull together a group that has the capability of building satellites. We had the good fortune that at this Laboratory, we had been building guided missiles for years, and therefore had a lot of people who had good background in building equipment that had to withstand being launched on a rocket. We had equipment to test acceleration, and shake tables to test vibration. What we had to learn was the vacuum technology." The Laboratory even created the systems, sub-contracting only a few components, such as the solar cells and telemetering transmitters.

The care with which the project was planned and the excellence of its execution are indicated by Kershner's statement, "I can honestly say that nothing proved more difficult than we had expected. In general, we found that we had been very wary in our estimate of how much work and how much effort it would be to accomplish each of our objectives.

The satellite was christened with a name in keeping with the tradition of APL—all of its projects begin with the letter "T," for Dr. Merle Tuve, first Director of the Laboratory. *Terrier, Tartar, Talos* and *Typhon* had emerged as creditable projects. Naming the navigation satellite *Project Transit* perpetuated the established policy. "I like the name because it means two things," says Kershner, who made the choice. "First, the word means a surveying or navigating instrument. Second, astronomically, *Transit* means the passing of a satellite across the face of a mother body. It is a most appropriate name."

Transit 1A was launched on September 17, 1959, and failed to orbit, due to a malfunction in the third stage of the booster rocket. "It simply was not given enough velocity to stay in orbit, but we were able to receive the Doppler signal from the satellite when it was at its orbital altitude. From this one piece of information we received at the APL, we were able to make a comparison with the orbit determined by the radar tracking, and show that we had achieved excellent agreement. So even though the satellite was not put into orbit, we were able to confirm the validity of our concept of determining of the orbits by the analysis of Doppler."

This first *Transit* was a very early satellite, as far as this country was concerned. Neither the scientists at APL or anywhere else had had much background in developing this product of the new age. Therefore, great caution was employed in several instances. Kershner points out, "Having had no experience with solar cells, we put in the satellite a much larger than necessary amount of chemical batteries; in that way, even if the solar cells didn't work, we would still get operation over a period of a month. *Transit 1A* was airborne long enough to give us a reading, but further ground testing indicated that we did not need this amount of 'insurance' in chemical batteries.

"So some of them were removed, but some had to remain, since solar cells work only when the satellite is in the sun. Part of every orbit is in shadow behind the earth; there, you must have some chemical storage batteries to tide you over if you intend to operate continuously."

After the failure of *Transit 1A,* many months elapsed before the next attempt. The satellite was ready, but another launch vehicle had to be secured, and the project had to "get in line" at Cape Canaveral to get onto the launch pad. The Air Force operates the facility, and the Department of Defense makes the determination about what is to be launched, and when.

Kershner relates, "I do not go to the Cape for launchings, because more telemetered information is available at our Laboratory. We set up a communications nerve center in our main auditorium, and receive data on a 'real time' (immediate) basis from our tracking stations. Because interest in space activities is so extremely high, we invite people from the Laboratory, together with their families, to come in and observe the proceedings. They have quite a feeling of participation.

"Though sometimes launch has been at two or three o'clock in the morning, the auditorium has been absolutely full—with standees in the aisles. It is always a suspenseful time. We hear relayed from Cape Canaveral all of the countdown information, including any difficulties that arise to cause a hold. We get a description of the liftoff, then await word from the tracking stations to indicate if it went into orbit.

"When it is finally determined that it has been successful, big cheers go up! It is quite moving to see the response from the group, and realize how deeply this work affects them. The effort put forth by a sizeable number of people is really tremendous, and long working hours are always involved to meet our short schedules. When a piece of hardware is finally completed, we feel at the mercy of the fates as we wait to see if the system performs."

Even the first *Transit* satellite performed perfectly. It was a malfunction of the booster rocket that caused the failure of the mission. At last, on April 13, 1960, the second attempt was scheduled, *Transit 1B* rose into the skies above Cape Canaveral atop a *Thor-Able-Star* booster configuration in a perfect launch! All systems functioned A-OK, and it transmitted on all four of its frequencies from the moment of liftoff. Within a few hours, its orbit was determined—an apogee of 469 miles, a perigee of 235 miles—as it circled the earth every hour and a half.

The satellite was flung from the launch vehicle spinning at the approximate rate of 180 rpm. At a preset time, two weights unwound from cables around its shell and stopped the spinning. The 36-inch sphere, gleaming white to help control the temperature, resembled a child's top in appearance, for it had spiral bands painted around it which functioned as broadband antennas. It contained two transmitting systems (with two frequencies each) and two command receivers.

Also in its instrument tray, which was like a bulging equator dividing the upper and lower halves of the Fiberglas shell, was an infrared scanner experiment carried aloft for the Naval Ordnance Test Station. Another experiment conducted was getting a navigational fix on Austin,

Texas; it proved accurate to within one quarter of a mile. Though the batteries on *Transit 1B* failed after two months, a wealth of data was gathered during the 1020 orbits of its operating life.

With this successful launch, ARPA's role in *Project Transit* was fulfilled; management was formally transferred from that Agency to the Navy. Scientific development of the project still rested, of course, with the Applied Physics Laboratory, under the excellent direction of Kershner. The first launch was but a sample of the store of scientific advancement that lay ahead!

Space exploration has proved upsetting—not only from the physical aspect of weightlessness, but also upsetting to the mental stability that men find comfortable. We are most secure, most reassured that we will triumph in this matter of living, when the elements and forces of nature are buffered by plausible explanations. When one of these man-devised principles will no longer hold up in the face of new discoveries, consternation is usually experienced. Only the truly detached mind welcomes the shattering of long-held beliefs, and recognizes the process as real progress.

The first major sacrosanct belief which space research vanquished was occasioned by *Vanguard I*. This recalcitrant satellite, so aggravating to launch, finally went into orbit on March 17, 1958, and justified the effort that had been expended by sending back the startling data that the earth is not round but is slightly pear-shaped!* Now, further findings are indicating that a more proper fruit-analogy might be a bunch of grapes.

Transit 1B provided this news. Relates Kershner: "The earth is found to be extremely uneven, with all sorts of lumps, bulges and bumps. These are much, much bigger effects than mountain ranges. Even the Himalayas are just barely noticeable to a satellite orbiting at 500 miles altitude. These newly discovered bumps on the earth are not necessarily very high, but they involve huge areas. The total mass of these protrusions is tremendous."

The significance of this in space technology is substantial. These bulges influence the gravitational field, which in turn influences the earth-orbiting satellite. "This remains the most challenging problem with *Project Transit*. The accuracy with which we can predict the satellite orbit depends upon how well we know the forces to which the satellite is subjected. We discovered that we did not know the gravitational field of the earth nearly well enough to do accurate prediction of orbits."

* These studies were conducted by the following persons of the National Aeronautics and Space Administration: Ann Eckels Bailie, J. A. O'Keefe, and R. K. Squires.

The very new trades upon the very old. Orbits are determined by means of celestial mechanics—a science whose foundation was laid by Sir Isaac Newton with the publication in 1687 of his *Philosophiae Naturalis Principia Mathematica*. This work consolidated the pioneer work of Galileo, and set forth the three laws of motion which are the principles of mechanics. These, plus Newton's universal law of gravitation, permit a problem in celestial mechanics to be stated as an equation.

"To define the problems inherent in the *Transit* program, Dr. Robert Newton was in our first study group. Newton (who is no relation to Sir Isaac!) is our Laboratory's leading expert, and is certainly one of the top men in the country," says Kershner, whose own background in pure mathematics includes celestial mechanics. Newton then formed a group solely for the celestial mechanics aspect.

A satellite would move in a perfect ellipse, were it not for the disturbances, termed perturbations, caused by other solar bodies, by electromagnetic forces, by radiation pressure from the sun, and other factors. The perturbations which result from unevenness of the earth's surface had not previously been a consideration because no project prior to *Transit* had demanded such accuracy. To meet these demands upon celestial mechanics for more exact computations, another branch of science had to be involved:

"This study is called geodesy," says Kershner. "It is the measurement of the earth and its gravitational field. The progress that has been made in this science in the few years since satellites have been launched is very much greater than all the progress in the field of geodesy up to that date."

On April 27, 1962, the wraps were taken off *ANNA*,* which for a period of time had been a secret military project. This geodetic satellite, one of the most complex payloads that has been developed, has as its purpose the gathering of information on two distinct, but interrelated, problems: the exact location of control points on the earth, and the earth's gravity field. These add up to knowing the exact shape of the earth. Lieutenant Commander Mark M. Macomber, of the Bureau of Naval Weapons, reveals that *ANNA* will carry three types of instrumentation: a radar beacon (transponder) for catching and returning signals from ground stations, transmitting equipment to enable the measurement of Doppler shift, and a high-intensity optical beacon producing a series of five light flashes spaced 5.6 seconds apart—which will make the satellite one of the brightest objects in the skies.

* The name is an acronym for Army, Navy, NASA (National Aeronautics and Space Administration), and Air Force, the agencies which originally collaborated on the program. It was later classified and NASA withdrew during that period; they have now rejoined with the project's declassification.

Dr. Harold Brown, Director, Defense Research and Engineering, succinctly described the extraordinary satellite when he said, "I would consider *ANNA* the use of space as a tool to learn more about the earth."[4]

The first attempted launch of an *ANNA* satellite on May 10, 1962, failed because of a malfunction in the launch vehicle. A second attempt was scheduled for August, 1962, but apparently because of the radiation created by the U.S. high-altitude hydrogen bomb explosion on July 9 (which was much stronger than anticipated), the launching was postponed for perhaps two to three months. Once the satellite has been put into orbit, and the intensive calibration phase has been completed to prove the accuracy of the instrumentation which it carries, and also the method of ground-data handling, a world-wide geodetic observation program will be initiated. The aim of this effort will be to improve knowledge of the earth's gravitational field.

A vast and continuing program will be required to provide comprehensive understanding, as Macomber said in his testimony before a Congressional committee: "A solution for the gravity field can be obtained which would be perfect for one inclination, but which would give completely erroneous results for a satellite in some other orbit.

"In order to reduce the correlation between terms of the gravitational field, and to define this field as it actually is, there must be a variety of orbits, both in inclination and in altitude, and the observations from all orbits must be analyzed together."[4]

The matter of locating a point—exactly—is of increasing importance, Macomber explained, citing this example: "The tracking stations are important because when you start out, say, for a shot to the Moon, you have stations that are separated by about the diameter of the earth that are tracking the vehicle. These stations have to be tied together very closely so that you get a good indication of where the vehicle is.

"Any error, in, say, a base line of some 4000 to 7000 miles would give you a tremendous error in range when you get out toward the vicinity of the Moon or going toward Venus."[4] At present, it is estimated that there is an error of 500 to 1000 feet in exactly locating tracking stations that are established on other than the North American Continent. This is due to the fact that each continent has its own geodetic system. The control point upon which every position in the United States is located is Meade's Ranch in Kansas. But it has not been precisely determined where Meade's Ranch is with respect to the control points in other geodetic systems, and with respect to the center of the earth. With *Project ANNA,* it is expected that the individual grids that cover each major continent can be related with increased accuracy. There are 14 different data systems which *ANNA* will tie together on a world-wide grid system.

"One essential feature must characterize any geodetic satellite program," said John D. Nicolaides, Director, Program Review and Resources Management, Office of Space Sciences, NASA. "This essential feature is teamwork. No single group or single agency or single service or single country can carry to successful completion this truly world-wide job."[4]

With this product of the Space Age, a long-standing hope will be fulfilled. The first action toward making geodesy an international science was taken by Lieutenant General Baeyer of Prussia in 1862, when the Central European Geodetic Association was organized. By 1883, the United States was participating, and at the next conference, three years later, the name was changed to International Geodetic Association. After World War I, a further reorganization occurred in connection with the newly created International Research Council, and the group became the International Geodetic and Geophysical Union.

It is ironic that space has been both the source of the world's greatest scientific competition, and the world's greatest scientific unification.

Kershner indicates the progress that has occurred in geodesy in a relatively short time: "When we launched the early *Transit* satellites, knowledge of the gravitational field was good enough to do tracking to about a mile accuracy. The apogee and perigee could be determined more accurately than that, but the main problem was when the satellite would reach a given point. It was as if the railroad track were well known, but as if the speed along the track were pretty uncertain. These uncertainties of about a mile meant only a quarter of a second in arrival time, because the satellite goes four miles a second. Greater precision was needed. The brilliant young mathematician, Newton, has done a fine job of pushing our knowledge of geodesy to a point where we now regularly are achieving a quarter-of-a-mile accuracy. This four-fold improvement reflects what we have learned about the gravitational field of the earth. It is interesting that *Transit* is so exacting in its demands, and also provides within itself one of the most powerful tools available for accomplishing these goals.

"As to the performance criteria of the navigation satellite, I can say that the goal from the very beginning was one-tenth-of-a-mile accuracy—and now we have demonstrated that it is possible to achieve it. This is a different measurement from the accuracy in determining the orbit —this is determining a location on the ground. Any uncertainty in the orbit is only one complication. There are other additional problems that can cause an inaccuracy, and all of them have to be kept low enough so that the sum of all these errors is less than a tenth of a mile."

Precision!

In every phase of the project, the demands were immense. The matter of the tracking stations was no exception. Kershner wrote in his *Progress Report* in the spring of 1961, "At the time the initial *Transit* Program proposal was being considered, typical satellite tracking or prediction errors ranged from 5 miles to as much as 50 miles. There was a widespread belief among even well informed people that there were mysterious or at least unpredictable forces of large magnitude acting on satellites which would for years prevent orbit prediction with an accuracy of better than a number of miles. Fortunately, most of the difficulties of that period were a result of poor measurement rather than a reflection of basic unknowns."[2]

Since no adequate facilities existed for tracking *Transit,* stations had to be especially built. At the time of the early launchings, the stations at Las Cruces, New Mexico; Austin, Texas; and Howard County, Maryland, had been completed—but there were no foreign facilities. The Laboratory began the expansion, but since it quickly became a tremendous logistic problem, the responsibility for establishing the world-wide network was assigned to the Navy's Pacific Missile Range, PMR, in November, 1961.* Commander James C. Quillan was named *Transit* Officer. The additional stations are located at Anchorage, Alaska; South Point, Hawaii; Misawa, Japan; San Miguel, Philippine Islands; Smithfield, Australia; São José dos Campos, Brazil; Pretoria, South Africa; and Lasham, England.

The tally of stations now stands at eleven, yet only four are required for the operational *Transit* system. Kershner explains the reason: "The additional stations have been for the expansion of our knowledge of geodesy, necessary for the precision of our orbit. We simply could not attain it until we learned more exactly, for example, where Australia is relative to the United States."

These stations, operating on a continuous basis, will soon have the function of tracking four *Transit* satellites, in polar orbit, at approximately 100-minute intervals; the typical horizon-to-horizon pass will be between 12 and 15 minutes. One of the stations must also monitor the time pulses from the satellite and make comparison with the time as determined by the U.S. Naval Observatory.

The Doppler data gathered by each of the stations are sent by teletype to a computing center; here they are used to determine the satellite orbit, and to predict the future orbit. This information is then sent to the injection station, and on the satellite's next pass over the station, former data are erased from its magnetic core memory, and this new computation is inserted. *Transit* immediately repeats back what it just has been given for verification, and the satellite's memory is then locked to prevent any further insertion of information until about 12 hours later.

Transit 2A, launched on June 22, 1960, was the first to carry the elec-

* When *Project Transit* becomes operational, jurisdiction for the entire program will be assumed by the Pacific Missile Range.

tronic clock. It also included an improved telemetering system, sending back data which Kershner equates in these terms: "One day's transmission makes a book that is approximately 12 inches by 16 inches, and 5 inches thick! One has to write computing machine programs to summarize these data to put them in useful form," reveals Kershner. "It finally winds up being a single number, you might say, or a better value for a single number. It takes that much information per day for a matter of weeks to get an improved value on one of these terms."

He speaks further of *Transit 2A* by saying, "It also carried more solar cells, so that its operating life would not be cut short as was *1B*. Even now, after two years, *2A* is still transmitting complete information, but only during the time it is in sunlight. This means it had a failure of the chemical batteries, though of a nature that it can still transmit whenever the solar cells are lit."

Transit 3B, the first to include a memory as part of its instrumentation, was launched February 21, 1961, and carried pickaback *Lofti,* a satellite, to be used in the study of low-frequency transmissions through the ionosphere. But malfunction prevented it from separating from the mother satellite, and prevented *Transit* from separating from the second stage of the launch vehicle. This caused *Transit* to be put into such a low trajectory that it orbited for only about a month.

Drum-shaped *Transit 4A* launched June 29, 1961, was a major advance toward a smaller, lighter-weight satellite. Two important space "firsts" were achieved with this satellite—it was the initial user of RIPS, a nonfissionable radioisotope power supply which was a modified SNAP-3 unit developed by the Atomic Energy Commission; the simultaneous launching of three satellites marked another first. *Transit 4A* carried pickaback the *Injun* and *Greb* satellites; although the latter two did not separate, a high percentage of the test objectives were still met.

Transit 4B carried pickaback *TRAAC* (Transit research attitude control satellite). Kershner explains, "Both satellites were launched together with a *Thor-Able-Star,* and separated in orbit. *TRAAC* was the first experiment testing a gravity-orientation system. It is shaped like a dumbbell, with a long boom that is supposed to extend. Although this boom did not extend, we did solve the basic problem of damping a gravitationally stabilized satellite by releasing a spring with a weight on the end. This tricky part of the experiment worked, and we now know that this is a workable mechanism, so we are employing it in the operational satellites.

"In addition, *TRAAC* is making many measurements of the environment in areas where previously we did not have enough knowledge to realistically predict the life of solar cells. *TRAAC* will give us information that will enable accurate computations to be made on the rate at which solar cells decay, and enable us to make close predictions on the lifetime of our satellites."

This remains the primary requirement for improvement of the *Transit* satellites—lengthening their life span. It is a critical factor for economic reasons. For the operational *Transit* system, four satellites must be continuously in orbit. If each lasts one year, the obvious requirement is for the launching of four satellites a year. But if the life of each can be prolonged to five years (which is the aim), the total number of satellites needed to keep the system in operation over a period of years would diminish to a fraction. So the maintenance costs for the system directly reflect the useful life in orbit.

Cost can be greatly reduced by another means—reducing the weight of the satellite. The early *Transit* satellites, weighing nearly 300 pounds, had to be launched by a giant *Thor-Able-Star* booster; the cost for this was between three and four million dollars. Now Kershner and his crew have achieved an amazing shrinkage in the weight of the satellite—by miniaturization of components and simplification of construction—so that it is now 100 pounds. The smaller payload can be launched by a four-stage, solid-propellant *Scout* booster rocket, at a cost of about one million dollars.

"The design of the present satellites meets all requirements for operational status. As the state of the art of geodesy advances, their performance can be improved by simply making a change in the computing program—and this can be done even after they have been put in orbit. But there is no need to delay the operational status for that, because even the present accuracy is very useful, and quite a bit better than is available now by any other means of navigation. So at the Laboratory we are building satellites as fast as possible. As soon as the program is on a real production basis, the Navy hopes to bring in either industry or a Naval laboratory to build continuing models."

Other Navy plans for *Project Transit* are vast and commendable.* Intention has been announced to release information so that all nations will be able to make use of *Transit* as a navigation aid, just as they presently use international radio aids. Writes Captain Freitag, "The *Transit* navigation system will be in operation in 1962. Then ships anywhere and everywhere can get not only navigational information but the exact time and the predicted future orbits of the satellites. This system insures reliable, completely passive, all-weather navigation. Ocean voyages for all ships of all nations can thus become safe and more efficient."[3]

Says Kershner, "There has been a great lot of international interest.

* Contact for Navy information was made prior to mid-March, 1962. Other sources were utilized subsequent to that date.

We at the Laboratory have been urged by the Navy to make scientific reports to the NATO organizations; in 1960, Bob Newton and I attended the AGARD* meeting in Istanbul and subsequently have made presentations in London and Paris on the present status of the program, and how they need to prepare to make use of it."

In the report made before a joint meeting of the Institute of Navigation and the Royal Geographical Society in London in the fall of 1961, Kershner and Newton gave a lucid account of the great service which this nation is making available to the world: "A user anywhere on the surface of the earth is always within line of sight of at least one satellite orbit. Hence he needs to wait at most one period of the satellite, about 110 minutes, in order to obtain data from a satellite pass, and to get a navigational fix. With more than four satellites, more frequent fixes can be obtained.

"It is expected, in fact it is anticipated, that there will be two classes of user. One of these will demand the utmost accuracy obtainable from the system (about one-tenth mile), and will be prepared to pay the price in the way of elaborate equipment and of elaborate computation. The other class will be content with lower accuracy (about one-half mile), making a smaller investment in equipment. . . . A 'bread-board' set of equipment for this class of user has been built and is being studied at the Applied Physics Laboratory. While it is not possible to estimate costs of building such equipment accurately at the present stage of study, it will be somewhere in the range of $5000. In complexity, it is comparable to a color television set, but will probably not have the volume of production, and hence will probably be somewhat more expensive."[5]

The general costliness of space development has been repeatedly emphasized. But comparison with other methods of doing the job—or even a fraction of the job—give the surprising revelation that it is not only the best way, but the cheapest way to attain certain capability. Just as it has been stated that the communication satellite may be cheaper than the cost of laying another transoceanic cable, so is *Transit* a bargain in its category!

"The radio aids to navigation upon which mariners previously had to rely have covered only high-density areas, because real global coverage would require such a tremendous number of stations in constant operation that the cost would be fantastic. In many large areas of the earth, as in the Indian Ocean area, there are simply no technical aids to navigation. So ships are dependent upon the stars. But the stars, unfortunately, can be seen only in favorable weather, and there are many areas of the world where the weather remains unfavorable for observations for quite long

* AGARD is NATO's Advisory Group for Aeronautical Research and Development.

periods of time. Consequently, the ships are without help, and have no way of knowing where they are except by dead reckoning—figuring from the last time they got a fix; and this might be as much as a week before.

"So there is great usefulness, value, importance to the world in having a navigational aid that is accurate and is available in all weather—whether the day is clear, or if there is a cloud cover, or whether it is day or night conditions. To have this system around the whole globe is a tremendous thing! In addition to the immediate usefulness for various naval missions, there is equal value for civilian use. Merchant marine vessels can know their exact locations, always; capability will be developed to channel permissible routes, diminishing the chance for collisions in any kind of weather condition."

Contained in *Space World* magazine is this tribute to the project: "This is the first application of space technology that will be of direct practical benefit to people on earth. . . . Stealing a march on NASA's world communications and weather satellite programs, the Navy predicts its *Transit* system will become operational before the end of the year. . . . With these lighthouses of space faithfully guiding all ships to port, a large group of skeptics will at last concede that space research is not a waste of money and effort."[6]

Although all emphasis on *Transit* has been toward its seagoing application, its benefits to landlubbers must also be recognized. "As a tool for surveying land, it is even more accurate than in locating ships. This is due to the fact that the motion of the ship is a factor, whereas in land survey you can have the added check of remaining in one spot and taking repeated measurements," says Kershner.

"Tremendous amounts of money have been put into surveying the world. For example, it is a very expensive operation to send surveyors down one coast of South America and up the other coast. Such working methods will be totally unnecessary in the future. With *Transit* surveys will be completed in areas where they have never been performed, and will be executed with even greater accuracy than previously would have been possible."

Although *Project Transit* has gained the greatest emphasis, it is by no means the extent of Kershner's activities. As the Director of the Space Development Division at Johns Hopkins University's APL, he has charge of any projects which involve the use of satellites or the exploitation of space technology. "I am also the supervisor of the *Polaris* division—in which we have the assignment to prepare the evaluation test phase, but I have such a superb second-in-command to oversee this that I actually spend most of my time in space activities," says Kershner.

"Here at the Laboratory, we prefer such assignments as *Transit,* for which we have the primary development responsibility, from concept to delivery." Somewhat pensively, Kershner recalls, "When I was a little boy, I used to have a dream that someday I would have a job in which I had an elaborate operation, with many people working with me, and in which I would make plans and decisions. I had the constant thought of developing a 'fancy gadget.' Aren't dreams ridiculous?" *Transit* is a very fancy gadget, indeed!

The general area of young Kershner's dream was certainly influenced by his highly educated and scientifically inclined father. Though headmaster of Franklin Day School, a boys' school in Baltimore, his particular interests were physics and mathematics. "Quite a remarkable man," Kershner fondly recalls. "He was a man totally without prejudices. His strongest impression on me was intellectual honesty. The truth was the only thing that mattered. You had to be very careful that you recognized it—give yourself every chance to be sure you recognized it—by listening carefully to both sides. By not making up your mind prematurely on the basis of hearsay, supposed authority, tradition or anything else, you remained open in your thinking until you had heard enough of all the facts to reach a really valid conclusion.

"This is the concept to which I was exposed as a child, and it was a wonderful thing, for I didn't have to wait and struggle to discover it for myself. By having it so convincingly demonstrated and handed to me, it proved a tremendous help in all my decisions. My sweet and charming mother also reflected this outlook."

Since seeking the truth is the basis of science, this pattern of thinking was especially compatible with Kershner's inclination toward mathematics. "This subject always came extremely easy to me. It was so simple in comparison with most things. There was never any trouble getting scholarships. When a person is fortunate enough to have something come so easy, it makes decisions very simple. There were no questions as to the subject in which I would specialize."

But even this predetermined subject for specialization had a sudden unfoldment. "When I was in my senior year in Baltimore's Forest Park High School, I had an extremely good mathematics teacher, Sophie Becker. With her help, I suddenly discovered that mathematics could be illuminating, rewarding, and just plain fun! Before this it had been easy but dull."

Kershner has strong memory of this early period: "In contrast to many of my friends who were having rough times, I had a happy, contented life, with parents who got along wonderfully with each other and with no problems. And I had an awareness that it was good." The first without the second is meaningless. If appreciation can be realized only in retrospect, the real reward of the benefit is never experienced.

Kershner earned his Ph.D. in mathematics at The Johns Hopkins University. His unusual flair for research was demonstrated by the publication of five papers prior to the completion of his graduate work, and honors included membership in Phi Beta Kappa and Sigma Xi. But toward the completion of his education, he lacked the faith to sustain his dream of overseeing the development of a "fancy gadget." The idea was abandoned in favor of a sensible decision. "By the very nature of my preparation, I was sure I had committed my life to only one thing—becoming a university teacher. Nobody hired a mathematician for anything else. I was really quite content with this idea—at the time." His first position was that of instructor of mathematics at the University of Wisconsin. After three years, he returned to his alma mater to become an Assistant Professor. In the concentric circles of science, words were being passed about this most promising young mathematician.

The cycle of his personal life had been fulfilled in 1935 with his marriage to M. Amanda Brown, whose talent as an artist included capability in production illustration—that cross between art and mechanical drawing. Some of this interest has spread into Kershner's life, as original paintings around his office evidence. Of his work he comments with candor, "I use only oils, because they have the virtue of allowing you to paint by successive approximation. You try, and if you are wrong, you cover up." Another manifestation does not allow such easy correction. With untutored architectural prowess, he has designed homes with scientific logic. A characteristic of his planning is that closets are placed in unexpected places, and have doors on both sides!

Their elder son, Richard, Jr., who has just been graduated from high school as a straight A student, has refuted the scientific side of his heritage and followed the artistic—in a different form. He is a poet. But Kershner points out there is some related interest there: "He does write poems about space!" The younger son, James, is now 13; equally bright but less inclined to apply himself, he has a current penchant for cooking. Should this persist, the world might be blessed with a hyperbolic version of Crepes Suzette.

The atmosphere of the Kershner home is one of relaxed and happy stimulation. It reflects what friends say of the master of the house: "He is a wonderful person, who is helpful to everyone, and tolerant of everything but intolerance."

Since Kershner's work is also his diversion and his hobby, there is little other regular activity. "I am an anti-golf man," he protests. "I feel that I have reached a reasonable status in life, and agree with the Chinese gentleman's expression, 'Surely you can pay someone to do that for you!' I like less strenuous endeavors—like listening to music."

The routine of Kershner's life abruptly changed with the advent of World War II. "I felt that the payoff for mathematical research was a little too long-term to be an appropriate activity for a fellow my age in wartime. So I moved into an area of mathematics that could be applied quickly and immediately in the war effort.

"I joined the Geophysical Laboratory which was operating under the Carnegie Institution in Washington, D.C., and became immediately engaged in research on ballistics, calculating powder charges for guns, studying high-velocity new guns, and things of that nature. As the War progressed and the lead time became shorter, I moved more and more into the practical phase, transferring to the Allegany Ballistics Laboratory in Cumberland, Maryland. Here I was in the rocket branch, because this was becoming the big new thing in weaponry, yet there was not as much tradition in this field as there was with guns; therefore they needed new mathematics and new developments more rapidly.

"During the last part of the War, I was building rockets and recoilless guns, and demonstrating them to the troops. I found that I had quite a taste for this and apparently a reasonable flair for this kind of hardware-development activity. In some ways it was more satisfying than mathematical research." The basis for giant strides that technology has undergone stems from World War II effort, Kershner points out: "It took years to bring all the potential into being, but just consider the list—rockets were developed during that period, as was the servo-mechanism theory, the communications theory, the high-speed digital computer, and many other concepts.

"There was another important product of the War, and that was spirit. Most of today's young people who did not participate in that effort have no understanding of the discipline entailed and the rewards that were experienced. The work was tremendously hard and demanding, but it gave a sense of gratification in return. Many people involved in the defense effort acquired a taste for the exacting standards and stringent pace, and have never slowed down. Once there is experienced the deep satisfaction of getting a job done a little quicker and better than anyone thought possible, one does not want to change to any other method of work."

Kershner by no means infers that all young people lack strong motivation. "It is quite possible to find large numbers of brilliant, dedicated, hard-working young people. They have not experienced a shooting war, but they appreciate that we are in a competition for our very survival. This group is as highly motivated as any people I saw in wartime.

"The people who worked to develop *Polaris,* for instance, felt an urgency and a conviction that this must be developed at the earliest possible moment to deter war and guard freedom. I don't think it would ever be possible to convey how deeply those of the Navy felt this responsibility. The effort which they exerted, without let-up until it was completed, would seem totally unbelievable to people who did not see it as closely as I did."

Writes the magnificent Carl Sandburg, "Nothing happens unless first a dream."[1] Those who stand as the vital contributors to today's progress possess the unique ability first to dream, then to transform visions into the most pulsating reality. Though not all people can possess the skill and genius to specifically enrich this technological advancement, anyone can become an "associate member" with merely the single qualification of awareness.

Of all the arbitrary divisions that might be made in our society, none has more significance than the separating of those who live as a part of the world and its happenings, and those who move about on the fringe in private little worlds. If it be a subconscious retreat, a protection from the vast problems that are besetting today's citizen, the shield effectively blocks the excitement of the unfolding of this dramatic cavalcade. Is the avoiding of the pain worth the price of denying the pleasure? If a sense of responsibility does not dictate participation, even selfish motives should prove sufficient to urge every individual into the mainstream of this challenging era.

Some speak the language and understand. To those who don't, words will not convey the picture. Relates Kershner, "Having enjoyed teaching, I fully intended to return to it after World War II. On leave of absence, I returned to the University one day to discuss plans, and I found a curious thing. My attitude had undergone a drastic change. As I talked with one member of the staff, I commented quite dryly that there had been some quite exciting times since I had last seen him—which I thought was a subtle way to describe the War.

"He agreed that there had been very exciting times, but he didn't know that I had realized it. The University had introduced a new trigonometry textbook, and the engineering department hadn't liked it at all, but they were fighting it through to the last ditch. He talked on, but I didn't hear. We just weren't communicating."

Kershner adds, "Such insulation from the world is common among college professors, but not to the point of being typical. On the contrary, there were many tremendous contributions by college professors during the War, and large numbers have been among the most important figures in our space research effort. But there are those like my friend, who simply lose touch."

There was another consideration of greater importance in helping

Kershner to determine the direction his career should take in that post-war turning point. "The fact that the A-bomb had been developed made it clear that the world was headed for very real and serious trouble unless international agreement could be reached on how to live in the presence of such a monster. Many of us fought very hard for the acceptance of some reasonable proposal for international acceptance; essentially, the Baruch Plan is what we thought ought to materialize. Its validity at that time lay in the fact that we were the sole nation in possession of nuclear capability. It was a generous offer to share, but it was refused by the Soviets."

Taking into consideration the world's need and the manner in which he might best make a contribution and also what would best satisfy his own sense of achievement, Kershner did a drastic thing—he abandoned mathematics, which is regarded as a lofty perch at the top of one of the pure sciences, and became an engineer. "There is a definite looking-down-the-nose hierarchy in all this. Scientists don't speak to engineers, physicists don't speak to chemists, mathematicians don't speak to physicists—in fact, I guess only the good Lord speaks to mathematicians. At any rate they are supposed to be at the top of the pyramid.

"But these pecking orders have become all mixed up in recent years. Biology is being done by physicists, physics is being done by chemists—nature just isn't that nicely categorized. And I can say that I made the move to an engineering type of activity of my own volition, and have had a wonderful time! I am not removed from mathematics, because with the tremendous complexity of our modern projects, a fairly profound understanding of mathematics is required. There never was such a thing, really, as simple engineering—people just didn't have full appreciation in prior days. Even in bridge building, if you don't have a good understanding of the physical problems, the bridges blow down—as one did in the state of Washington because they had not consulted an aerodynamicist."

Of the various avenues that he might have traveled, Kershner chose the Applied Physics Laboratory, APL of the University from which he resigned as teacher. He joined the Lab in February, 1946. It was the time of eventful activity, not only for this scientist in his new surroundings, but for the entire area of rocketry and space. *Talos,* a surface-to-air guided missile developed by APL, was successfully flight tested by the Navy. The first United States flight testing of the captured German V-2 rockets took place at White Sands Proving Ground. *Project Rand* was established at Douglas Aircraft Co., and the first highly classified report issued by this group was entitled *Preliminary Design of an Experimental World-Circling Spaceship*. The War Department Equipment Board rendered the decision that missiles would play an important part in future warfare.

Kershner's first activity at APL was in the development of booster rockets. His next activity was the responsibility, from plans to production, of the solid-propellant *Terrier* missile, which is the primary anti-aircraft armament on our Navy ships today. He also assumed over-all supervision of the Navy's *Tartar* surface-to-air missile.

"There is a proud tradition at APL which everyone absorbs when he becomes a part of the team. Their first program during the War was the development of the proximity fuse, which they accomplished in an incredibly short time. This fuse figured very very importantly in a number of engagements, for it actually turned the tide of battle. Such a rousing success helped to instill a pride which everyone feels in the importance of the APL projects. The batting average is very high. There is no program we have ever been allowed to carry out that has not been a success."

Others share Kershner's deep exhilaration at seeing this materialization of ideas. "This is called the Applied Physics Laboratory, and you mustn't pronounce the 'Physics' any louder than you pronounce the 'Applied.' We like projects that are pushing the boundaries of knowledge—that are not just physics or just engineering. It is a middle ground between university research and industrial engineering which we try to inhabit.

"In 1946 when we got into the business of making guided missiles, the weapon had never been demonstrated as being feasible. It is the kind of problem we like—turning laboratory concepts into reality. We feel that an organization that tries to operate without carrying the project to the point of building hardware will lose a sense of reality and a feeling for the practicality of problems, even causing a long period of perfecting to make their output useful. We don't just turn out paper. We build actual prototypes of anything that will eventually be produced by industry. Thus APL has both the understanding of the basic physics and the capability of building pieces of engineering hardware. This can speed up the entire process tremendously. It is this capability of rapid advancement to which most of us are so dedicated."

APL utilizes the developmental technique which has made available to this country some of the vital advancements of the Space Age. It is used by Dr. Wernher von Braun and his team to develop booster rockets; he terms this method the "arsenal approach." Dr. James A. Van Allen employs the same method at the State University of Iowa in preparing his cosmic ray experiments. Kershner is convinced it is the most efficacious method.

Dorothy Thompson has said, "Vision is needed by the democracies. It is needed more than armaments!"[1] It is also needed to make inroads into the future, for those thoughts that are restricted by present capacity are obsolescent before they emerge. Ideas must be dropped into the fluidity of imagination, and be allowed to expand as ripples into the infinity of tomorrow.

An oft-used phrase in space development is: "The state of the art." It has a transitory connotation that conveys the attitude of the scientists, for they say, in effect, "This is what we can do at this instant, but. . . ." Their aims ever leap to increasing capability. Beyond satisfying today's requirement, they are flailing about in the realm of tomorrow's possibility. Distinguished from the more common thought process which strives to meet current needs, the proclivity of science-oriented perception is to create a competency for its own sake. "The use will follow," says Kershner.

"Applications arise that were never contemplated. The mere ability to do a thing brings about the usage. The satellites themselves are the best illustration of that. Twenty years ago, it was known that satellites were technically possible, yet at that time no one projected any terribly good uses to which they could be put. As soon as it was clear that they were not only technically feasible but were actually going to exist—and that there would be economic support for making them, which was the critical question—uses just came tumbling out. Navigation is one, weather observation is one, communication is one—these are now accepted by everyone.

"The big payoffs from space will be things of which we have not yet dreamed. They will be the by-products of discoveries that I can't predict—discoveries when we get to the Moon, when we get to the planets. They will have what I can only term 'incalculable benefits,' since there is no way to estimate them now. We only can be guided by the lesson that history teaches: whenever new areas open up, discoveries are made that are extremely significant to your well-being, and which modify your way of living for the better." Progress is the word which says it best—progress today at an unprecedented pace!

Kershner refers to the interesting point that the "things" may not be as noteworthy as the "thoughts" which space manifests: "Though certainly astronautical applications will have great impact upon the lives of the average person, we cannot overbalance them against the mental stimulus. The tremendous emotional lift that this country experienced from the successful orbiting of Astronaut John Glenn, for instance, is an immense gain in its own right."

When the geographical frontiers of this nation vanished, there was marked a gradual disappearance of a spirit that implanted greatness in every individual; the stagnation of sufficiency has permeated our attitude to a disturbing degree. Bold idealism is embedded deeply within the American soul, however, and it is only resting in a torpid state. The land and the gold were but lures toward the West. The real motivation was the relentless challenge of conquest. Adventure has ridden in chariots, sailed the Spanish Main, and joggled in covered wagons. It is now orbiting in a weightless state.

When tribute is heaped upon Kershner and his staff for their remarkable record of success, he most modestly answers, "We could make satellites work the first time only because they were very simple satellites, not because we were geniuses." He elaborates on the point: "I believe that there has been an attempt to make giant technological leaps without taking certain small easily accomplishable steps on which you can build. It must be determined which of the possible directions is more practical, which pays off better.

"The approach to some of the satellite programs distresses me tremendously, because no efforts are being expended to solve the smaller problems first. They are plunging ahead, building an extremely sophisticated device. The odds are very much against your building something that elaborate and that complex and having it work the first time."

Kershner's words are underscored by his accomplishments—of such importance that he has received the highest recognition which the Secretary of the Navy may bestow upon one who is not an employee of the Department of the Navy, the Navy Distinguished Service Award. Kershner has received this not once, but twice—in January, 1958, for his work in the *Terrier* missile program, and in February, 1961, for his outstanding contributions to the successful development of the Fleet Ballistic Missile System, *Polaris*.

The originality of some of his contributions has earned him patents, and his scientific thinking has produced about 40 papers, plus a book which he co-authored with L. R. Wilcox, *The Anatomy of Mathematics*. The volume is an exposition of the modern axiomatic approach to the basic branches of mathematics and includes much original work in the development of axiom systems. A number of schools and colleges have created courses based on the book. Its preface contains an attraction also for the lay reader: "The only prerequisites for reading this book are the desire to start and the perseverance to finish. The reader does not even need to know the sum of 7 and 5; incidentally, if he does not know this sum, he will not learn it from this book."[7]

Dual aspects of the authors—as scientists and as philosophers—are noted in a passage which conveys their viewpoint: "Now it must be admitted that an understanding of abstract reasoning as exemplified by modern standards of rigor in mathematics, does not automatically make for clear and careful thinking on all subjects. It is even admitted, reluctantly, that there may be mathematicians with a considerable aptitude in exacting fields of thought, who are as opinionated politically, bigoted ecclesiastically, and intolerant generally, as anyone you are likely to find.

In addition to an understanding of the nature of a proof, there are needed also the desire to transfer that understanding into other fields and the open-mindedness to permit the transfer to be made. But certain it is that the transfer is impossible if there is nothing to transfer. With a firm conviction that logic can be of great value to any open-minded man, this book will be devoted to an exemplification of modern standards of logical thought, as applied to the simplest branches of mathematics."[7]

In his own attitude toward his activities, Kershner at first seems highly illogical: "I have always used in my programs a philosophy of under-budgeting and under-staffing." Then he plausibly continues, "This way, people are forced to be geniuses. If you give them a lot of money, they buy a vast amount of equipment and beat the problem to death with a sledge hammer. If you don't allow people enough time and money to do it the hard way, they'll find an easier way!

"Let's take, as an example, one of the primary problems of space—stabilization. I am somewhat disturbed to see what might be termed a 'brute force' engineering approach to it, where one uses, with appropriate modifications, techniques that had been applied in guided missiles.

"There has not been enough resourcefulness toward seeking a solution unique to the environment in which the satellite operates, which would make it simpler to accomplish the desired objectives." Having erected the framework for an hypothesis, Kershner suggests this alternative: "There are a number of features that the usual engineering approach says we have to fight which I feel can be utilized to advantage—such as radiation pressure from the sun. This force pushes on a satellite. Instead of lamenting that this is what we have to compete with, I say, 'Use it.'

"Because you are weightless while in space in a satellite, there is a belief that there is no gravity. That is, of course, not true if you look even closer to another decimal place. You are in free fall, and don't feel gravity when you are on board a satellite—but since one side of the satellite is nearer the earth than the other, there is a difference in the level of gravity in the near and the far side of the satellite. This gives a torque. If a satellite of the right shape is built, this torque becomes large enough to actually point the satellite at the earth.

"This tendency to twist has been used by nature to stabilize the Moon and keep one face always looking at the earth. It could be used by a satellite in the same way. If this is accomplished, one side is always looking at the earth, which means all the antennas can be placed there to pour all the power down to the earth where it is wanted instead of scattering power out into space where it is not needed."

Citing advantages, Kershner says, "This obviously improves the design of the satellite tremendously, for it eliminates limited-life approaches or mechanisms that are inherently unreliable and will fail in a matter of months. There is no reason why this kind of stabilization should not work for years and years. So I advocate using what's available in space, taking advantage of it."

There is a distant attitude about Kershner as he describes this new satellite design. The vision appears very real to him as fabricated by his thoughts. It emphasizes another truth of nature—life moves in a cycle. Dick Kershner, the man, still dreams as the boy of a "fancy gadget" that he will develop. The very advancements of space are made up of imaginative wanderings such as this within the mind of a brilliant mathematician-engineer!

REFERENCES

1. Adams, Franklin Pierce: *FPA Book of Quotations,* New York, Funk and Wagnalls, 1952.
2. Kershner, R. B.: *Progress Report on Transit,* Silver Spring, Maryland, The Johns Hopkins Applied Physics Laboratory, May, 1961.
3. *United States Naval Institute Proceedings,* 87:5:77–84, May, 1961.
4. *Project ANNA—Geodetic Satellite System,* Hearings before the Subcommittee on Space Sciences of the Committee on Science and Astronautics, U.S. House of Representatives, May 14, 15, 16, 1962.
5. Kershner, R. B., and Newton, R. R.: *The Transit Navigational Satellite System,* presented before the Institute of Navigation and the Royal Geographical Society, London, England, September 26, 1961.
6. *Space World,* May 14, 1962.
7. Kershner, R. B., and Wilcox, L. R.: *The Anatomy of Mathematics,* New York, Ronald Press, 1950.

Outstanding director of our tremendous space science program

HOMER E. NEWELL

"Winged words." The phrase is attributed to Homer. The concept that it conjured up in the Greece of several centuries B.C. may not have been far different from the attitude of today. Men have aspired to the heavens since the time imagination bestirred them from the cave.

The principal difference today rests not with the dreams, but with the possibility of transforming them into reality. "Man is reaching for the stars."[1] The Homer who wrote that is not a poet but a scientist—Dr. Homer E. Newell. As Director of the Office of Space Sciences* of the National Aeronautics and Space Administration (NASA), he is responsible for the programs which utilize rockets, satellites and space probes to conduct scientific experiments in space.

Newell well measures up to the enormous responsibility demanded by this key position of guiding our nation's scientific space effort, in that he is highly intelligent, greatly respected, conservative, and utterly dedi-

* The Office of Space Sciences is one of the four major offices of NASA. The others are: (1) Office of Applications, which handles such programs as the meteorological and communication satellite systems; (2) Office of Advanced Research and Technology; (3) Office of Manned Spaceflight, which directs Project *Mercury*, Project *Gemini*, and Project *Apollo*.

cated. This is not a man of spectacular personality to be quickly quoted and as quickly forgotten. Newell, instead, possesses the attributes found in a friend of 10 or 20 or 30 years standing. He wears well. His thoughts are considered; his ideas, soundly formulated.

This man is the very personification of the spirit that exists in our government space agency. Seldom have attitudes matured into tradition as rapidly as with this organization. Catalysts in the evolvement of NASA have been men such as Newell, Dr. Hugh L. Dryden, the quiet and eminent Deputy Administrator, and the extremely competent Dr. Robert Gilruth, Director of the Manned Spacecraft Center.

Space, to such men, is an advancement to be pursued with full awareness of its potential—not a new gimmick to be exploited and propagandized. When the flash and dash of the world's introduction to space has faded from the scene, when the headlines and hoopla are forgotten and the major factors emerge, the United States' accomplishments will be perceived clearly as a giant contribution to progress.

Newell explains: " 'Space science' has become a familiar term, but it has taken on a mystical tone that it really shouldn't have—because it is nothing but science done in space, in the rocket, the satellite, or the space probe. The techniques are modified, adapted, extended, to do research out beyond the atmosphere. Otherwise it is the same ideas and the same people. An important point is that the process of becoming a space scientist is simply first to be a scientist, then to start working on space problems—perhaps the study of the earth's atmosphere, or interplanetary space, or the solar system.

"A physicist, for example, might in the normal course of things become involved in the study of nuclear reactions in the accelerators and equipment that we have in the laboratory. Or he might just as naturally become interested in all the reactions and interactions that go on out in the interplanetary space. He'd still be a nuclear physicist; but in the latter case he'd also be a space scientist."

Why does a man become a space scientist? The question begets a broader one, which Newell has applied himself to answering in many of his books and addresses: "Why space? What, precisely, is the United States program?" As he writes, "Before we can discuss the program intelligently, or criticize it, or attempt to evaluate it, one must know what the program is."[2]

This scientist-administrator, who has exercised a strong voice in the formulation of much of our nation's astronautical planning, explains, "Basically, the space program is designed to use the rocket and related equipment and techniques to extend man's sphere of action, to advance his knowledge about the universe, and to advance technology and the applications thereof."[2]

The moon, planets, stars and sun will be investigated and explored with the vehicles that have emerged in this age. And one phase of this search is so important, so fraught with implications and possibilities that it overshadows all other considerations—the search for life beyond the earth. "What a tremendously exciting thing it would be to find life, either as we know it, or different from that we know, on one of the planets!"[2]

As we learn more of the conditions and environments of other areas of the universe, we unravel more of the mysteries which shroud our own relatively little world. The bioscientist suddenly has open to him a laboratory as vast as our solar system in which to pursue the enormously complex question of the origin of life.

In addition to this bioscience branch, which ones are adaptable to space and which are earth sciences? "An example of the latter is oceanography," Newell says, "since at the moment we do not know of any oceans on Venus or Mars that we would be studying. But aside from that, it is difficult to think of sciences that really concern the earth alone. Just about all are involved in one way or another in space—if not actively now, they will be eventually. Consider them—physics, geophysics (which includes geodesy, atmospheric physics and ionospheric physics), solar physics, cosmic ray physics, astronomy, chemistry, seismology, meteorology, radiations, studies of magnetic fields, gravitational fields, studies of the structure of the planets similar to structure of the earth."

The scope of the activity suddenly becomes as limitless as the very nature of space. Within the framework of these collective sciences Newell mentions some of the typical researches that are being conducted: "There is research on materials; fuels; chemical, electric, and nuclear propulsion; solar, nuclear, and other varieties of power supplies; communications; guidance and control; computing techniques; measurement techniques; life support systems; etc."[2]

Though these efforts are still focused upon space exploration and spaceflight, the irrefutable rule comes into play: No advancement is so specialized but that its peripheral boundaries encompass an enormously broad area. So even at this very short-range view, when the Space Age is less than 5 years old, we are seeing valuable applications of the knowledge and techniques which have accrued to it.

Man's favorite topic for idle conversation—the weather—is a prime example. Meteorological satellites outstripped the initial plans of those who were responsible for launching them! The satellite *Tiros I* was intended as a research vehicle, but its worth was so quickly apparent that it was determined that a *Tiros* satellite should be kept in orbit at all times until the follow-on program (utilizing the *Nimbus* satellite) is in operation.

It has happened repeatedly in this expanding development phase. The scientist conceives and produces a research tool—only to have this progeny snatched from the domain of the laboratory, forced to immediate maturity, and applied to practical usage. It appears to be human nature—to set up a dike of resistance against the pressure of advanced research, then throw open the flood gates of acceptance once a trickle of result has been indicated. Often it is the experimenter himself who must then hold back his brainchild, begging for the necessary time to fully test and prove its capabilities.

Another system which will soon affect peoples the world over is the communications satellite. The wonder of transoceanic, instantaneous television has become a reality by bouncing the signals off *Telstar,* which was launched July 10, 1962. Telephone service between the United States and other continents will be faster, cheaper, better by this means. An unexpected application of the principle was indicated by a recent visitor from Mongolia. He expressed interest in the use of communications satellites to improve the whole communications system throughout his country, without the expense of putting up extensive cables. So even though the earthly distance traversed might be but tens or hundreds of miles, the signal would travel up to a satellite orbiting at an altitude of more than 22,000 miles and be bounced back.

Not only the land but the sea will draw from the wonders performed in space. *Transit,* the navigational satellite, has been developed from a concept of the Chairman of the Research Center at the Johns Hopkins Applied Physics Laboratory, Dr. Frank McClure. This innovation can serve all ships at sea. The military utilization is obviously of interest to the U.S. Navy. Under the auspices of NASA, the system is now undergoing evaluation for civilian application.

The exactitude of the requirements for this system involved many sciences in many ways. Perhaps the most surprising of them was the spill-over into geodesy! When orbits were being determined with preciseness heretofore never attempted, it was discovered that the satellites were being influenced by perturbations (disturbances) which could be explained only by the existence of huge lumps on the earth's surface! These protrusions, so huge they dwarf the Himalayas, had never before been revealed.

Suddenly, unexpectedly, the equation became a double-yielding one, and space reached back to earth to involve the science of geodesy when the satellites above revealed another tremendously significant fact. Discovery always involves a high degree of ebullience, for a rearrangement of all accepted beliefs must take place, and new concepts evolved.

Dr. Hugh L. Dryden states, "The early discoveries of new phenomena in space, and the very rapid advance in knowledge of such things as the interactions between the sun and the earth, has stirred up tremendous interest. Dr. Robert Jastrow has compared the excitement in scientific circles with that of other days of great advance in science, similar to when high energy physics was new, or when nuclear physics was new."

So space research is feeding back into myriad areas. Newell enumerates some of them: "The results of materials research—ceramics, metals, plastics, for example—will inevitably find their way into industry and to the consumer. The values of new fuels, new methods of power generation, and supersonic transportation are clear."[2]

He continues his recounting, "From the effort to place man in space will come a host of direct and indirect benefits. The study of man himself will advance the fields of medicine and psychology. Studies of human performance will show us how to use men more effectively in industry and elsewhere. The advance in technology brought about by the requirement to provide for man's needs when he is in outer space, either on the way to the moon or a planet, or on the moon or planet, will contribute significantly to human welfare here on earth."[2]

Space research may well make a major contribution toward the solution of one of the gravest problems facing civilization—food! The population explosion gives rise to the threat of world famine, unless more ingenious ways of utilizing our resources are developed. The study of special foods being evolved for the feeding of astronauts on prolonged space journeys may well contribute to such knowledge.

The impressive list continues, into such diverse areas as medicine, transportation, the development and conservation of our resources, the generation of power, fields of engineering, even road building and general construction.

In consideration of all this, a new light falls upon our stated national goal of sending three men to the moon and returning them to earth. That is the end objective in this first big step in space exploration, but the means of attaining it will push the limits of almost all scientific disciplines, and lift the level at which men on this earth will live.

"The problem of getting across to the people why their support should be given to the space program is one of making them aware of the value that will derive from the program. I think that the first line of attack is to show that dollars invested in the space program are just that—an investment! They will have returns!"

Not only is the investment in space research and exploration providing us with knowledge and accelerating progress, it is also stimulating the economy. Referring to the lunar mission, Vice-President Johnson writes, "Many billions of dollars would be required to do this. One may naturally ask why we should thus plan to shoot so much of our resources to the moon. But it should be pointed out that virtually all the dollars and resources expended upon the space program remain at home on earth in the form of jobs for thousands of people, and in the form of numerous benefits."[1]

It is estimated that the force mobilized for this effort will tally about 435,000 people—ranging in skills from learned professors and scientists to technicians and typists. The cooperation of about 10,000 companies will be required before the project is completed. The Administrator of NASA, the dynamic businessman, James E. Webb, has pointed out major benefits in the form of "spin-offs," which result in the creation of entire new areas of industry and of individual services, tailored to meet the demands of this astronautical expansion.

There are returns beyond all of this that defy appraisal in monetary terms—those of national self-respect, of the confidence born of capability, of esteem in the eyes of other peoples of other nations, of the initiative of leadership of the free world. Such priceless elements will be enhanced as we continue with a space program that is directed toward good for all people.

Beyond that which can be estimated, Newell adds what is perhaps the most elusive yet promising of all: "Past experience has shown that the most important benefits of our research are probably unforeseen."[1]

Those happy accidents of science which can be lumped under the term "breakthrough" are multitudinous. Dual circumstances must be present to permit them: Proper sequencing of conditions must be present for research to be undertaken, and the researcher must have sufficient acumen to make him aware of the discovery if it is different from the result he had anticipated. Without the second factor, a disillusioned scientist has considered his experiment a failure—only to have the data re-examined by a more perceptive colleague who saw in it the unanticipated but amazing findings.

The plus side of the space ledger is heavily weighted. We have the individual stimulus of challenge such as has never before faced men. The satisfaction of present attainment is noteworthy yet minuscule in view of the future potential. Our economy is already enriched with the civilian and military space contracts and business activity, and is still mushrooming. The fall-out of benefits is raining down in every area of living, and the advancement of knowledge is but beginning!

The most dramatic show in the cavalcade of civilization is unfolding. Alert persons are appreciative spectators; and the fortunate, chosen ones are participants helping to write this dramatic chapter in history. Among the other effects arising from the study of space, there might be added that of a "disease"—one from which the members of the select society never wish to be cured. The heady promises of it evoke most stimulating curiosity, and each new attainment produces the symptom of throbbing satisfaction.

This affliction is, perhaps, one of the few things shared by those who make up the space world which is, in most ways, an agglomerate collection of individuals. From industry have come both scientists and businessmen to contribute to this sprawling new effort. Universities have been tapped for some of the high-ranking intelligence demanded by the seemingly unsoluble problems that beset the missions and projects. From the ranks of civil service, faithful personnel have applied themselves to the positions with NASA with renewed vigor. The military services have charged forward, perceiving in space new means of guaranteeing the freedom of this nation. Converging from these and countless other areas, the personnel has rallied, bringing a variety of viewpoints yet unanimity of aims to the space effort.

Homer E. Newell stands out in the bas-relief of this picture much as the consummate actor does by underplaying.

Were the FBI searching for an agent who could get lost in a crowd by virtue of his lack of unusual, visable characteristics, a man such as Newell might be the choice—average height, average weight, no marks or scars, an inconspicuous manner. In the realm of appearance, he could be placed in many backgrounds—a bank, a university, a church.

Remarks his long-time colleague, Dr. John Clark,* "I don't readily bring to mind any single incident that could be used to characterize Dr. Newell—which is in itself interesting. The impression he conveys is not by individual, unusual acts, but by his consistent attitudes and methods. His outstanding qualities are those of being even-tempered, philosophically consistent, and intellectually honest in attempting to apply a basic set of ethical principles to any job. These qualities are somewhat rare in today's world."

The opinions concerning the man, Newell, vary but little as other associates add pieces to the mosaic. Comments Dr. Hugh Odishaw, Executive Director of the National Academy of Sciences, "Dr. Newell is a very thoughtful, painstaking, deliberate, and considerate individual—one highly talented in science administration and in the organization of technical programs. He has an unusual capacity for synthesizing, as demonstrated by many of his publications which constitute splendid reviews. Being characterized by a high seriousness, he has admirable objectives and a profound concern for the interests of science and the nation. He is an extremely hard and effective worker."

Some of the qualities enumerated by Odishaw are inherent within the man; others have come through application and experience. Wandering back through the 40-odd years of Newell's life, there seems an effective blending of the two categories.

It was spring of 1930, and High School Day in Holyoke, Massachusetts. The ninth-grade pupils were visiting the school they would enter in the fall. In the chemistry class the instructor was asking questions of

* Dr. Clark has recently been appointed Associate Director and Chief Scientist of the Office of Space Sciences of NASA.

his students—who did not respond. After being tempted by several questions, one of the visiting ninth-grade students timidly put up his hand. Somewhat surprised, and a little skeptical, the teacher said, "Well, if you know the answer, what is it?" The young visitor gave a most thorough and correct reply. The teacher posed other questions. His own class continued to fail to respond. The visiting student continued to give correct answers. The teacher, Omar Hebert, was intrigued at the unusual capacity of this youngster who would be entering his class the following year, and inquired as to his name. It was Homer Newell.

A somewhat surprising revelation is that he had acquired this advanced ability through only a year of application. "I had been getting B's and C's in my studies up to the time I came across a book in my grandfather's library, *The Friendly Stars,* by Martha Evans Martin. It was a complete turning point in my life, for it suddenly awakened an interest in me. Though there were elements of science in the book, it was primarily a narrative style of writing about the beauties of astronomy." The book, which still has a place in his library, entices Newell with such passages as these:

" . . . if by chance we come to know by name one bright star, it immediately separates itself from all the others and becomes an individual. If we enlarge our acquaintances in the skies, the whole aspect of the heavens is changed, and, instead of a brilliant assembly of impersonal points of light, we see a host of individuals that we know as bright Capella, sombre Betelgeuse, and others. . . . When he has come to know them, there is no greater delight than to lie stretched on a cot in the open with the whole expanse of the heavens above him, and watch them as they rise and pass and go again. This is the stage of acquaintance that binds one forever in friendship with the stars. . . . The moon comes and goes. She is the symbol of inconstancy. The planets wander from place to place—most of them easy enough to find, but continually changing in brightness and position. Only the stars are always the same."[3]

Newell suddenly gained a focal point for his alert mind, and curiosity was so aroused that he eagerly turned to other astronomy books from the large library of his grandfather, Arthur James Newell, who lectured on scientific and historical subjects. Homer Newell's interest broadened to the field of chemistry with equal fervor. In such an example as this, it is intriguing to consider the big "if"—if the fascinating book on astronomy had not been handy for his perusal, would he have been transformed from an average student into an avid science enthusiast? How often do students wander the middle ground, because the particular instance has never transpired to trigger their real potential?

Educators know that there is fallacy in classifying students as "bright, average, slow," for when some bit of learning, or some experience lights the spark, a transformation can occur. It may come early in childhood, or it may come at a rather late period—when it is more difficult to catch up on the basics of learning.

Newell was fortunate to have been guided into the right channel at such an early age. As a student, he learned an important habit—to take the initiative of added reading and study. "I did not rely on the teachers, but sought out more material to study in the areas in which I was interested. There are three things that I feel a good teacher should provide to students—study at a reasonable pace, the presenting of a reasonable challenge, and the attitude of reasonable enthusiasm. When these are present, I think most students will respond, as did I."

When Newell enrolled in the high school chemistry course at the beginning of the year, the teacher, Hebert, gave him the final examinations. Newell passed with a top mark, so throughout the following months he was assigned special advanced projects. Hebert, aware that this bright and budding mind should be provided with all possible encouragement, helped Newell to set up a chemistry laboratory in his home—complete with alcohol lamps, flasks, glass tubing, beakers, scales and weights.

Young Newell mowed lawns, shoveled snow and did other odd jobs to save money with which to stock his lab. His father, an electrical engineer, obtained some of the chemicals from the laboratories of paper and textile mills of Holyoke upon which he called.

Newell has kept the laboratory, and is looking forward to the time when his 10-year-old son, Andrew, will experiment in it. "He is not old enough yet," says Newell, recalling the kind of incident that proves the wisdom of his attitude:

"During high school days I had a friend—who now, incidentally, is a well-known chemist—who became interested in chemistry. One day I happened to tell him of reading how to make nitroglycerin. I thought no more about it until later when I went to his house, and he handed me a little bottle filled with a light-yellow liquid. He proudly announced that it was nitroglycerin. Astounded, I said, 'Good night! When I told you how to make this I didn't tell you all the other things about how to wash it clean so that it might not explode spontaneously. You'd better get rid of it.'

"Well, my friend got rid of it—he told me later—by pouring it out in the backyard. This, of course, gave him a patch of dynamite! Luckily the rains washed it away before it exploded, but I've never quite forgotten the possibilities of the situation."

Newell was alarmed at one experiment he himself conducted—one that was described in a "playbook" of chemistry. "Substances were mixed in a test tube, and each time seemed to produce a minor explosion. Fortunately, I always took the precaution of keeping the test tube aimed away from myself, so that when this chemical volcano precipitated all the material out of the test tube, it only caused a purple splotch on the ceiling—which was easily covered by paint. This experiment was certainly one which should never have been included in the book."

Though chemistry continued as Newell's primary activity, interest started to generate in another direction as a result of the teaching of Miss Esther Barry. "She was a remarkable person, who used to read the classics in Greek and Latin, and who quoted Shakespeare to meet any situation that would come up. The subject she taught was mathematics, and during the time I was taking courses from her, she began discussing with me the theory of relativity. Under her guidance I did some additional reading, and it led to a deep interest in mathematics."

Newell, habitually "best" in all his studies, also excelled in the lighter art of punning! This is a flair he has never lost, and a friend warns, "Don't try to compete with him—he will outpun you every time." When Newell was asked to repeat one of his little "gems," he replied with a chuckle, "Puns are on the spur of the moment and vanish on the air—they should not be revived unless they are of the Shakespearian quality, which I do not claim to have."

This student's other thoughts were on serious matters. His interest in science might appear to have taken many turns—from astronomy, to chemistry, to mathematics. But evaluation indicates that each tangent fed into the mainstream of his career. Mathematics remained the focal point throughout the rest of school. "I had a really inspiring collection of instructors at Harvard," he relates. "The most outstanding, perhaps, was Professor George David Birkhoff, who at the time was rated as the world's leading mathematician. I was fortunate enough to have him as my tutor—Harvard has the tutorial system, in which each candidate for a degree has assigned a professor who guides the student in extra reading in his special area."

The junior class of which Newell was a member was most unusual. Birkhoff, finding that his students were already at the level of advanced calculus, and were interested in moving as fast as they could, guided them through the year's text, *Statics,* in the first quarter. "We then moved on to Routh's *Rigid Dynamics*, and went through a goodly portion of that in the next quarter. Before the year was over, we went into advanced topics, such as Lagrange's *Equations,* Hamilton's *Equations,* Relativity, and Celestial Mechanics."

In such a manner did Newell gain a thorough foundation in mathematics. This science has traveled far indeed from its beginnings with a notched paleolithic tally stick to indicate a number base. In its evolution through the pre-Hellenic age, the period of classical antiquity, the medieval interlude, up to its modern emergence, mathematics has formulated the launching pad for today's leap into space. Within every astronaut's capsule rides the spirit of Pythagoras, Archimedes, Hipparchus, Cardan, Newton, Lagrange, Gauss, Hilbert.

Newell had taken charge of classes on many occasions at the requests of professors. So when graduation brought him the offer of a scholarship in mathematics and education, he accepted with alacrity. "I had always liked teaching. But during this period of graduate work, I became very much disillusioned about the field of education—and my disillusionment has continued ever since.

"I found on the part of many education people a preoccupation with the tools of the trade, and not concentration on subject matter of the things being taught. The tendency is toward taking 10 education courses, and feeling one course in the subject matter is enough. I feel it should be just the reverse, with 10 courses in mathematics, or whatever the specialty is, and the few courses in education."

With conviction, Newell continues, "A teacher must know his subject, or he can't teach it. He can't inspire students if he doesn't know what the real problems are. In sharp contrast to the teacher who gave me so much guidance, Miss Barry, I remember another high school teacher who probably knew his education, but didn't know his mathematics. Many times he said, 'Oh, you don't need to know that. You'll never use it.' Time and again I have remembered that remark when I was in the midst of using the knowledge in the most fundamental things I was working on."

Newell feels there has been a deplorable decline in engineering and mathematics standards in college courses. "It has gone on so long now that not only must one try to inspire youngsters, but must also deal with parents who aren't inspired and don't care.

"Another situation has arisen—our youngsters all want to be alike. This, of course, is a natural tendency, but the education approach which often emphasizes adapting to the situation has gotten youngsters to the point where they'll adjust even to situations to which they should not adjust."

Newell specifies what he feels is a great weakness: "I know of teachers who take the progressive education maxim that if a student likes something, he will put forth the effort to learn it well. But conversely, this attitude can be turned in the student's mind to justify his not trying to learn something simply because he doesn't like it. Youngsters don't like drill—so, too often teachers don't make them drill. Yet, if a person wants to be a top-notch golfer, he practices and practices. If he wants to do well with reading and writing and arithmetic, he must practice, also."

This man of science sees a very big and very broad job to be done—that of selling a real appreciation of science for its own sake. "There is an aesthetic aspect to it, a philosophic aspect to it, that ought to be appreciated by the people. People must want to know for the sake of knowing; this, unfortunately, is a quality seldom found in the large percentage of those coming out of high school today. Instead, each is inclined to say to himself, 'What good is it for me? Can I make a faster buck with it? If my house is bigger, my automobile is bigger, then I shall have succeeded.' "

In concluding his thoughts on the matter, Newell points out, "I hold a Master's degree in education, so I feel I have a certain privilege to express this strong opinion. This nation was sold a bill of goods. We are a country founded on the highest ideals and principles, as stated in our Constitution and our Declaration of Independence. These principles grew out of a national philosophy that was non-materialistic, and yet our educational system of the past 30 years has been based on John Dewey's philosophy of pragmatism—which is a completely materialistic theory."

Though, undeniably, this rages as a controversy, Newell feels that there is coming about a recognition from educators that such a problem exists. "The National Science Foundation has been holding periodic Saturday morning seminars on problems of this sort, which bring together teachers and educators. The present trend seems to be to try to introduce more drill, more substance. I think if you explore this with the people downstairs* in the U.S. Office of Education, you'll find they are quite aware of this difficulty and are working on it."

Since this "scientists' viewpoint" on education has been expressed several times in various chapters of the *Men of Space* series of books, the suggestion of Newell's was followed. In the interest of hearing the other side to the debate, an opinion was sought from Dr. Albert Piltz, Science Specialist, U.S. Office of Education. Piltz painstakingly answers the "materialistic" charge in these words: "Attempts to trace the ills that have befallen education all too often converge on the philosophy of education as proposed by John Dewey who is probably the most maligned, misunderstood, misinterpreted and little read (with understanding) of all educational philosophers of our time.

"What all else may be said of John Dewey he is noted for his dedication to spiritual and moral values. A product of New England puritanism, he had a passion for the purity of life, for the values of life and American civilization. He made all of education a moral enterprise and was highly critical of acquistion and materialistic endeavor. He renounced the old curriculum because it did not teach morality. He was especially concerned that science and mathematics be taught with a moral awareness."

Piltz continues, "John Dewey's mission was to make ideals meaningful and relevant and bring them into everyday practice. He wanted them vitalized. He wanted living ideals rather than empty slogans. How elo-

* NASA is presently sharing Federal Office Building No. 6 with the U.S. Office of Education at 4th and Maryland St., S.W., Washington, D.C.

quently he makes his points in his writings: ' . . . The business of the educator—whether parent or teacher—is to see to it that the greatest possible number of ideas acquired by children and youth are acquired in such a way that they become "moving" ideas, motive forces in the guidance of conduct. This demand and this opportunity make the moral purpose universal and dominant in all instruction—whatsoever the topic. . . . The direct and immediate attention of teachers and pupils must be, for the greater part of the time, upon intellectual matters.' "[4]

In further emphasis, Piltz says, "Dewey's message is powerful, almost evangelistic, as he emphasizes human values: ' . . . What we need in education is a genuine faith in the existence of moral principles which are capable of effective application. We believe so far as the mass of children are concerned, that if we keep at this long enough we can teach reading and writing and figuring. We are practically, even if unconsciously, skeptical as to the possibility of anything like the same assurance in morals. We believe in moral laws, and rules to be sure, but they are in the air. They are something set off by themselves. They are so "very" "moral" that they have no working contact with the average affairs of everyday life. These moral principles need to be brought down to the ground through their statement in social and in psychological terms. We need to see that moral terms are not arbitrary, that they are not "transcendental"; thus, the term "moral" does not designate a special region or portion of life. We need to translate the moral into the conditions and forces of our community life and into the impulses and habits of the individual. . . . The teacher who operates in this faith will find every subject, every method of instruction, every incident of school life pregnant with moral possibility.'[4]

"Dewey was often called a pragmatist and this may have led to some confusion since there is widespread misconception of the term. By common definition it implies concern with practical matters, opportunism, and utilitarian motive, but in the philosophical and educational sense it means that to know whether or not anything is true or right, you must test the consequences. The worth of actions should be appraised in terms of consequences so one might act intelligently instead of blindly.

"With Dewey, morality was the fountainhead of education through which he believed ideals could be realized—his writings abound in the word 'ideal' of men. Although Dewey was a deeply religious man, he was opposed to the narrow, dogmatic interpretation of theology but was more strongly concerned with a view of life that would serve society as a whole where ideals of men might be fulfilled."

A fear expressed by many is that the trend toward science and engineering is endangering our cultural development. Newell has this astute explanation of science's influence on culture: "I do not see it as a situation where the humanities must give way to the sciences. I feel that science is becoming such an integral element of our present-day living and thinking that it must be regarded as one of the humanities—inseparable from them."

Certainly there is no lack of appreciation or participation in the humanities and the arts on the part of Newell and his friends. "Most of the people I know who are scientists are interested in history, music, the graphic arts, in geography and political science. This I want to stress—the scientists who are pushing for the conducting of a strong space science program, and the exploring of the solar system, regard this as an advancement of humanity, not as a conquest of all the other interests of humanity."

The broad, interrelated view must be taken, if the developments of this era are to be regarded in their proper perspective. Writes Aldous Huxley, "For modern science, there are no substantial and separate things; there are only processes, there are only transient knots in the universal interconnectedness of events."[5] Just as developments are connecting the individual disciplines, much as a spark might bridge separation, subjects are converging into a common area of utilization and application.

Space technology demonstrates a devastating eclecticism. It has sucked dry entire areas of learning, and goaded the ever-constant search for knowledge. It has pulled taut threads that reach far back into the history of human advancement, and has spun forward a web that promises to ensnarl temporarily isolated disciplines in the future. But lest the image of space be conjured as a greedy giant, its quality of generosity—still so little appreciated—must be fully recognized.

It is quite remarkable that man's surroundings and environment can undergo such drastic change, while man himself changes so little. With pathetic monotony he persists in doubting each advancement. The benefits of progress have been demonstrated efficaciously throughout history, but still the question persists: "What good is all this space development when I just want to live here on earth?"

Newell has an observation, "I think what is needed is a very active group of good writers who will do extensive research into this great process of feedback into the economy and into the everyday application, then inform the reading public about it.

"There is so much to tell—about such things as the mass spectrometers that are now being used in industry, although they were developed for sounding rockets; the two or so million dollars we are saving each year in the communications industry because of the ionospheric rocket research; the pressure gauges that were developed first for upper air research but are now being used in industrial processing; the materials being developed for exploration of the moon which are now being made into clothing. These illustrations are but few of the total applications of knowledge from space research to earthly benefits."

This NASA scientist-administrator is himself uniquely qualified for the crusade he advocates, having remarkable talent as a writer. Comments Dr. Hugh Dryden, "Dr. Newell has shown considerable ability in exposition of the scientific problems and the scientific results. You notice this in many of the books he's written—some of them for children, but most of them adapted to popular exposition in the field."* Though Newell has wanted to take on this added writing—and may yet do so when he has retired—his present work does not possibly allow it now.

The very qualities of spaceflight—speed, stress, pressure—are translated into the atmosphere that pervades the NASA offices. Calendars are crammed with appointments, the phones jangle perpetual interruptions, mail arrives and is dispatched in copious quantity, and there are endless numbers of meetings and conferences, both scheduled and spontaneously convened. Always there are pressing questions to be answered, and decisions to be rendered regarding never-before-experienced situations. Into unexplored areas, facing unknown difficulties, coping with unexpected developments, men and machines are being sent on pioneering missions. Reliance is upon the key men of this space effort to insure survivability—and they do not carry the responsibility lightly.

"The people of this office are working most of the time—evenings, Saturdays and Sundays—to keep the program moving at the pace which we feel is necessary. I arrive at the office at quarter-past seven each morning, and leave after six. I take home two satchels full of work each weekend, and come in Monday with as much as ten dictabelts of dictation."

The rigorous schedule extends to others beyond the executive level. Dorothy Baxter, Newell's most capable secretary, gets to her desk at a quarter-past eight. Newell states, "I want that first hour when no one is around to get started." After he has gone she always remains to finish up the work.

The effects of such a schedule extend even beyond the office staff. "This is not a job for anyone whose wife isn't also dedicated—because she has to make her contributions," says Newell. There scarcely can be the routine of a normal family life with such work loads on the husband.

In only one way does Newell endeavor to compensate for such a schedule. "I make a point of taking a rather lengthy vacation every year. I take three or four weeks off on the thesis that if the family can put up with

* Newell is the author of the following books: *High Altitude Rocket Research; Vector Analysis; Space Book for Young People; Guide to Rockets, Missiles and Satellites; Sounding Rockets; Window in the Sky;* and *Express to the Stars.* He has also written over 50 articles and scientific papers.

interrupted week-ends during the year, they deserve a full summer vacation.* Secondly, when I come back to work, I do a better job. Thirdly, I just plain need rest. And fourthly, in my position as Director of this Office, if I take the time off, then the other men of the Office feel that they should, and can if I can. We all do a better job for it." Considering the burdens that are upon Newell and his associates, they are wise to realize that their own productivity is increased by an occasional surcease.

The pace, and the stress, have steadily mounted since the inception of NASA. It was born in troubled times; *Sputnik I* had orbited on October 4, 1957, and introduced the Space Age to the chagrin of those who automatically assumed that our nation would always lead in pioneering efforts. In the scramble that ensued to formulate policy and institute long-overdue action, there was a wide range of discussion about where responsibility in space should rest. There was talk of the program being put within the Atomic Energy Commission.

Recalls William G. Stroud, who is now Chief of the Aeronomy and Meteorology Division at the Goddard Space Flight Center, "Newell played a big role in formulating the principles of why it would be the best thing to have a civilian space agency, and then in convincing men like Wernher von Braun that all interests would be best served with civilian rather than military leadership. A meeting was held in Vice-President Nixon's office in the Capitol Building with six of us—von Braun, who arranged it, Krafft Ehricke, William Pickering, John Townsend, Newell and me. It was Newell who was spokesman for the group, and provided leadership.

"Then, when NASA was decided upon at the top level, it was Newell again who helped write the scientific program. I know a number of his ideas are policy, and we operate under procedures which he has created. What is outstanding is the fundamental direction he has given the programs with which he has been associated. He is not an originator of new ideas, but has a real ability to get people to recognize the fundamental issues and to enlist their assistance in seeing that these are done."

Another colleague comments, "It has been said that Newell picks people's brains, puts all the data in the hopper, grinds it up, and produces results. Those who object to this fail to realize that even though you don't generate information, you must put all the various pieces together and come up with answers that are integrants of the individual inputs. This is a very important function in any social group, and particularly in science."

Newell's first title at NASA was Assistant Director for Space Sciences,

* Newell and his wife, the former Janice May Hurd, have two married daughters, Judith Deborah Kehoe and Sue Ellen Olsson. The two children still at home are Jennifer Dianne and Andrew David.

then Deputy Director of Space Flight Programs. The opposition facing all in that founding period was substantial. The scientists who strongly favored a vigorous space program were largely outside the circle of the old-line Cosmos Club.

Relates one member of the fraternity, "From the beginning of the space program there was a hard core of scientists who strongly questioned that the few million dollars allotted to space was being wisely spent. What is even more surprising, many still question it. They are obviously very, very wrong, and do not begin to recognize that the returns already—and we have just started—are beyond anything initially expected."

Congress had long heard expression of the negative view, as exemplified by the testimony of the highly regarded Dr. Vannevar Bush, who, soon after the end of World War II, expressed his belief that any vehicle such as the intercontinental ballistic missile was an "impossibility."

In view of such strong attitudes, and the lack of executive decision, it is to the credit of Congressmen that they displayed prescience in wanting to amply fund the effort. As former Congressional aide, Frank Gibney, relates: "The result was a paradox. Congress was painfully anxious to give the new space program every penny it needed. The committee to which I was attached, made this abundantly clear. Yet the budget estimates presented were worked out with the caution of the controller's office in a small-time factory—hardly the mentality expected of people supposed to trail-blaze a new and only partly known frontier."[6]

Space missions were not defined as among our national goals until May 25, 1961, when John F. Kennedy stated, " . . . I believe that this nation should commit itself to achieving the goal, before this decade is out, of landing a man on the moon and returning him safely to earth."[7]

A fluctuation of attitudes from the general public has continued to plague those of NASA. The pendulum of opinion has swung from disinterest during the lulls, to unreasonable expectations that we should immediately surpass our rival in space each time that nation has accomplished a new feat. An on-again off-again approach is not effective in any undertaking, and is quite impossible in astronautical research and development. Throughout, NASA* leaders have displayed equanimity, and have not been swayed from their carefully calculated objectives, toward which planned programs are being carried out at the fastest pace which is felt commensurate with practicality.

* The role of the military in furthering the nation's space efforts is not intended to be overlooked in this profile of an administrator in the civilian space agency. The accomplishments of military advocates have been detailed in previous volumes of this series, in such biographies as: Bernard A. Schriever, John Paul Stapp, Wernher von Braun, Don D. Flickinger, William F. Raborn, Jr., H. N. Toftoy, Jack Armstrong, and Malcolm Ross.

Their projects have been conducted in the sharp glare of the spotlight—an innovation in the field of research and development. "The traditional approach of the scientist," says Newell, "is to do something first and then talk about it. This whole open approach, of saying that we are going to try for a launching, that we are going to try to get certain measurements, that we are going to orbit an astronaut, is new to science. Although it has presented us with certain difficulties—and occasional embarrassments—most of us in NASA, including myself, feel that there has been a great salutary payoff to this open conduct. It has its hazards if there are failures; it becomes tremendously damaging as well as humiliating. But our average has been good. In the manned spaceflight program, it has been 100 per cent. We have said that our efforts are toward scientific advancement, intended to benefit all people. And our proof has been that we have conducted it right out in front of the whole watching world."

Project *Mercury,* because of its human element, has quite naturally captured most of the attention and adulation from the general public. It has loomed, and rightly so, as the giant accomplishment of our over-all space effort. But other programs of research must not be minimized or overlooked. Though findings such as those from the orbiting geophysical and astronomical observatories are admittedly less glamorous and exciting, they may prove to render benefits and broaden knowledge on a basis that will endure long after current projects are but footnotes to history.

Newell heads the Office of Space Sciences, and has the responsibility for the unmanned research program. By means of rockets, satellites and space probes, the Office is diligently studying the general areas of geophysics, astronomy and space biology. The over-all activity has been broken down into what one staff member terms "six manageable chunks." These subdivisions and their directors are: *Grants and Research Contracts,* Thomas L. K. Smull; *Geophysics and Astronomy,* Dr. John E. Naugle; *Launch Vehicles and Propulsion Programs,* Dr. Richard B. Morrison; *Program Review and Resources Management,* John D. Nicolaides; *Lunar and Planetary Programs,* Oran W. Nicks; and *Biosciences Program,* Dr. Orr E. Reynolds.

Toward the objective of putting men on the moon, the greatest need for additional data rests within the domain of the last-named office. Explains Reynolds: "The challenge of extraterrestrial travel and exploration demands a significant development of biology, in both conceptual rigor and methodology." The office is directing concerted effort toward investigation of the two major problem areas in manned spaceflight—weightlessness and radiation.

Concerned lest the comparatively short duration of the zero-gravity so far experienced by Astronauts and Cosmonauts may not be an accurate indicator of the effects over longer periods, Reynolds is undertaking weightlessness experiments with monkeys, chimpanzees and rodents for periods of up to 14 days.*

In addition, he plans similar tests on simple biological systems, such as bacteria, fertilized eggs, tissue cultures, multicellular organisms, and plants. He explains, "Only in this way can we detect and characterize the subtle cellular and subcellular effects on basic life processes, which would be masked by compensatory mechanisms or delayed in appearance in more complex organisms such as man."

When data from *Explorer I* revealed the inner Van Allen Radiation Belt, and *Pioneer III* indicated the existence of a second ring of cosmic radiation, grave added hurdles were placed in the path of man's journey into space.

Reynolds says, "The problem of ionizing radiation is one of the most apparent and potentially handicapping to successful manned space flight. To meet this problem we have enlisted the great competence of the U.S. Atomic Energy Commission in formulating and conducting a program ranging from theoretical radiobiology to use of laboratory accelerators and balloon and satellite borne space experiments."

The third major effort of NASA's Biosciences Program is an undertaking that could well supply answers to one of science's—and mankind's—most intriguing and perplexing questions.

For many decades, the keenest scientific intellects have been ingeniously unraveling the complex evolvement of life. Significant strides have been made with the advancement of the understanding of the nucleoproteins which Reynolds terms "the templates upon which the replication process of life is based."

This investigation in the past has been conducted within the confines of the earth's surface. Satellites and probes now offer the opportunity to carry instruments and specimens into space, to land them on other planets, then through intricate devices return information and samples to earth for analyses and evaluation. In this application, it is clearly indicated that space is an arena where the individual disciplines, such as biology, may be researched in a unique and efficacious manner.

This phase of Reynolds' activity is the most exciting adventure which any scientist might undertake—*the search for extraterrestrial life!*

Emphasizing the importance of this investigation for life forms on other planets, he states, "There is urgency in the search, not because of some planned application of the knowledge gained, but because of the passion of man for understanding his place in the universe. The hour of discovery

* The most extended periods of weightlessness which men to date have undergone are those experienced by two U.S.S.R. Cosmonauts: Major Andrian Nikolayev was launched on August 11, 1962, into 64 orbits, and Lieutenant Colonel Pavel Popovich ascended the following day to complete 48 orbits. They both landed on August 15, 1962.

is near and the significance of the discovery will have profound impact not alone on biology but on the whole of science and philosophy."

The activity of the Biosciences Program has strong and direct feed-back into the manned space flight program, for the ultimate study of extraterrestrial life will transpire when men are landed upon the surface of Mars—a feat scheduled for the 1970's.

This was one of the points extensively discussed at the Space Science Summer Study, an effort planned by the Space Science Board of the National Academy of Science at the request of NASA's Administrator, James E. Webb.

The goals of the Study were broad and fundamental: to examine the scope, quality and objectives—both current and future—of our space science program. Held at the State University of Iowa from June 18 to August 10, 1962, the General Chairman was Dr. James A. Van Allen, and Dr. William W. Kellogg served as Vice Chairman; in attendance were some of our nation's most distinguished scientists.

The report which was produced will help to guide the NASA program over the coming years. It also had reciprocal advantages in that members of the scientific community gave important briefings to NASA personnel, and NASA in turn more fully acquainted scientists with the opportunities for basic research that exist within its programs.

In NASA's Office of Space Sciences, Newell concentrates his attention on the scientific programming aspect of the activity, and delegates the engineering management to his Deputy, Edgar M. Cortright.

Available to this office, and the other three major program offices of NASA, are the facilities of its nine field installations. These centers, their locations and directors are: *Marshall Space Flight Center,* Huntsville, Alabama, Dr. Wernher von Braun; *Ames Research Center,* Moffett Field, California, Dr. Smith deFrance; *Lewis Research Center,* Cleveland, Ohio, Dr. Abe Silverstein; *Flight Research Center,* Edwards, California, Paul Bickle; *Goddard Space Flight Center,* Greenbelt, Maryland, Dr. Harry J. Goett; *Jet Propulsion Laboratory,* Pasadena, California, Dr. William H. Pickering; *Wallops Station,* Virginia, Robert L. Krieger; *Langley Research Center,* Hampton, Virginia, Floyd L. Thompson; and *Manned Spacecraft Center,* Houston, Texas, Dr. Robert R. Gilruth.

"Our Office of Space Sciences uses six out of the nine centers. They are, in effect, like contractors—except being our own centers, we make particular use of them. Our program also involves the universities of the country, because in them there is to be found the biggest single resource in research talent in this country. We plan for the participation of people like Dr. James Van Allen of the State University of Iowa, Dr. John Simpson of the University of Chicago, Dr. John Winckler of the University of

Minnesota, and Dr. Bruno Rossi of the Massachusetts Institute of Technology.

"Our program is made up from ideas which come to us from these university people, from those in industry, from non-profit institutions, from our own NASA centers, and even from scientists of other countries. These experimenters are the sources of the ideas which are presented as formal proposals to NASA Headquarters and are reviewed." To handle the needs of the experimenters, observatory-type satellites are now designed with a more or less standardized arrangement for accommodating the experiments. Space in these satellites is as eagerly sought by scientists as are seats on a crowded bus.

Choosing the package to be placed aboard each satellite is truly a difficult matter. "Primarily, we determine the scientific problems that must be undertaken in order to advance a given discipline or science in general—then we determine in broad terms that we will support activity in these various areas, and plan the resources necessary to support each at a certain level."

For the actual selection of the experiments, even the erudite members of the Space Sciences Steering Committee* do not render the final choices without seeking extensive expert advice. Says Newell, "A small group such as this is incapable of containing within itself all the knowledge that is required in so broad a program as space sciences, so it is necessary to bring into our planning, evaluating, and selection a much broader knowledge. We do this by having subcommittees in the various discipline areas concerned in our program: Astronomy, Bioscience, Ionospheres and Radio Physics, Particles and Fields, Planetary Atmospheres, Planetology and Solar Physics. These subcommittees are comprised of NASA people, plus consultants from the outside scientific community.†

* Newell is Chairman of the Space Sciences Steering Committee. Dr. John F. Clark is Vice-Chairman. The members are: Edgar M. Cortright, Oran W. Nicks, Dr. John E. Naugle, Dr. Orr E. Reynolds, John D. Nicolaides, Dr. Charles P. Sonett, Jesse L. Mitchell.

† Past and present consultants of the subcommittees include: Philip H. Abelson, Carnegie Institute of Washington; Kinsey A. Anderson, University of California; Dirk Brouwer, Yale University Observatory; Allan Brown, University of Minnesota; Harrison Brown, California Institute of Technology; Melvin Calvin, University of California; J. W. Chamberlain, University of Chicago; Leverett Davis, Jr., California Institute of Technology; Freeman J. Dyson, Institute for Advanced Study, Princeton; Maurice Ewing, Lamont Geophysical Observatory; Sidney Fox, Florida State University; William A. Fowler, California Institute of Technology; Herbert Friedman, Naval Research Laboratory; Thomas Gold, Cornell University; Richard N. Goody, Harvard University; Jesse L. Greenstein, Mt. Wilson & Palomar Observatory; Fred T. Haddock, University of Michigan; David S. Heeschen, National Radio Astronomy Laboratory; Robert A. Helliwell, Stanford University; Harry Hess, Princeton University; Hans E. Hinteregger, Air Force Geophysics Research Directorate; Norman H. Horowitz, California Institute of Technology; Francis S. Johnson, Lockheed Aircraft Co.; William W. Kellogg, RAND Corp.; John Kirby Smith, Oak

"Numbered among these are some of the top minds in the United States, including a number of Nobel Prize winners. These men are always on the rolls, but are paid only when they are working on a project, at the rate of $100 per day."

Each of these subcommittees' drafts recommends short- and long-range programs. At times they assist in the evaluation of specific proposals by rating them in various categories of eligibility; but the subcommittees are not asked to select one proposal in preference to another. That remains the responsibility of the Steering Committee. From the advice provided by this subcommittee, each subcommittee chairman makes recommendations to the Steering Committee for experiments to go into a given spacecraft. Thus is the complex entity of space science broken into parts which are individually manageable, so that all possible consideration might be given by experts.

"In addition, we have available to us the Space Science Board of the National Academy of Sciences, under the chairmanship of Dr. Lloyd Berkner. This is really an outgrowth of the Satellite and the Sounding Rocket Committees of the International Geophysical Year. At the present time, NASA and the National Science Foundation provide financial support for this Board, and it is available for advice and counsel to all government agencies—not just NASA."

So it is possible to bring into play a tremendously powerful body of scientific minds to apply to the problem of planning the program, and selecting the experiments which are to be conducted in space. The parallel factors which must be considered are: (1) which are the good and sound experiments toward solving the most important problems, and (2) what are the resources in the way of vehicles, and what performance capability do the vehicles have compared with what is needed to carry out a certain collection of experiments?

Guided by these considerations, certain collections of experiments are assigned to particular satellites or space probes. Funds are then made

---

Ridge National Observatory; Gerard P. Kuiper, University of Arizona; Joshua Lederberg, Stanford University; Henry Linschitz, Brandeis University; S. R. Lipsky, Yale University; C. Gordon Little, Central Radio Propagation Laboratory, National Bureau of Standards; Edward P. Ney, University of Minnesota; Eugene N. Parker, University of Chicago; A. Keith Pierce, Kitt Peak National Observatory; Colin S. Pittendrigh, Princeton University; Ernest C. Pollard, Penn State University; Frank Press, California Institute of Technology; Bruno B. Rossi, Massachusetts Institute of Technology; Carl Sagan, University of California; Gerhard F. Schilling, RAND Corp.; Erwin R. Schmerling, Penn State University; J. Carl Seddon, Goddard Space Flight Center; Bengt B. Stromgren, Institute for Advanced Study, Princeton; George W. Swenson, Jr., University of Illinois; Gordon Tomkins, National Institutes of Health; Richard Tousey, Naval Research Laboratory; Harold C. Urey, University of California, Los Angeles; James A. Van Allen, State University of Iowa; Kenichi Watanabe, University of Hawaii; Fred L. Whipple, Smithsonian Astrophysical Observatory; John R. Winckler, University of Minnesota.

available to the experimenters, and if it is for a satellite, the Goddard Space Flight Center is most likely designated to assume management of the project. If such is the case, the Center lines up contractors—for example, on the Orbiting Geophysical Observatory, Space Technology Laboratories, Inc., was chosen as the prime contractor. The Center also forms a working group of the experimenters and the key engineers on the project. It is the responsibility of this group to make sure that the scientific experiments which are being prepared will be of the proper physical specifications and dimensions to fit into the satellite, and that all efforts are coordinated on a proper schedule to be completed at the time of launch. Should the group of experiments be in the lunar or planetary area, the Jet Propulsion Laboratory would probably be assigned the management, and would work with the scientists and contractors in a similar way; the monitoring group is determined by the kind of satellite or probe.

"The experiments are selected," explains Newell, "on the following basis: the importance of the scientific problem that it is trying to solve, the soundness of the proposed method, the likelihood of success, and the adaptability to space technique. In some cases we do not assign payload space to an experiment because it could be conducted as well or better by a ground-base method, which is generally much less expensive than conducting it in space. Of prime importance, of course, is the competence of the proposer. In our lunar program, we have teams of experimenters; though each man may be excellent individually, we still feel the over-all competence is broadened by their working together."

With Newell's office, the half-billion yearly budget is a pie, sliced in appropriate-sized wedges between the various areas. The biggest piece goes to lunar and planetary programs; the reason for its having the greatest funding is that the vehicles and spacecraft required to send experiments to the moon and planets are the most expensive. He comments, "The project of sending a spacecraft out to the moon, landing it on the moon, and continuing to work and send back scientific data is much more difficult than a project where a satellite is only put into an earth orbit. Also, a larger number of attempts will likely be required for one success."

The other areas in the Space Sciences Office—astronomy, biosciences, geophysics—receive smaller portions of the budget. The program director of each of these areas has the responsibility of further dividing the funds; as an example, in geophysics there are ionospheric studies, atmospheric studies, studies of the solid earth, etc. The sub-program director must make allocations; for instance, the ionospheric studies money must be divided between propagation studies, radio propagation studies, use of satellites for identifying and measuring the individual ions, etc. Meticulous care is thus exercised at every level to wrest the most from the investment.

Though the NASA management chart shows Newell's office as one separate from the other three, each must in reality be regarded as cross-feeding the others. Project *Apollo*, the great mission of this decade, will be the recipient of substantial help from Newell's office. "Once that mission has been achieved, it must be remembered that one of the major reasons for sending three men to the moon was to place them in a position to explore and to investigate the lunar surface—which gets right back to space science. So we go in a circle. We help each other as we go along, and we are all traveling the same direction—toward the advancement of knowledge!"

With insight, Newell has written, "Of great interest in all considerations of manned flight into space is the new environment that man will encounter. During such flights we may expect to learn more about the environment itself. But we may also expect to learn more about man, as he faces and copes with that environment. In the course of time, we may expect to learn how to live with the new environment or, rather, to live in spite of it."[8]

Mature people today are still reeling under the impact of the innovations of this age. Basically, feats are being performed that most adults assumed impossible only a few years ago. Adaptation to such wonders have varied with the flexibility of the individual. But none of this restriction, none of the limited preconceptions are present in the young. Their eager minds accept spaceflight, and are reaching out to the distant horizon of discovery with relish.

In fact, youngsters might be regarded as "salesmen of space," in Newell's estimation. Through their appreciation, there has come about an entire transformation in the general attitude. "Not too long ago, I was amazed at how many were almost unaware of the existence of the space program. It was surprising to run into people who had never heard of NASA. You wondered if they ever read the newspapers. But since courses and information on space have been introduced into the schools, and the young people are becoming informed, it is quite different. They are probably one of the best sources of information for the parents.

"I've found, at least in our local schools, the courses in physics and chemistry bring in these new problems. I've had the privilege of taking over high school or junior high school classes when teachers were off to conventions, and am very much impressed with the fact that these youngsters are more alert and more up to date on what's happening in these areas than the parents are."

These youngsters will be the parents of the next generation—where space will be an accepted way-of-life. But to properly strengthen the accomplishment of this, space must be integrated into areas of learning beyond the science courses. Students must be made aware that this present activity does not end with rockets and spacecraft, but is rendering widespread influence. Says Newell, "I don't know of any courses that deal with the sociological implications of space. But we here at NASA are trying to interest universities in considering this aspect of the problem. We are prepared to support an interdisciplinary activity that combines with our space science research—social, political, and economic courses that can study the impact and feedback of this tremendous program on our nation's growth."

How urgently are such measures needed, for what a deprivation it is to be alive today, and not be cognizant of the single most decisive scientific event that has transpired to change the course of civilization. Challenge and opportunity are sounding with many-decibel tones for those who have not surrounded themselves with a vacuum to bar the vibrations.

Eyes see and ears hear, but the brain interprets like a giant data reduction facility, allowing into consciousness only that which we choose to receive—and that is almost inevitably what we can understand.

In the majority of cases it is the women who come more slowly to the realization that they can become a part of this effort. This fact is partly caused by, and at the same time contributes to, the lag in general acceptance of women in important positions in science and technology. Newell's youngest daughter, Jennifer Dianne, has shown inclinations toward a career in science. But Newell is realistic in his appraisal of what she will encounter: "I think that women who enter this field have to recognize that they are facing odds. They are pioneers not only in science, but in the field of women in science. But they can overcome the obstacles. Eleanor Pressly, who works for NASA at Goddard Space Flight Center, started out as a mathematician, and developed into a good rocket engineer. Now she is to the point where she can go out into the field and direct the project. Nancy Roman, in the field of astronomy, has developed one of the best programs at NASA. So it can be done, and we would like to see more of the girls do it. It is certainly a wide open field, and needs the women, because they are just as brainy as the men."

A survey has indicated that most women scientists come from a home where the girl is the only child, and where the father has a scientific background. The influence of family and home continues to be the major one in shaping pliable young minds. Newell recalls how his own mother's and father's alert interests in the events of the world proved a strong force in his life. "My father, being an electrical engineer, exposed me to interesting thoughts—although my inclinations were always more scientific than engineering. My mother was highly interested in the more advanced thinking of the day—in science subjects, political and social subjects—and conveyed her interest to me just through talking about it. She was, and still is in her 70's, an extremely expert pianist and organist. I used to go to sleep at night listening to Chopin."

Newell's own talents for the arts have been expressed in his writing. His power of expression has served important purposes in his speaking, as Dr. Hugh L. Dryden points out:

"Dr. Newell is very effective before public groups in communicating some of the enthusiasm for scientific research. This job of forming the link between the scientist and the lay person is a never-ending one. Often the scientist tends to get a little too technical for the public, and finds difficulty in being understood. I think that Dr. Newell has been more successful than some others on our staff. For that reason, he is used quite frequently for briefing others on the program. He is very effective before Congressional committees."

His presentations—so giant that they assume the proportions of a book—are rendered the more effective with lucid explanations of the fundamentals of which he speaks. This is illustrated by a paragraph from his Congressional Presentation of NASA fiscal year 1963 plans:

"As is well known, all matter is made up of atoms and molecules. Aggregates of these atoms and molecules go to make up macroscopic matter as we know it. These atomic and molecular particles are exceedingly small. An atom of hydrogen, for example, is in size to a 2-inch-diameter stone as that stone is to the entire earth. Each cubic inch of air, at sea level, contains something like a hundred billion billion such atomic and molecular particles."[9]

His ability to simplify and succinctly express ideas comes from thorough knowledge of the subject, which stems from two things—Newell's well-trained intellect, plus his long exposure and association with space. His career has traveled in as straight a line as a rocket trajectory, never veering from the sciences that are important in astronautics. After earning his doctorate in mathematics from the University of Wisconsin in 1940, he joined the staff of the University of Maryland, teaching mathematics. As World War II created special needs, he became a ground instructor in navigation for the Civil Aeronautics Administration. Later, in 1944, he joined the Naval Research Laboratory in a scientific capacity. "In the guided missile subdivision I headed up the theoretical work, primarily in physics, and was also involved in electronics communications; all of this, of course, was then classified.

"At the end of the war, a group of us considered what we should recommend that our group do that would take advantage of our experience, interest, talents and competence in special fields. In one session we were listing various suggestions on a blackboard when Milton Rosen voiced the idea for research in the upper atmosphere, which was listed as Project 8 on the blackboard. As we discussed and eliminated the various other ideas we realized this field was a natural. So Project 8 was our recommendation for future work, and it was accepted by the Laboratory."

The Rocket Sonde Branch was founded early in 1946, with Dr. Ernst Krause as head and Newell as his deputy. With the area of the work thus determined, thoughts next turned to the means of accomplishing this research. Newell relates, "We considered very carefully whether we should begin our work with sounding rockets or with artificial earth satellites. In January, 1946, I gave a series of lectures to the group on the mathematics of satellite orbits, concerning energy requirements, and the physics behind the operation of satellites. Other members of the group lectured on such problems as the engineering and the aerodynamic aspects.

"We concluded at that time that although it was possible to consider putting a satellite into orbit, the effort involved would be too great and too expensive—considering the state of the art at that time. It was deemed wiser to start with sounding rockets and wait until rocketry had developed a bit more, since the missile field was supporting the development of rockets."

Newell continues, "This was the beginning, really, of upper atmosphere research with rockets, although it must be remembered that the scientists of Jet Propulsion Laboratory had launched their first WAC *Corporal* rocket in 1945. However, it was able to carry only 25-pounds payload to about 40-miles altitude."

The V-2 could carry a ton of payload to 100-miles altitude. This German-developed rocket which was launched against the Allies at the closing of World War II became the vehicle used by Krause's (later Newell's) group. The work was possible at this time because of the actions of far-sighted Colonel (now Major General, retired) H. N. Toftoy of the U.S. Army. He instigated Operation *Paperclip,* which brought to this country the great bulk of the brainpower which had developed the V-2, including Dr. Wernher von Braun. Toftoy also prompted the shipment of the components for 100 V-2 rockets to this country, to be deposited at White Sands Proving Ground in New Mexico.

In order to determine how these rockets might be put to best use, the Army called a meeting in January, 1946. Among the groups invited to be represented were those of the Naval Research Laboratory (the host-organization), several universities, and General Electric Company; the latter had been put under contract to provide supplementary personnel. When these former military weapons were put at the disposal of scientists for research, a veritable clamor ensued, the requests were so numerous from individuals and groups wishing to have experiments flown. To evaluate the research and to allocate the limited room, the V-2 Rocket Panel* was formed, under the chairmanship of Dr. Ernst Krause.

"The first experiments called for some ingenuity," recalls Newell, "not

* The name was later changed to Upper Atmosphere Rocket Research Panel, and is now designated as the Rocket and Satellite Research Panel.

only because everyone was new to the business, but also because of the haste with which the equipment had to be prepared—Army Ordnance scheduled a firing about every two weeks. I recall one instance in which Dr. Ralph Havens prepared a pressure gauge to measure pressures in the upper atmosphere by taking an automobile lamp, knocking the top off it, and calibrating the filament. It sounds primitive, but the physics is good and it actually worked. With it he got the first upper air pressure measurements that were obtained."

Science, by its very nature, is divorced and devoid of emotion. It is factual, detached, systematic. Yet the science of rocketry has evoked a powerful reaction from men at its "moment of truth." When individual vehicles roar forth from the launching pad, pulses quicken and hearts are stirred—even of the men of disciplined natures. Dr. Walter Dornberger, for instance, in his book, *V-2,* describes the launch of October 3, 1942:

"The rain of sparks rapidly coalesced to a flame and changed within a second to a jutting jet of reddish-yellow combustion gases. . . . With an acceleration practically corresponding to that of a falling stone, the rocket climbed straight and steadily upward from the launching table. . . . It was an unforgettable sight. In the full glare of the sunlight the rocket rose higher and higher. The flame darting from the stern was almost as long as the rocket itself. The fiery jet of gas was clear-cut and self-contained. . . .

"My heart was beating wildly. The experiment had succeeded. For the first time in the history of the rocket we had sent an automatically controlled rocket missile to the border of the atmosphere at Brennschluss* and put it into practically airless space. We had been working ten years for this day. I am not ashamed to admit that I wept with joy."[10]

A few years later, on another continent and in utterly different surroundings, Newell beheld the specter of this mighty rocket at launch. Despite the almost impenetrable quality to his New England reserve, he described the moment in these words: "Fully loaded, the V-2 now awaited its release to roar away into the azure heights above it. From within the impatient missile—or was it I who was impatient—trails of white vapor streamed, caused by the constant boiling of the intensely cold liquid oxygen in one of the propellant tanks. . . .

"At the count of zero, flame burst forth from the tail of the rocket. . . . All about us the air thundered with the noise of the motor. The ground trembled. In only a matter of seconds the rocket had climbed so high that we had to crane our necks to watch it. . . . The V-2 firing was the first rocket launching that I had ever witnessed. Nothing could match the excitement, the thrill, the exhilaration that went with that beautiful, inspiring, awesome sight."[1]

There occurs in the early stages of any developmental cycle a period

* The German term for "end of burning" of the rocket.

which comes to be fondly remembered by those who have participated in it. Before the inevitable departmentalizing that splits the essence of a project into its components, the whole of an idea is throbbing with promise and the stimulation of discovery. The early days experienced by Newell at White Sands followed this pattern.

"For the individual who likes pioneering and roughing it—and that includes me—things were more fun! We had to make do with what we had, so everybody cooperated and shared equipment, and assisted in getting tasks done. We ate in primitive style, but somehow the food tasted better—even though maybe it was worse. Sometimes we worked in cold weather—often our fingers became so cold it was difficult to work with the equipment. Other times it was terribly hot, and sometimes we worked in the dust storms and the sand. But there was a wonderful spirit of adventure to it. We were doing something really new! Even a small sounding rocket was really big news for the papers—whereas now even the launching of a satellite is very often back-page news. All this combined to make it more fun—and not just a business."

Does such a circumstance and the flavor of such surroundings call forth more ingenuity, more resourcefulness than people are inclined to employ at the later period when the routine is more regulated? Newell does not think so, and explains, "We're trying to do more difficult jobs now, and they require the same resourcefulness, the same ingenuity—only the make-do that you had to have in those early days is now missing."

Many a man has forged links onto the chain of important events without cognizance of his function. Such was not the case with Newell and others in that time of experimentation. "We knew what we were doing. We knew that we were heading toward the eventual exploration of space. I was among the 'newcomers,' when compared with people like Dr. Robert Goddard, Dr. Herman Oberth, Dr. G. Edward Pendray, and Dr. Wernher von Braun; they had been thinking about this from the 1920's and 1930's.

"I benefited from the vision of von Braun, who was working for the U.S. Army as consultant on the firing of the V-2's. In 1947, when I took over as head of the Rocket Sonde Branch, one of the first things I did was to have a series of conferences and discussions with him on the various experiments we wanted to perform, and what these might do to affect the rocket." Recalling those first meetings, Newell relates, "My initial impression of von Braun is the impression that I still have today—of an intensely interested man, a dynamic man, a highly competent individual, an enthusiastic man in this area."

"Nothing great was ever achieved without enthusiasm." Ralph Waldo Emerson stated. Repetition has perhaps dulled the impact of his words, but not their validity. The exuberant, contagious spirit of men such as von Braun has lent incalculable added thrust toward attaining the rockets that have put this nation into space!

A paraphrasing of the quotation could express another unquestioned truth: "Nothing great is ever achieved without planning." Dr. Ralph Havens* says, "Homer Newell is willing to sacrifice himself to administrative work. He has a potential as a research man, but with his conscientiousness, he feels it is his duty to push these programs. This is something most research people would not do.

"He is an excellent administrator. His main grace is his ability to take a group of research people, obtain funds for their efforts, and review what they do. Though he has not originated the work, he can certainly understand everything about it, and has written books on it. Speaking as one who was formerly under the direction of Homer Newell, I'd say he is one of the most capable men I've ever been associated with—he has excellent knowledge, excellent logic, and excellent vision."

The adjective "logical" recurs as other colleagues speak of Newell. One individual phrases it this way: "His business dealings are so logical, always on such an intellectual plane, that he is a very cool customer. He's all business. It makes him somewhat remote in the eyes of people who tend to approach things from a more emotional basis.

"But this self-possessed quality of Newell's surely does not imply a closed mind. There is always an open door to valid concepts from his associates. Even when Newell has made a tentative decision, it is not too late to have him give the matter fair consideration. This may lead to a reversal of his tentative decision—if it doesn't, it is because he can show that he was right and not just being stubborn about it."

Another individual, who terms the reserve "aloofness to all personal matters," adds: "His appearing somewhat of an enigma makes certain problems, but on the other hand it may have certain advantages. Sometimes you shouldn't get too close to the people you work with, so I couldn't say whether it is good or bad. It is just his type. People who do good work will get on well with him. He cannot tolerate mediocre people."

In an era, and an area, where technological excellence is imperative, this refusal to compromise has been a most commendable trait. Complexity brings increasing need for reliability.† An early airplane, with a few hundred parts, might average out a fraction of a percentage of failure in each individual part and still fly. But the spacecraft which has one million parts, must have a margin for error which is reduced by magnitudes, since the chance for failure does not add but compounds with each additional part.

Therefore, the demands for excellence are great indeed. "Newell possesses an exceptionally keen mind, and a comprehensive understanding in

* Newell's former associate at the Naval Research Laboratory, Dr. Havens is now a consultant.

† NASA has a Director of Reliability and Quality Assurance, Landis S. Gephart, whose efforts are devoted exclusively to the matter of maintaining highest possible standards. Aero/space corporations maintain similar departments.

depth of these complex problems relating to space sciences," says G. K. Megerian.* He points out that Newell envisions future plans, developments and problems with remarkable clarity.

In no way was this more forcefully demonstrated than in Newell's early advocacy of a satellite. He relates, "We had started rocket sounding research in 1946, so had those years of experience in the early 1950's when it became clear to me that there was going to be an International Geophysical Year (IGY). By this time the V-2 Rocket Panel was called the Upper Atmosphere Rocket Research Panel; it was an unofficial body, unchartered by any government agency or any agency, and was a gathering together of people of common interest in the sounding rocket area. I prodded them to turn their thinking to a rocket program under the IGY, for I felt it would be a powerful way of developing study of the earth."

The United States was not alone in performing such research. "I think the Soviets were conducting some rocket research just as we were, and the two programs were going along a parallel, although we never heard of their work because they kept it under wraps. The fact that the IGY encouraged an open program, an open effort to put satellites in orbit, together with the fact that we said we were going to participate, I feel did stimulate them."

Newell's interest led to his participation in the actual setting up of the structure. Dr. Hugh Odishaw, who was Executive Director of our IGY Committee, tells how Dr. Newell played an important role in the development of our satellite effort: "It was my responsibility to develop the program for presentation to the government. Unfamiliar at that time with the rocket system technology, I turned to Dr. Newell for help. In turning to him, I was not turning simply to a member of the staff of a government laboratory (Naval Research Laboratory), but to a very knowledgeable individual."

The Chairman of our IGY Committee, Dr. Joseph Kaplan (Professor of Physics, UCLA), was most favorably inclined toward the satellite program, which he called LPR—long-playing rocket. He made known this strong support to certain Congressmen, and in July, 1955, President Eisenhower made the formal announcement that this country would initiate a satellite program.

Perceiving the need for a powerful booster rocket to hurl the balls into space, Milton Rosen and Dr. Joseph Siry of the U.S. Naval Research Laboratory made performance calculations on *Viking,* a U.S. Navy rocket developed under Rosen's direction. Many felt this rocket was too marginal for the job of launching satellites. A proposal was then drawn for *Vanguard,* a new rocket which was a modification of the *Viking.*

* Mr. Megerian is Project Manager, Project *Celescope,* Smithsonian Institution, Astrophysical Observatory.

There were at that time 3 proposals being considered for the launching of a satellite, as listed in a Report of the House of Representatives: "Before the Committee (Ad Hoc Group on Special Capabilities) for consideration were (1) an Army proposal based on a modified *Redstone* missile with three additional stages; (2) a Navy proposal based on a modified *Viking* rocket with two additional stages; and (3) an Air Force proposal based on the ICBM booster with one additional stage."[11]

There were many considerations, much controversy, then a complete reversal of decisions by the Research and Development Policy Council, which finally gave the nod to *Vanguard,* with an Aerobee-Hi second stage, and a solid-propellant third stage. Dr. John Hagen was named Director of Project *Vanguard,* and Newell was named the Science Program Coordinator.

Dr. Kurt Stehling,* in his book, *Vanguard,* states: "The Vanguard rocket was a new vehicle, the result of many disciplines and technologies, many yet untried, and would require close monitoring by the NRL group. The Navy's contract with the Martin Company gave that organization the prime responsibility for launching of the vehicle with the understanding that the NRL group, and any others who would be called in by the Navy, would do the technical monitoring of the project and be finally responsible for it—that is, would sign for a sealed and delivered rocket when such a rocket was ready for firing."[12]

Vanguard became many things—our first attempt to orbit a satellite, a political football, a tremendously expensive project, a source of scientific advancement. The evaluation of each of these integral parts is a study in itself, and is filled with equivocal elements. Whether it was an experience, an attainment, or a disappointment depended upon the position and the viewpoint of each participant in the program. Only one claim can be made positively for the project—it was certainly the most widely discussed of all our IGY activities!

The IGY was built upon an interesting structure. It was a coordinated cooperative activity of the International Council of Scientific Unions (ICSU), a group which has two classes of memberships—unions and nations. To manage and plan the IGY, ICSU formed a committee, known by the French name, *Comité Special de l'Année Géophysique Internationale* (CSAGI). The Committee, with Dr. Sidney Chapman as Chairman, and Dr. Joseph Kaplan and Dr. Lloyd Berkner among the members, recommended at the termination of the IGY that ICSU form a new committee to further space science activity.

* Dr. Stehling was the Vehicles Branch Head during the Project *Vanguard*. He is now Scientist for Propulsion in the Office of Plans and Program Evaluation, at NASA Headquarters.

This was done. Its name is the Committee on Space Research, and it is known by another set of initials, COSPAR. Newell was asked to act as the original convener of COSPAR at the first meeting in November, 1958, in the Royal Academy Buildings in London.

"It was most friendly," Newell recalls. "Everyone was interested in creating something that would serve as an international focal point for space research." The members drew up a proposal charter, a set of bylaws, and elected a set of officers. The first President of COSPAR, Professor H. C. van de Hulst of the Netherlands, held the office until the spring of 1962, when he was succeeded by Professor Maurice Roy of France.

Van de Hulst, a tall and distinguished man, a respected scientist, conveys much of his attitude when he writes: "Most scientists will agree that cooperation in scientific research between individuals or groups requires *mutual confidence* first, *mutual understanding* in the second place, and *efficient organization* only in the third place."[13]

The two Vice-Presidents of COSPAR are Dr. Richard Porter of the U.S.A. and Academician A. A. Blagonravov of the U.S.S.R. Newell relates, "Opposing politics came to the surface in the early meetings because there was an imbalance between the Eastern and Western representation. The U.S.S.R. was the single member from the former category—all other members were either Western or neutral. It wasn't intended that way, but just happened because the membership was set up largely on the basis of the people and nations which have an interest or an activity. The Committee immediately agreed that it would have to be changed, so a better balance was achieved by bringing in countries like Poland and Czechoslovakia. Once that was settled, other such problems have not frequently arisen. The emphasis is directed toward the scientific problems—not toward the political."

COSPAR is characterized by its scientist-to-scientist type of activity, not governmental, except insofar as the national academies in various nations are governmental. Newell enlarges upon the areas of agreement by saying, "The scientific community is pretty much aligned in the important areas of research. Whenever a good experiment is presented—one that is well thought out and has some competent people behind it—there's usually agreement that it is worthy and ought to be done."

The organization is made up of four Working Groups. Newell, following the usual course of a convener to bring together members to set up a structure, has dropped out of that activity. He now attends the yearly meetings* as an adviser to Porter, as a NASA delegate, and as a member of one of the four Working Groups which constitute COSPAR, the one on Scientific Experiments.

* Following the initial meeting in London, meetings have been held in Nice, France; Florence, Italy; and Washington, D.C.

COSPAR has come close to attaining the original objectives, in Newell's opinion: "It has done most in bringing together the scientists from different countries to discuss the results of space experiments, and to prepare special reports. For example, there was produced a weighty technical report on the Solar and Geophysical Events that took place in the summer of 1959. There is a report on the International Reference Atmosphere in which all the available data on the earth's upper atmosphere have been brought together and analyzed and synthesized to make up a set of tables.

"In other words, to publish the results of past research, and to hold symposia on the various aspects of space research—this has been one of the biggest achievements of COSPAR. An output of these symposia—which are held at the time of the yearly meetings—has been very large and valuable books, proceedings and transactions that present to the world the latest results in the space science field."

As to where responsibility should rest in space activities, it is the general approach of our State Department and the National Academy of Sciences that it should be separated into two headings: matters of scientific bearing and nature should be handled within the International Council of Scientific Unions, which puts it in the COSPAR arena; matters of practical applications, or a legal or regulatory nature should come under the purview of the United Nations Committee on the Peaceful Uses of Outer Space.

President Kennedy in his 1961 State of the Union message, and again in September of the year when he addressed the U.N. General Assembly, urged U.S.–U.S.S.R. cooperation in specified areas of space research. Though the initial suggestion was rebuffed, a repetition of the proposal in March, 1962, led to a meeting of representatives of the two nations, Dr. Hugh L. Dryden and Academician A. A. Blagonravov at the United Nations in New York. Kennedy suggested five areas for discussion: establishment of a weather satellite system; an exchange of technical tracking equipment and data; mapping study of the earth's magnetic field; intercontinental communications network; pooling of data on space medicine. The first three met with favorable response, and seven counter-proposals were made by Premier Khrushchev.

A second meeting to further discuss the possibilities was held in Geneva, beginning in May, 1962. This brought together a new 28-nation U.S. Committee on the Peaceful Uses of Outer Space, and Newell presented for the U.S. one of the important proposals—the establishment of an international sounding rocket launching site near the equator. A great forward step appears to have been taken when an area of agreement was reached, as reported in an Associated Press release which appeared June 14, 1962:

"The plan provides for a worldwide exchange of scientific data, encourages a series of international space research and training projects, and provides for establishment of international launching ranges for sounding rockets near the equator."[14]

Data will be gathered and made freely available to U.N. members. The plan further specifies: "The projects include a worldwide survey of the earth's magnetic field, rocket and polar cap experiments, international cooperation in the fields of space communications, meteorological satellites, scientific assistance, education and training, and a program for 'The International Years of the Quiet Sun' in 1963–64. This is the period of minimum solar activity allowing more accurate measurements in the earth's space environment."[14]

It has long been clear to thinking people that cooperation is essential. Reinforcing the seriousness of the potential of space—which may be turned toward the destruction of civilization, or toward its greatest benefit—Secretary of State Dean Rusk stated: "The right time to subject activities in space to international law and supervision is now, before possibly untoward developments occur."[15]

Dr. Hugh L. Dryden underscores the obvious with the simple statement, "Space science deals with the phenomena on a global scale. International cooperation in space is almost a necessity, as compared with other forms of research which might be conducted in a laboratory."

Through the earnest efforts of NASA, and the spirit of receptiveness encountered from nations throughout the world, there is now in existence a widespread International Program, under the direction of Arnold W. Frutkin. Newell feels, "This is one of the most fascinating aspects of our effort. The initial activity of the sounding rockets and the launchings of satellites occurred, as we know, in the United States and the Soviet Union. The power of this technique has caused interest in a large number of countries.*

"These countries are working out sounding rocket programs to study the earth's atmosphere, to do rocket astronomy, and similar projects. Our cooperation is based on mutual interest, and on an ability to assist one another. There is no exchange of funds, although there may be an exchange

* AID, the Agency for International Development, has been growing quietly since 1959. There are three major categories to its activities—personnel exchanges, operations support, cooperative projects. The following nations are involved in one or more aspects of cooperative space efforts: Argentina, Australia, Belgium, Brazil, British East Africa, Canada, Canton Island, Chad, Chile, China, Colombia, Costa Rica, Czechoslovakia, Denmark, Ecuador, El Salvador, Fed. Rep. of Germany, Fed. Rhodesia/Nyasaland, Finland, France, Greece, Hong Kong, Iceland, India, Indonesia, Iran, Ireland, Israel, Italy, Japan, Korea, Mauritius, Mexico, Netherlands, Netherlands New Guinea, New Zealand, Nigeria, Norway, Pakistan, Peru, Philippines, Poland, Portugal, South Africa, Spain, Sudan, Sweden, Switzerland, Turkey, United Arab Republic, United Kingdom, U.S.A., U.S.S.R., Venezuela, West Indies Federation, Zanzibar.

of equipment—one country supplying the rocket, another the launching facility, observations being taken by another, for instance. One of the ground rules is that the results from this cooperative project will be published in the open scientific literature, so that it will be available to the whole world."

NASA will send all the results of its Space Science Program to the IGY Data Centers which are still in existence. Other countries are free to choose that, or any other method—as long as they make the data available to all. This activity is not restricted to Newell's office alone, but involves other offices of NASA.

The Office of Manned Space Flight, directed by D. Brainerd Holmes, is engaged in the most publicized phase of this—which is the tracking of the orbiting *Mercury* capsules by stations that are spread around the world. In this instance, the degree of the cooperation varies from the foreign country allowing NASA to establish a station on its soil, to a foreign country's actually assuming responsibility for the operation of a station. There is joint effort in the Deep Space Network which tracks deep space probes and lunar probes, and also in the communications and meteorological satellites.

The world's first international satellite, the 133.6-pound *Ariel,* was launched with a three-stage *Delta* rocket from Cape Canaveral on April 26, 1962. Named after the spirit of the air in Shakespeare's *The Tempest,* its mission is to learn more of the ionosphere and its complex relationship with the sun. The experiments were prepared by the United Kingdom; NASA's Goddard Space Flight Center provided some 112 man years for the project, bearing the responsibility for the design, fabrication and testing of the spacecraft; for the power supply, telemetry, command receiver, temperature control and data storage.

On the same date, NASA launched from its Wallops Island Station a *Nike-Cajun* sounding rocket which was the joint scientific effort of the U.S. and Japan. This, the first of 3 such shots which are planned, was also a Goddard-managed project. These are but the forerunners of closer working arrangements between the world's space science efforts. Other activities on the Continent reveal the deep interest on the part of many nations to figure in this remarkable scientific advancement. The European Scientific Research Organization (ESRO) is being formed to conduct space research, e.g., in astronomy and planetary studies. Another group is under consideration, the European Launch Development Organization (ELDO). Their aim would be to build a vehicle capable of launching European satellites.

Such pooling of interests, and the cooperative efforts through NASA, have been the only feasible means for most individual nations to enter into the costly business of space research. But there are other, more vital considerations. Frutkin, NASA's most capable Director of the Office of

International Programs, views the program: "Above all, perhaps, we know that space is inherently international in character. It is already a widely accepted principle that no one nation should appropriate to itself regions or natural bodies in space. There is strong feeling everywhere that we must not extend cold wars and armaments competitions into the vastness of space. We, for our part, hope to demonstrate by the openness of our program and our readiness to participate in cooperative projects, that we subscribe in fact as well as in word to these principles."[16]

Congress was so aware of the importance of this broad view and embracing attitude that when the Act was written which established NASA in 1958 there was specified as one of the purposes: "Cooperation by the United States with other nations . . ."[16] Frutkin makes this significant comment: "NASA has accepted this objective not as a pious pronouncement but rather as a substantive obligation."[16]

The potential of concerted combined world-wide efforts exceeds present capabilities to project. In long-range terms, even our own nation's effort can be stipulated in no more than general terms. Newell restates the known direction: "We now have a vigorous program going in space science and in spaceflight. We will continue to press forward, will put men on the moon. Obviously journeys to the planets will follow the lunar event. Mars is the first likely planet for human exploration—the temperatures are reasonable, and it does have an atmosphere, so that it is possible to work out ways of moving around on the planet. Venus is a much more difficult planet to consider because the temperatures are 600° F. at the surface—at least, as far as we can tell now—and that's quite a problem.

"As far as setting a timetable for these events, I don't believe in trying to state dates, because it is anyone's guess right now; it does no good, and can do a lot of harm. We should follow a sound step-by-step process."

The statement has been made, and frequently repeated, that in our short-range predictions we have been overly optimistic, and in our long-range predictions not optimistic enough. Newell does not agree with this view. "I think this misses a point. We know pretty much what we can do short range. When it is predicted that we are going to fly a certain mission on a certain date, then the schedule undergoes delays, that fact is not in my estimation an error in prediction. The important point was that we knew when we started that the objective could be accomplished, and it was finally done in the manner we specified.

"In our long-range predictions, we are not really able to detail just how everything will be done. There are many engineering hurdles that we are going to have to get through first before we will even know how certain things will be accomplished."

In the earlier period of our space effort, considerable attention was given by various people to the fact that lack of budget was holding back the activities. Newell has a slightly different thought on this: "Generally, the area is moving pretty close to as fast as it reasonably can. It must be clearly defined that there are two phases to scientific investigations: First, there is an exploratory or preliminary phase in which you are feeling your way; this might be expressed in military terminology as the advance guard that moves ahead. Then, the advance is consolidated when the whole army moves up.

"In the space science field, the advance research is moving ahead quite rapidly, and a goodly portion of the consolidating work is being done. However, with added budget, the consolidation could be much more extensive. So I would say that more money would in many cases allow us to move ahead more thoroughly, but not necessarily more rapidly—for the present.

"There will be a point where the advance guard simply can't move any further and will just have to wait for the other to catch up. This is because a part of the consolidation efforts will be back in the lines of supply, so to speak—the scientists of tomorrow. The knowledge we have recently acquired and will continue to acquire must find its way into textbooks and classes. The techniques we are evolving must be made known and become adopted by industry. If these things fail to happen, our support of available personnel and manufacturing capability will lag so far that eventually it will be completely out of phase."

All areas must maintain a pace commensurate with today's progress, if bottlenecks are to be avoided. Nowhere is this urged more strongly than in basic research, or pure research, which is the essence of the productivity of Newell's office. "It is so important because the basic research that you do provides you with facts—new facts and new insights into principles. The basic research that we have done in the past has provided us with a whole collection of facts, insights and principles. If we were not to do any more, we could go on using those facts forever, for they would never cease to be true or to be applicable.

"However, the applications would tend to fall into a pattern after a while, because of not having new insights and new facts to generate new ideas for applications, or new approaches to solving problems." The research performed for space science has already provided an enormous store of new and useful facts. The promises being held forth now—some so faint they are but a glimmer—are for such incredible wonders as finding an electronic means of giving sight to those who cannot see.

Newell's approach is invigorated by one little-known phase of his activity. Dr. Hugh L. Dryden reveals, "One of the conditions of his appointment to this administrative position was that he be allowed to maintain intimate contact with scientists and what is going on in the laboratory.

So each Friday, he is at Goddard Space Flight Center with an unlisted telephone extension that only a few people know."

Such activity helps Newell to remain updated on the constant changes that space science is undergoing. He is "extremely well liked by his colleagues," as Dr. G. K. Megerian testifies, partially because he speaks their language.

"Newell is one of the few 'ivory tower' scientists in the hurly-burly of the Washington space program," says the eminent Dr. Fred L. Whipple, Director of the Smithsonian Institution Astrophysical Observatory. "I have great respect for Homer Newell as a man of great integrity, ability and energy for the most difficult task which he is now carrying out."

Whipple then pays a rare and deserved compliment when he says, "I would call him a 'scientist's scientist!' "

REFERENCES

1. Newell, Homer E., *Express to the Stars,* New York, McGraw-Hill, 1961.
2. Newell, Homer E., *Why Space,* Address presented before the American Society for Engineering Education, Texas Technological College, Lubbock, Texas, April 6, 1962.
3. Martin, Martha Evans, *The Friendly Stars,* New York and London, Harper, 1907.
4. Dewey, John, *Moral Principles in Education,* New York, Philosophical Library, 1959.
5. *Esquire,* 45:43–44+, May, 1956.
6. *Harpers,* 220:1316:38–45, January, 1960.
7. Kennedy, John F., *Special Message on Urgent National Needs,* address to Congress, May 25, 1961.
8. *Science,* 131:3398:385–390, February 12, 1960.
9. Newell, Homer E., Statement in *Hearings before the Subcommittee on Space Sciences of the Committee on Science and Astronautics, U.S. House of Representatives,* 87th Congress, 2nd session, March 6, 1962.
10. Dornberger, Walter, translated by James Cleugh and Geoffrey Haliday, *V-2,* New York, Ballantine Books (no date on this paperback edition. Copyright 1954 by the Viking Press).
11. *Organization and Management of Missile Programs,* 11th Report by the Committee on Government Operations, 86th Congress, 1st session, September 2, 1959.
12. Stehling, Kurt R., *Project Vanguard,* Garden City, New York, Doubleday, 1961.
13. *Bulletin of the Atomic Scientists,* May–June, 1961.
14. Associated Press, *Los Angeles Times,* Los Angeles, California, June 14, 1962.
15. *Los Angeles Times,* Los Angeles, California, May 26, 1962.
16. Statement of Arnold W. Frutkin, Director, Office of International Programs, before the Members of the Inter-American Defense Board, Washington, D.C., February 16, 1960.

Forceful President of the company which has produced Polaris, Agena *and other space projects*

L. EUGENE ROOT

"Gene Root will confront squarely any problem that comes along. Many people are wary about undertaking any project of very great magnitude. This is not so of Gene Root. Furthermore, he has great perseverance; if he gets knocked down once, he will bounce up to try again. And a combination of qualities that he possesses is quite rare—while he has a good share of self-assurance, at the same time he has great humility. Often the former quality alone will cause a person to shy away from tasks if there is an element of doubt as to their successful execution, because they do not wish to risk appearing in an unfavorable light. But it is in these problems of greater challenge that Gene's humility has enabled him to undertake—and succeed in doing—some very big jobs." The man who paints this character portrait is Arthur Raymond of the Rand Corporation, who has known Root since the 1930's when Raymond was a professor and Gene was a student. The years of their association have been over a period of time during which there has been great evolution in the air/space field, as well as impressive technological development generally.

Root moved to the forefront very early in his career and has consistently maintained a position of leadership. Stresses a colleague, Leo A. Carter,

"It is definitely leadership—not drivership. Root drives only himself. His intense application provides inspiration to his associates, of course."

In an industry which is highly complex, extremely competitive, and is always striving to acquire more knowledge, more economical production and higher reliability and greater performance, Root occupies a prominent and very high position. As President of Lockheed Missiles and Space Company, he has spearheaded some of the most impressive projects of the Space Age. The respect of him and regard for him by his colleagues were demonstrated in 1962 when he was elected President of the Institute of the Aerospace Sciences.

In part, Root has been able to pursue this activity in addition to his already very full-time occupation because of substantial assistance from his own "secret weapon." This is in the form of a notebook! In describing his use of it, Thomas V. Jones, President of the Northrop Corporation relates, "Gene takes notes, but not as many do, who scribble them on the back of envelopes. His are printed, most carefully, in large bound notebooks. I'll bet he has a file of them eight feet thick, covering every discussion or meeting that he has ever attended. He documents, follows through, refers to them; consequently, he has remarkably extensive and detailed understanding of whatever subject he is occupied with at the moment."

Someone not acquainted with him, and witnessing his note-taking only, might classify his as an unimaginative or overprecise personality. But Root is refreshingly inconsistent in this matter, as Jones goes on to explain, "I have never before seen this methodical trait combined with the gift of an entrepreneur—and I mean that in the finest sense. Without being any 'scientific spellbinder,' Gene has the real ability to look forward—he has a perceptive understanding of what is required for advancement. He can see a technical capability, then push toward making it useful for future concepts. And most importantly, with his knowledge and sincerity he can convince policy makers that it is right."

Though normally these dominant character traits can be by-products of maturity, they have been a part of Root since boyhood.

The early years, spent on ranches and farms in Idaho, Washington, and Nebraska, encompassed a series of activities that might have fitted young Root to be an aerial artist! Though scarcely more than a toddler, he used to grab the tail of a pet calf and get pulled about in a wild and rugged ride.

When of school age, the determination to be punctual was so mighty that one day when he was delayed in leaving for school, he pleaded with a friend to let him ride on the fender of his truck in order to get to school on time. But as he drove, the friend forgot about his fender-riding passenger, and young Gene, not to be prevented from getting into class before the bell sounded, leaped off the truck as it sped past the school. He still recalls the horrified expression frozen on the face of his teacher who was in the yard at the time and saw one of the truck wheels pass over Gene's right leg. Incredibly, no bones were broken.

There were other acrobatic-like incidents during Root's school days. For example, one day a classmate was questioned as to his excuse for being late to school so many days. The boy said that a freight train had delayed him. The teacher asked how this could be when Gene Root, who came from the same direction, was on time. The boy replied that he did not like to jump between the cars of a moving train, as Gene did! "That activity of mine came to an abrupt halt," admits Root. After that, the teacher didn't question tardiness.

The Root home was the scene of perpetual activity, as well might be expected with four lively boys. The youngest, red-haired Melvin, used to delight in boasting to all the other kids, "My big brother can lick your big brother." Root still recalls some battle scars as he says, "I was that big brother, so I finally had to be firm with Melvin and tell him it was pretty rough going to cope with the challenges he flung around."

Gene Root used to make a Saturday ritual out of taking his brother, Donald, 4 years younger, to the movies. Hand in hand, they would walk the four blocks, gleeful in anticipation of a thrilling matinee. But the happy habit came to an abrupt end when the admission was raised from 5¢ to 6¢ and Gene balked at the exorbitant price! "I am a quarter Scot," Root mentions, "as you might surmise from that. The other quarters are English, Irish, and Dutch. It has been said that the traits popularly associated with these nationalities come to the fore on different occasions—either singly or in combination. But somehow," Root ruefully admits, "it always seems to be said where there is a slightly negative trait showing."

Root's father was engaged in a variety of activities, each one of which his sons found interesting. The one that they liked most was his candy and ice cream business—for reasons that are not in the least obscure. Ranching was another endeavor that intrigued young Gene Root. "Dad was business manager for the 47,000-acre Cantrell Ranch.

"I worked in the harvest fields during the summers, and I remember that one season I was a 'fire bug'—that member of the harvester crew who rides some distance back of the Caterpillar threshing machine and watches for fires; it was flooded peat reclaimed area, and any fire that breaks out on such land burns for a long time, until it reaches the water level. I also worked as a 'sack sewer,' but I had trouble with their arrangement because I am left-handed. The most fun was when I 'tended header.' This meant watching to make sure the big header cut the grain just at the right height." Farm and ranch life has taught many a boy the qualities of resourcefulness that are vital helps in future "big city" life.

The machinery to which Root was exposed took on a different form when his father became chief accountant for an automobile agency. "I recall how impressed I was when Dad would come home with different cars—an Auburn, Willys-Knight, Willys-Overland, or Peerless!"

Root's boyhood interest in the scientific field produced one highly spectacular experience which he recalls: "We had a home in Stockton, California, three blocks from the last street-car stop. Soon after my mother got off the street car one late afternoon she heard a high-pitched commotion that caused her to run the entire distance home. When she arrived, the fracas had all the appearances of an Indian war dance—or maybe scalping party. The kitchen was full of kids who were screaming, jumping and hollering, and trying to scrape pieces of hot molten lead from their heads. I had been responsible for creating the confusion by attempting to cast a long lead rod. I had poured the molten metal into a long green bamboo stick. I didn't have enough sense to know it shouldn't be green wood. When the lead hit the bottom, it bounced out again like a Roman candle, spouted to the ceiling, and bits of it ricocheted down on the brotherly group who were all watching the experiment."

It was a considerable attainment when the family managed to move to a large enough home for each of the four brothers to have his own room—and each was promptly declared "off limits" to the others. This condition had a decidedly beneficial effect on Root's scholastic record. Study in the midst of family palaver had been difficult.

This industrial leader, who is unusually articulate, recalls that English composition was a difficult subject. Mathematics, physics, mechanical drawing, and engineering were his favorite courses. He set goals to continue his education which were beyond the financial grasp of the family, even with the earnings that Root could manage from constant summer- and after-school jobs. Two Stockton, California, service clubs figured in the solution: a Rotary Club scholarship was the means of his entering the College of the Pacific; his second and third years were made possible through an athletic scholarship from the Lions Club.

"This was a combination scholarship which embraced athletics and attendance at the weekly Lions Club meetings. Since I was on the College of the Pacific football team, my single obligation each week was to report on the progress of the team. At the end of two years, I was given a prize for the ingenuity of my explanations of 'why' when our team lost."

The financial aspects of the fourth year of college presented a serious problem to Root. Even though an athletic scholarship from the school covered tuition and books, he could not possibly save enough from odd jobs to cover remaining expenses. As a solution to this dilemma, he finally decided to call upon Harriet West Jackson. This lady had been a customer on the *Stockton Record* paper route he had had in grammar-school days, and she had been most appreciative of his willingness to pedal several extra miles, no matter what the weather condition, to deliver her paper. She expressed her gratitude by a warm friendly interest in all of Root's activities and future plans.

In view of her generosity to many organizations, and her expressed interest in higher education, Root conceived the idea that she might help him with a loan for the last year at the College of the Pacific, and two years of graduate work at the California Institute of Technology.

"Reluctant though I was to have to ask it of her, I saw no other way. So I prepared my case in as thorough and logical a manner as if it were a court trial. I called at her home at the appointed hour, and we talked casually for about a half hour as to what I had been doing. When she asked about the prime reason for my visit, I said I wanted to borrow funds for 3 years of school. I was all primed to launch off into my formal presentation, but she interrupted by asking how *much* I wanted to borrow! I told her, and she asked how I would like to have the necessary amount! I was flabbergasted! I got the loan all right, but I recall being a little let down that I had not had the opportunity to state elaborately all the reasons why I needed it."

There was long-range thinking behind Root's request to Mrs. Jackson. In his sophomore year he had made a decision, based primarily on his exposure to two teachers who had joined the staff of the College of the Pacific after having received their Ph.D.'s from Cal Tech. Root recalls, "These chaps were very impressive to me, because they were so thoroughly trained in their fundamental grasp of mathematics and physics as it related to my specialty of aeronautical engineering. The classes in this field were very small—perhaps five or six students—so we received what amounted to individual training from these men of such high caliber. One of them was Dr. George Thomas Harness, who later became a professor of electrical engineering at Columbia University."

With foresight, Root recognized early in his college days that he would have to make great effort to meet the requirements for entrance into Cal Tech as a graduate student. So he carried very heavy courses of study, taking 21 units a semester in preference to the normal 16. "Gene never did anything half-heartedly," says one of his closest friends. Leslie C. Drury, who went through the four years at the College of the Pacific with Root, continues, "Above all his other fine points is the fact that he always reached for perfection. He was willing to spend the time that he felt was necessary to accomplish a given assignment to the best of his ability. If this meant foregoing some of the pleasures of college life, he stuck to his studies. This determination no doubt contributed largely to qualifying Root for the position in his field which he holds today."

Drury hastens to add, "But I should not give the impression that Gene was strictly a grind. Nothing would be farther from the truth. He participated in and enjoyed the organizations and the social life of the campus to a greater extent than did the average student; but he somehow always managed to get the important things done before the fun started."

They drove to school together in Drury's Model T Ford, and shared many trials and tribulations. Recalls Drury, "During those depression years, we helped to finance the school months by many activities. I remember one summer we picked apricots near San Jose. We camped in the orchard, cooked our own meals, and most of the time wore only pants and shoes in order to save washing so many clothes."

Root's work, interestingly, has taken him back to the "apricot" area. Now, in the well-earned position of President of one of the nation's most successful space companies, he can afford a smile at memories of the rigors of those experiences.

At the time, they were regarded in only one context—they were the means of moving toward a clear purpose. "I was completely fascinated with the thought of designing airplanes! In the early 1930's, aviation was relatively new and of great interest to everyone. Technically, the emphasis was on advances in aerodynamics and improved performance."

The progressive College of the Pacific acquired an airplane, the "Flying Bengal," and instituted a flying school. The Stockton Lions Club stretched a point and assisted Root to the extent that he could take flying lessons and qualify for a commercial pilot's license by his junior year! Says Drury, "Pilot's licenses were somewhat scarce at that time."

Another of Root's close friends was a fellow flier, Carlos C. Wood, who now holds the position of Manager of Engineering, Sikorsky Division, United Aircraft Corporation. "We competed for grades not only through the College of the Pacific, but also at Cal Tech," Root recalls.

The other prime interest of his extracurricular activities continued to be football. Says Harold E. Cunningham, now with the City College of San Francisco, "I was assistant football coach under C. E. 'Swede' Rightor at the College of the Pacific when Gene Root was attending. He distinguished himself as a blocking guard, was sharp and resourceful on both offense and defense, and possessed a remarkable amount of drive and determination."

As with any other activity he undertook, Root plunged into the game with his whole heart. Comments Cunningham of this attitude, "When the great coach of Notre Dame, Knute Rockne, was accused of over-emphasis on the winning of football games, he replied, 'When I'm in need of a surgeon, I would like to have one who doesn't give up too easily.' "

Striving for touchdowns is a reflection of spirit and drive—two qualities which have true meaning when applied to other endeavors. It is interesting that the coach, Cunningham, also taught in the engineering department, and so had opportunity to observe this transfer of qualities by Root. The instructor sums up Root's all-around capability with a simple statement, "He was the kind of a student who makes teachers look good."

Dr. Robert A. Millikan, the distinguished Nobel prize-winning scientist who was then President of Cal Tech, delivered the commencement address at the time of Root's graduation from the College of the Pacific. The College President, Dr. Tully C. Knoles, singled Root out for honor when he chose him to meet Dr. Millikan at the train. The two had a conversation that provided great encouragement to Root. "Dr. Millikan was strongly in accord with my desire to become an aeronautical engineer, and he foresaw that the field of aeronautics was just beginning to come into clear focus at that time."

It is to be expected that the development in the fields of air travel and space travel would have many parallels. First was in the reaction of the general public to the simple fact of its being, a fascination with the sheer novelty of it and incredulity of the new science. Following that, people were overawed at the daring feats of the pioneers. In the earlier period, Lindbergh and Doolittle were counterparts of Glenn and Shepard.

But the third and significant phase to the history of the evolution of each is the applications aspect. Air became an accepted part of life when it provided a better or faster way to deliver mail, to dust crops, haul cargo, and carry passengers. Space has now entered the age of applications with the advent of *Telstar,* the communications satellite, *Transit,* the navigation satellite, and *Tiros,* the weather satellite. These are but precursors to limitless practical utilization of the new science.

Just as the Space Age has had its wild-eyed enthusiasts who have waged ceaseless battle to bring rockets and satellites into reality, proponents of air power and prowess persisted in their time against the barriers of shortsightedness. Notable among them was Brigadier General William "Billy" Mitchell, who proposed such "radical" ideas as the use of airplanes for strategic bombing and for coastal defense.

But advancement has the inherent force of a wall of water. Though it can be temporarily dammed, crevices eventually will let through a trickle, and then the avalanche follows. Aviation underwent serious blockage after World War I—when the number of men in the Air Service was slashed from 200,000 to 10,000, and orders for 13,000 airplanes were summarily cancelled—but this vanguard of a new dimension in living soon pressed forward.

The aviation industry was beginning to sprout in California, though the founding of the company that has become the world's largest manufacturer of airplanes was not exactly auspicious: Donald Douglas established his business in a small office in a back room of a barber shop in Los Angeles. In nearby Burbank, a self-taught barnstorming pilot, Allan Haines Lockheed, was among those to form another aircraft company. This was sold in bankruptcy proceedings during the depression for $40,000 —a sum that seemed so exorbitant that the presiding judge admonished the new owners, "I hope you know what you are doing." They knew.

Every era has its trends. Many of today's bright students gravitate to thoughts of a career in the space sciences. The cycle before that was toward nuclear studies. In Root's college days, the highest excitement in engineering circles was generated by aeronautics. The Great Dream of many an ambitious student was to attend Cal Tech, where the Guggenheim Aeronautical Laboratory was making history!

The first hurdle was to gain entry into the graduate class, for there was fierce competition from the cream of colleges and universities, nationwide. The second, and even graver challenge, was to stay in the highly select group. The class which Root entered was extremely small and select, yet only about half made the grade. He relates, "It was a very invigorating curriculum that had to be attacked with a vengeance. The scholastic competition was pretty terrifying, and the amount of work required was fantastic."

Dr. Theodore von Kármán, the brilliant Hungarian-American scientist who is a living legend, had moved his residence from Europe to Pasadena to accept a post in GALCIT (Guggenheim Aeronautical Laboratory California Institute of Technology). Root studied not only aerodynamics but also advanced engineering concepts with the great Doctor.

Another of his professors was the young but already outstanding Dr. Clark B. Millikan, son of the man who was then President of Cal Tech. Structures was taught by Dr. Ernest Edwin Sechler, and Dr. Arthur Louis Klein specialized in wind-tunnel instrumentation and mechanical design. Since Root was planning to continue his education to the doctorate level, he was also engrossed in learning conversational and scientific German which was to serve him in a most unexpected way at the end of World War II.

Root relives the remarkable experience of that Cal Tech period by saying, "We were completely absorbed in aeronautics. There was a most remarkable concentration of knowledge heaped upon us, to the extent that we seemed to be carried far beyond our actual capabilities by the superb teaching of the staff. Not only did our studies cover the complete aeronautical field as it then existed, but we were pushing it beyond subsonic into supersonic theory. One fascinating technical area was that of turbulent flow measured in flight and correlated with theory; in this I recall specifically how Dr. von Kármán could clarify the complex matter with his simplifying lectures."

GALCIT augmented its powerful teaching staff with visiting lecturers and part-time teachers who came from industry. Among them was Arthur E. Raymond, then Chief Engineer at Douglas Aircraft Company, Inc., who conducted a weekly seminar on airplane design. "We thought Raymond was being pretty tough on us at the time by being so exacting," Root recalls, "but we later realized he was merely conveying how things really were in the actual practice of aeronautical engineering in an aircraft factory. He properly depicted it as hard, precise work, and stressed the great responsibility that the engineer carries."

Raymond, too, has memories of that first contact with Root: "Although I was at Cal Tech primarily to instruct and not to recruit people for Douglas, I could not help but gain strong impressions of the relative merits of my various students. I invited Gene Root to go to work for me."

This placed Root in a real quandary. The offer promised to fulfill the exact dream that he had held for many years, yet it had come too soon. He had planned to complete his graduate work before joining industry. "But I was dissuaded from continuing for the additional year at Cal Tech that it would take to earn my doctorate when it was frankly expressed to me that if I were to accept the position at Douglas now, I might well be hiring Ph.D.'s to work for me in a reasonable time. It seemed the propitious moment to make the move."

The series of planes known as DC (Douglas Commercial) have substantiated the saga of flight for three decades. It is estimated that the DC-3's have flown more than 87 billion passenger miles! Over 10,000 were manufactured—and over a third of these are still in use! There is a saying, "You can crack 'em up, but apparently you can't wear them out."[1]

Root entered a field that was young and a business that was relatively new, yet it was already rich in reputation. Above all was the spirit that prevailed—with goals as limitless as the sky itself. The objectives were to be attained by techniques which were already shadows on the drawing boards and in the wind tunnels. Root's first assignment was in the engineering department of the Santa Monica plant, under Leo A. Carter, who relates: "My first impression was of a very solid citizen. He did some work in special design, but was soon transferred to the area of his specialization, aerodynamics. There he became the number two man in the department under Dr. W. Bailey Oswald, and was soon a dynamic force in that department.

"I can remember a few instances in which there was a disagreement—for the aerodynamics business was more of an art than a science at that time—and the vehemence with which Gene Root presented his side of the controversy. Even though he was pretty young, he would stand on his own feet and say what he thought, and generally he was right. This was evidenced by the fact that he was soon promoted and left the Santa Monica plant to take charge of the entire aerodynamics work at the El Segundo Division of Douglas."

Men do not rise spectacularly in business by mysticism or levitation. The character traits that set leaders apart are usually apparent from the time of their first positions. Root specialized first in wind-tunnel testing of scale models of designs along with performance calculations and guarantees—but this was not the extent of his influence.

"At that time, I doubt that Douglas had more than 1000 people in the entire company, and Gene was one of their bright engineers." So says Lieutenant General Laurence C. Craigie, USAF (Ret.), now a Vice President, of American Machine and Foundry Corporation. Craigie was then at Wright Field as the Project Officer for transports and trainers, and had much occasion to work with Douglas as a predominant producer of transports.

"If I were to pick out the characteristic in Gene that has impressed me over the years, it would be his solidness, his soundness of thinking. He is extremely intelligent, has good judgment, and when he comes up with a recommendation you can be sure it has been thoroughly considered from all appropriate angles," says Craigie.

And there were difficulties to be faced in that stage of the airplane's growth. "The major problem," Root states with candor and simplicity, "was in getting them to fly correctly!" He is a little more definitive when he says, "My job was to design, or to obtain through flight testing, proper stability and control characteristics in an airplane." As initially designed, some of the early Douglas DC models had deficiencies in yaw stability and control. Root did not feel constrained by the convention of the time, and solved the problem with the addition of an impressive vertical stabilizer called a "dorsal fin." A friend remarks, "It was quite a running gag to tease Gene about this monster tail—but it surely licked the difficulty."

Root's contributions to Douglas aircraft add up to a most impressive tally, and include one or more of the varied functions of aerodynamic design, the improvement of flying qualities, wind-tunnel work, stability, and control flight testing on many of their models, including five of the most reliable craft ever to become airborne—the DC-3, B-18, B-23, DC-4, and the cargo version of the latter, C-54.

Dr. Robert S. Schairer, now in Development Planning at the Lockheed Aircraft Corporation, was a Cal Tech student on the wind-tunnel crew when he first met Root. It has been said that without the well-designed wind-tunnel facilities offered by the Pasadena institution, the DC series of airplanes could never have been developed to such a state of performance. Schairer recalls the extensive use of the facility.

Of the attitude that Root held in all of this work he says, "It was evident that he relished tackling difficult problems—ones that were new and different. He had the forcefulness to make up his mind, but by no means has he ever run a one-man show in the sense that he does all the study and doesn't pay attention to anyone else. Quite the contrary, he makes extraordinarily good use of the people around him by seeking inputs from them, then mulling over the combined opinions, and arriving at a decision based on this." Schairer went to work for Root at Douglas upon graduation, and remained with him when he moved to Rand, so the thoughts span long duration.

Elmer Wheaton, now a Vice President of Lockheed Missiles and Space Company, is another whose association dates from the early days at Douglas. "Gene has a key capability in working with people, and that is his ability to kid with business associates in a serious vein. He can convey the idea that he holds no grudge against them personally, but expects them to 'get with it.' He has a real talent to turn the phrase at the right moment."

Behind this talent is a strong desire to help the people who are working for him. Though it happened 20 years ago, one highly successful man relates an incident that transpired when he was a fledgling engineer: "As is so often the case with young people, I apparently was doing satisfactory work from the technical point of view, but was not putting my best foot forward from the standpoint of getting along with my fellow employees and supervisors. I, of course, did not recognize this, but apparently Mr. Root did.

"There are a number of ways that a supervisor could relate this problem to an employee—one would be to call him into his office and give him a stiff lecture. The manner in which he chose to handle it was extremely effective, and certainly demonstrates his interest in people and his desire to help them improve themselves. He invited me to his home on a Sunday afternoon, just saying he wanted to talk about some things. After some refreshments and light conversation, he told me he had noted I was having difficulty with some of the people with whom I worked—although he was sure I had not realized it or I would have corrected the situation.

"He assured me that he realized that I had done what I felt was right, so he was not seeking reasons for my actions. This set the stage so that I was immediately in a listening mood instead of putting forth all sorts of excuses. He then emphatically pointed out in considerable detail the things I had done which caused friction." This man adds, "The incident had a major effect on me, and in my advancement in the company. I was deeply impressed that so important and busy a man as Mr. Root would spend his Sunday trying to help me to help myself. Mr. Root left Douglas soon after this, to my regret. I am sure that had I remained working with him, I would have benefited still more from his counsel."

Root has given a special consideration to the human element in all situations. Such an attitude has done much to buffer the great transitions which have taken place in the aircraft industry during the span of his career.

Aviation began as a novelty, an endeavor suitable only for daredevils. However, the time required for it to gain general acceptance, was, in reality, surprisingly short. A "breakthrough" came in the late 1930's which signified sanction from the world of business—vending machines were placed in air terminals from which travelers might purchase life insurance.

But the real potential of aviation was completely beyond the thinking of too many policy-makers. Even as late as 1936, the great air advocate, Henry H. "Hap" Arnold, then holding the rank of Brigadier General, was steadfastly refused funds for his "wild schemes" of acquiring fleets of planes to provide supply lines to bases throughout the United States, Alaska, and the Canal Zone.

Yet Arnold persisted in his requests for a build-up of airpower. Unbelievably, in the summer of 1939 when Arnold went before Congress he was asked, "Why should we expand our air force?" All too horribly soon, the Luftwaffe and the Kamikaze pilots supplied the answer. Arnold was finally issued a "blank check" to start the long-overdue build-up.

Writes the Air Force historian, Dr. Alfred Goldberg, "By the close of 1939 the two Allies (England and France) had ordered 2,500 aircraft in the United States; before the end of March, 1940, they had arranged for the purchase of 8,200 combat planes of the latest types. Such orders, piled on top of the Air Corps' twenty-four-group program adopted in the spring of 1939, gave a tremendous boost to the American aircraft industry. From a production rate of 100 military aircraft per month in 1938, the industry reached 402 in April, 1940, and was tooling up to produce at double that rate."[2]

Instant airplanes! It seemed that by no computation, logic or hope could they be produced—yet they were. The government helped to protect the aircraft industry against the over-expansion bankruptcies that followed World War I by allowing the cost of the extensive new manufacturing facilities to be amortized over five years instead of the usual 16. Much of the financing was provided through the Reconstruction Finance Corporation. Manpower was a shortage not so easily supplied.

The burden that fell to those in key positions of the aircraft industry was overwhelming. Root then headed the Aerodynamics Section at the El Segundo plant of Douglas, and worked in closest cooperation for the tremendously talented Chief Engineer, Edward Heinemann, and Leo Devlin, who was Chief Designer. Their productivity as a working team resulted in: the SBD *Dauntless* carrier-based dive bombers, which proved the backbone of the Navy's air strength in the Pacific during World War II; the AD *Skyraider* series of all-purpose Navy attack airplanes, of which there were 18 versions; the DB-7; the A-20 *Havoc* bomber, which was utilized on every front by the French, British and Dutch, as well as the Americans; a remarkable series of experimental craft, including the XSB2D-1, D-558-1 and D-558-II *Skyrocket*.

Such a record of performance by this team affirms the validity of a thought expressed by Henry David Thoreau: "Man's capacities have never been measured; nor are we to judge of what he can do by any precedents, so little has been tried."[3]

Not only did the tasks have to be done fully and quickly, but perfectly—or as nearly perfectly as men could accomplish. The Air Force had a motto which it tried to instill in the 700,000 men who were assigned to aircraft maintenance: "A pilot depends on you." The greatest taskmaster of all, man's conscience, set the standards toward which they aimed.

Of the important traits which characterize Root, none has proved more valuable than vision. While still deeply preoccupied with the demands of wartime production schedules, he and a prescient few at Douglas looked toward tomorrow's aircraft requirements. When they did, they faced a wall—a wall of sound. In an age so enlightened and so reluctant to admit superstition, there was a mystical aura which surrounded the legend of the Sonic Barrier. Pilots who never relied on a rabbit's foot would wipe beads of perspiration from their brows, as they related tales of the forces that seized their craft when speeds approached Mach 1. The more the devastation of fear pervaded reason, the greater this imaginary barrier became.

Supersonic flight was being seriously investigated in many quarters by late 1943. Ezra Kotcher, a most talented engineer at Wright Field, was drafting designs for an airplane with such capability. The National Advisory Committee for Aeronautics, NACA, the government agency which was the predecessor of the National Aeronautics and Space Administration (NASA), had discussed high-speed craft in an important meeting with members of each branch of the military and industry. Within a year, Air Force and NACA launched the X-1 rocket airplane at Bell Aircraft Company, and the Navy instituted a research airplane program at Douglas.

Root relates, "We started working on the design of the D-558 *Skystreak,* a straight-wing research airplane that would push near Mach 1. In 1945 I was interrupted in this effort by an extremely interesting assignment. At the suggestion of Captain Walter S. Diehl of the Navy,

I was sent to Germany for six weeks—these 'six weeks' lasted for six months!"

Even before the beginning of World War II, there had been authoritative reports that Germany's scientific skill was being pushed in the areas relating to aviation. The V-2 rocket was proof that it had also gone the step farther into space. It behooved this nation to garner as much of this advanced technology and planning as was possible in the wake of the Allied forces' advance into the Rhineland in 1945.

Root was a member of the U.S. Navy Technical Mission in Europe, headed by Commodore Shade. This group worked closely with the Air Force Scientific Task Group (USSTAF), headed by Dr. Theodore von Kármán and Col. Donald L. Putt, with similar groups of the Army, and with several government agencies, including NACA. The purpose of the combined effort was to seek out data, examine facilities, and talk with the leading German scientists.

"We were quartered in Paris," Root relates, "and went out in jeeps on 14-day tours throughout the whole of Germany. I had U.S. Navy Lieutenant Uellendahl as my interpreter, the same fine officer who had accompanied Lindbergh earlier. He was of great help to me, because he had gone to school in Munich and spoke German fluently. It was a completely fascinating, if chaotic, experience, to find and examine the German scientific advances in aeronautics.

"As these teams moved about, practically following the tracks of our advancing forces, there was a great sense of urgency because of the terms of the agreement between the Allies which authorized occupation of certain areas by the Soviets. This triggered a fierce competition between us and the Russians for the top German scientific talent. We were at a great disadvantage, because our policy at that time would not allow us to promise the Germans anything—not even that they would be brought to this country, though some of us took it upon ourselves as citizens to invite them.

"We were so distressed at the prospect of this exceptional talent getting away from us that a few of us just went ahead and gathered together outside of Paris some of the finest scientists, until we could make some other kind of arrangements. I feel that our nation finally secured a good number of these leading men."

A notable example of this joint effort was Operation Paperclip, the Army coup which garnered 127 scientists, including Dr. Wernher von Braun, of the Peenemünde group which had produced the mighty V-2 rocket. H. N. Toftoy (now Major General, USA, Ret.) deserves the greatest credit for this valuable action, which has resulted in a substantial boost to our over-all space effort in the intervening years.

It was a tremendously difficult and confused period, and the over-all aim of the missions was not helped by the fact that much of the initial interrogation had been conducted by individuals without scientific background. Realizing that the full potential of the situation was not being explored, the urgent request was issued for design specialists from industry to hurry to Europe to help in the interrogations to determine the extent of the German advancements.

The attitude on the part of German scientists and engineers abruptly altered when they were interviewed by men for whom they had professional respect. They took deep pride in their accomplishments; they were eager to talk and to substantiate their discussions in every way. Root says of the episode, "It was perhaps the most accelerated mental effort that I have ever experienced outside of Cal Tech graduate work!

"My specific assignment was to investigate their advances in high-speed aircraft. They were far ahead of us, primarily because they concentrated in high-speed aerodynamics, and had available excellent wind-tunnel facilities. They had achieved penetration into the supersonic speed range through the use of sweepback of the wings, the jet engine, and proper air-inlet design. The development of the sweptback wing was the one which was most interesting and somewhat ironic as we found out later."

Root explains why it was ironic: "One of our own U.S. engineers, Robert T. Jones, who worked for NACA at their Langley Field installation, had evolved this concept, but it escaped us in its theoretical form. It was formulated to overcome shockwave effects at very high speeds. Only after Americans saw the tremendous work that the Germans had performed with the radically different wing design did we appreciate Jones' idea, and hasten to utilize it."

Root appraises, "Truly, the advances that the Germans had made produced nothing short of a state of shock to us. We found so much that we considered valuable, for instance, that we microfilmed an entire top-secret library—one which Hitler had ordered destroyed. It is interesting to speculate why his orders were not carried out. Perhaps the German scientists could not bear to see the fruit of their arduous efforts wasted, so they hid it all in a mine shaft where our Allied team found it.

"There were such large amounts of material gathered that I assigned every available person the duty of sifting out the important parts. It became a grave problem just to keep it in our possession, since it had been agreed by the Allied powers that all of the technical material would be concentrated in a massive storehouse in London. But knowing this would mean great delay in ever getting the vital data into the hands of our people so that they might make use of it, we feverishly sifted through and microfilmed what we judged to be the most important."

Dr. Clark B. Millikan, who was one of the most valued members of the technical mission, flew back to Washington, D.C., for the purpose of conveying to the top-level Navy people the importance of what had been found. Root says, "He stressed to them for our Navy team that great advancements really had been made by the German scientists—that we had documentary proof of it.

"Further, we urged that their developed data be accepted immediately, and that we *not* start proving out the answers by duplicating their experiments one by one. Since our nation was still at war with Japan, we said it was imperative to start making use of the material, without even waiting for translations of it, for a sufficient number of our people could read German."

The plan was accepted. It was Root's full responsibility to assemble the data gathered by both the Navy and the Air Force into a 5000-foot roll of microfilm, and get it to the United States—it was "hand-carried" by Abraham Hyatt (now with NASA), a Marine Corps officer on the team who was a friend of Root's. The film was duplicated into 35 complete sets, and, along with an index, was rushed to key people in the military and industry.

From two to five years were saved!

This is the estimate which Root makes of the impact of the German data on our aircraft development. "We were able to accelerate our effort in high-speed aircraft to this extent because of their advancement in aerodynamics and in power plants. For example, George S. Schairer of the Boeing Airplane Company was in Europe with the Air Force mission, and returned to Seattle to plunge immediately into designing the B-47. Other companies also employed the knowledge, including application toward the design of commercial craft. At Douglas in El Segundo, we got busy on swept-back-wing fighters for the Navy. Working with our ace aerodynamicist, A. M. O. Smith, we also applied the swept wing to a Phase II version of the D-558, *Skyrocket,* research airplane." This became a record-setting craft in due time,* and one of Douglas' proudest contributions to the annals of aviation.

The responsibility which Root had accepted in this assignment had been noticed, and his manner of performance was so outstanding, that recognition came to him in a particularly unexpected and gratifying manner. He received the Junior Chamber of Commerce Award as one of the Nation's Ten Outstanding Young Men of 1945! This is given only to men 35 years of age, and further emphasizes the fact that maturity is not a matter of how many years an individual has lived. Too many people grow old without ever growing up for this to be the guideline.

* In the *Skyrocket,* Colonel Marion Carl, USMC, set an altitude record of 83,235 feet in August, 1953. In the following November, A. Scott Crossfield became the first man ever to travel twice the speed of sound, when he piloted the *Skyrocket* to Mach 2.04.

In college, it had been said of Root, "Dedicated—reached for perfection." At keenly competitive Cal Tech, fellow students and teachers alike agreed, "Top integrity. Great application, and infinite attention to detail." Then there is added a comment from a colleague, "Gene Root is not as quick as 20 people I could mention. *But,* it has been my observation that this quickness to catch on can be a real disadvantage, for often it makes people jump to a particular decision without properly considering all aspects.

"When Root gives an answer, you can be sure that he has given the problem tremendous intelligent thought, explored it from all sides, isolated the salient points, and that the opinion he renders is the most soundly based. I would consider Root a fine example of what a man with real capability can do in the way of truly applying himself. It is certainly to his credit that he used self-discipline, painstakingly acquired the knowledge of how to think and what to think."

The next major happening in Root's life echoed this tribute. He was invited to join with Project RAND.

In the closing days of World War II, the far-sighted General Arnold—who had been proved right repeatedly in the issues for which he fought—turned his primary attention to the means by which future conflict could be averted. It was he who had personally requested of Dr. von Kármán that the Air Force Scientific Advisory Group be organized to search out scientific advances not only in Germany but later in Japan as well. Arnold was also one of the prime forces behind the instigation of Project RAND, a study which began under contract at Douglas late in 1945.

The purpose of this effort was defined in Air Force Regulation 20-9: "Project RAND is a continuing program of scientific study and research on the broad subject of air warfare with the object of recommending to the Air Force preferred methods, techniques, and instrumentalities for this purpose."

Though that was the statement of work, its interpretation varied. "It was quite difficult to find the right questions to ask—and answer," says Dr. Robert S. Schairer.

Arthur Raymond, who helped to recruit the staff for the Project, says: "Each individual who had the idea of the broad need for such an organization had a somewhat different concept. It was like the story of the blind man who tried to describe what he thought an elephant looked like; every person had a slightly different idea of what Project RAND should be. There had never been one like it before, so we had to plow new ground as we went along."

General Craigie explains it in this manner: "RAND is a rather unusual company, in that the work they perform for the Air Force is not prescribed in great detail. From the beginning, we requested certain studies in certain areas, then RAND was given the latitude to do independent thinking. They did a great deal of studying for us relative to various concepts:

" 'What would be the pay-off of speed vs. range? Should we go for a small bomber that would be re-fueled, or should we go for a larger bomber that would carry all its own fuel for the flight? What are the various ways of performing the bomber mission, fighter mission, air defense mission?' To help find some answers, Gene Root headed up one of the most important efforts in RAND, the Airborne Vehicle Section."

The first six to join Project RAND, in order, were: Franklin R. Collbohm, J. Richard Goldstein, James Lipp, L. Eugene Root, John D. Williams, and Charles J. Hitch. Space studies were immediately begun by this remarkable group, indicating the advanced scope of their entire approach. Rand Report #1, a document of greatest historical importance, was dated May 2, 1946, and entitled *Preliminary Design of an Experimental World-Circling Spaceship*.

Project RAND continued for two years at Douglas, then it became apparent that the nature of the work done required that the group be set up as a separate organization. The RAND Corporation was formed to administer Project RAND, and offices were established in Santa Monica, California.

Tom Jones, who joined RAND as Root's executive assistant, recalls, "There was great awareness of the importance of our mission. Everyone had a consciousness that the leverage of technology—in the sense of changing the future—had grown so horrendous that it was humbling. When the more doctrinaire members of RAND's staff disagreed on 'far out' projections, the others understood why. Over-all, the people at RAND have always been very practical in their thinking."

Collbohm, the Director of RAND Corporation, said of initial aims: "Our objective then, as it is today, was to make it possible for a group of civilian scientists to work full time on the analysis of military problems of importance to the Air Force. At the same time, to be effective, such a group would have to maintain a real working relationship with industry and with scientists in our universities."[4]

The scope of RAND has grown to include these technical divisions: Aero-Astronautics, Computer Sciences, Cost Analysis, Economics, Electronics, Logistics, Mathematics, Physics, Planetary Sciences, Social Science, and System Operations. Collbohm explains the utilization of these categories in approaching a problem:

"In RAND this diversification of skills is used to broaden the perspective of our major studies. When such a study is planned, we are able to draw on the various technical divisions for specialists and to assemble these into a team having the skills to examine the problem in a broad context. The team then delegates to the technical divisions the job of making the substudies that produce the detailed components for the larger analysis.

"By using mixed teams, our specialists, who are of necessity limited in number, are often able to contribute to several different studies at one time. The technical divisions from which they are drawn devote a major effort to keeping up with the state of the art."[4]

The extensive degree to which RAND has fulfilled its giant aims is due in no small measure to the ones who initially helped to shape it. Jones says, "A strong camaraderie exists between those of us who were a part of it, for we feel that we were in at the birth of something most important."

Those early sessions had many interesting sidelights. A colleague recalls how Root's exuberance pervaded the atmosphere, and that he made colorful use of football expressions to spur on his "team." The man adds, "The eggheads moved in a somewhat different aura, but they made a great mistake if they ever underestimated Gene Root. Even at that time, the mark that he had made in industry was significant."

The best in each man was needed to approach some of the developmental paradoxes that befell aviation. One of the most evident, yet complex, of these was in the mere matter of standardization. Root's drive and courage, coupled with his technical competence, caused him to be called in on this project.

At Wright Field, he met with the man who had prompted the Air Force to take action to fill this need, Colonel Donald L. Putt. (Now a retired Lieutenant General, Putt is President of United Technology Corporation, and has offices very near Root's offices.)

Putt recalls, "The great problem that faced us in 1939 was that of trying to compare performance characteristics of different airplanes. It was especially difficult when the Army Air Corps and the Navy vehicles were being compared, because the two organizations would not calculate the performance in the same manner. Since some airplanes fly low, some high, some best at one speed and some at another, comparison between them simply could not be accomplished until a formula was established to measure each airplane's performance by certain standard flight paths."

He explains, "By a flight path, I mean this as an example: in a bombing mission, you take off, have a certain time to climb to a specified altitude, travel a given distance to the target, operate at full power while in that vicinity, then fly a predetermined path to return."

At the request of the first Secretary of Defense, James E. Forrestal, Putt and Root tediously evolved the standardization procedures that are still in use throughout the Air Force for quoting the performance of aircraft. It is a classified document often referred to as the "Black Book," officially entitled *Standard Aircraft Characteristics,* published by the Aeronautical Systems Division of the Air Force Systems Command. This led to a follow-on assignment, to formulate a basis for comparing United States aircraft and those of other countries. Root performed this work on special assignment to the Secretary of Defense, during the spring of 1948, and it resulted in the document: *Comparable Military Aircraft Characteristics Summary Project.*

At one of RAND's staff meetings, Root made this suggestion, "In order to get closer to the matter of advising the Air Force, it seems clear to me that we need to get closer to the Pentagon. In that way, we might be able to help with more immediate problems, as well as thinking of those far into the future. I feel that the senior members of the RAND group should rotate on taking tours of duty in Washington, D.C., for a year or so, and thereby gain a better viewpoint of our objectives." It was a good suggestion—so good, in fact, that the proposer found himself assigned to the Pentagon on July 1, 1951!

The atmosphere that existed within this stronghold of defense planning and policymaking was one of considerable controversy at that time, occasioned by the upheavals that were transpiring in the relationship between science and technology and future military operations.

Root was assigned as special assistant to the office of his friend and associate, General Putt, who was then Deputy Chief of Staff of Development. Putt was in the process of setting up a new organization. To the position of Director of Development Planning he appointed Colonel (now General) Bernard A. Schriever. The function of this post was to do forward planning—work for which Schriever was eminently qualified.

Root says of him, "Then, as now, he was a dedicated and extremely able man. Under Don Putt's fine leadership, Ben was trying to determine in a very real sense what the Air Force should be doing, and faced such basic questions as: How should we go about doing the future job of the Strategic Air Command? How should we go about lining up our defense forces? It was our combined task to write 'Development Planning Objectives,' for each one of the five task areas of the Air Force."

There, as in all other assignments, Root proved his worth. J. H. Carter, another of his associates, relates, "Gene has an outstanding ability to distill, out of a mass of information presented to him, the critical elements of any new idea or problem. He will arrive at a clear conclusion from these elements, and be doggedly persistent in implementing the resulting decision. This persistence has usually paid off because Gene has a way of inspiring enthusiasm in his associates, both superiors and subordinates."

Though Root was supposed to have remained in this post for only a year, many projects were under way that required his excellent analytical thinking—so the time accumulated to almost two years before Putt's successor, General Craigie, felt it reasonable to agree to Root's leaving the responsible post.

When he returned to California to resume his position at RAND, Root says, "I found I was in the embarrassing position of replacing a couple of fellows who had done and were doing my job very well. This prompted my decision to go back into industry."

Root had a most unique experience in looking about for his next position. While in the Pentagon, he had collected about thirty-five offers from various places for future employment.

"I asked Frank Collbohm if I could go examine which of these should be accepted. Frank gave his OK if I would report back on my research, as an economic exercise in the supply and demand of RAND graduates."

When word got around that Root was available, the offers were repeated. The very number and diversity of them intensified the difficulty in making a decision. One day he was doing some deliberating while lost in the midst of a crowd—at the Men's Bar of the Statler Hotel in Washington, D.C.

Hall L. Hibbard, Vice President of Lockheed, relates, "I walked in there and spied Gene over in a corner. He had one leg draped over a cocktail table, one arm thrown around the empty chair next to him, his eyes were on the ceiling, and his thoughts obviously were in another world. In fact, he was looking a little disappointed with this world."

The two friends laughed at the ludicrous picture that Root presented, then Hibbard told him, "You need a tonic. The best tonic I know would be a job at Lockheed. We have been doing advance planning at Lockheed, of course, but no one person is concentrating on forecasting as a full-time job. It is being done mostly by corporate officers who sort of 'do it on the back of an envelope' as they ride back and forth to work.

"Our corporation has reached the stature where we need full-time effort, at the highest level. We should get topside people and put them topside—where they will not be concerned with the day-to-day 'fire fighting' that goes on in a large corporation."

Hibbard was most persuasive, but Root is not one to make snap decisions. With his family, he flew to Hawaii to have time to deliberate on this and other offers while he enjoyed a long over-due rest.

With a smile, Root relates, "You know, it is an honored custom in China for the parents to select the future spouse for their child. In a way, that is what happened to me. Dad found Beryl before I did, when he was in the printing business in Stockton. Orders for printing yearbooks took him around to the various schools. At Walnut Grove High School he was impressed with a very charming able girl who was editor of the yearbook. Since she was planning to enter the College of the Pacific the following fall, he suggested to her that she look me up."

From Beryl's viewpoint, it proved a most interesting suggestion, and she recalls, "I soon found I didn't have to 'look.' Everyone on the campus knew Gene Root. He was an outstanding football player, was in all of the college social activities, as well as being an honor student. So I spotted him, but he didn't know me from all the other hundreds of freshmen."

By the second semester, Beryl had lost some of her timidity, and began speaking to Gene Root each time they passed in the halls. Being a gregarious and gentlemanly fellow, Gene spoke back—not really knowing that this was the girl his father had described. She relates, "I finally got up courage to invite him to our spring formal."

Gene Root continues the story by saying, "The telephone connection was not too good. I misunderstood her name, and thought it was another girl whom I had been dating. When I discovered my error, I began to wonder who had called me. While in this puzzled state, I was walking past the freshman dormitory one day and a very pretty head leaned out of the window and called to me: 'The date of our spring formal has been changed to next Friday.' I was downright grateful for this clue, but still didn't know the name to attach to this smiling face. So I spent the afternoon in the college office, poring over the files of all the freshmen girls, trying to recognize her picture—a privilege accorded the Chairman of the Student Affairs Committee."

Luckily he did, and the episode had a happy ending—though not for three years. Root finished Cal Tech and allowed himself time to become established at Douglas before asking Beryl to set the date for their marriage. "By then Gene was earning $24.48 a week, so we felt it was ample to establish a home," recalls Beryl, amused at the comparison with today's scale of living costs.

Three children comprise the Root family. Kirby, 19, now makes a fine figure in a Marine Corps uniform, standing 6 feet 4 inches. Attractive and serious-minded Karen, as small as her brother is tall, is in her last year of high school. Red-haired Brian, 10, appropriately has a firecracker kind of disposition.

While Beryl has to admit that the tremendous demands of Gene Root's work constantly deprive his family of his companionship, she is deeply appreciative of an opportunity that has been afforded the family to expand their outlook and to meet many outstanding people. Visitors into their home have included some of the world's leading figures in business, the military, and science, and have imparted to the family's consciousness a great awareness and appreciation of the meaning of this present period in history.

One of the indications of what a man deeply believes is revealed by the basic philosophy which he tries to instill in his children. To Kirby, Karen, and Brian, Root has stressed the quality of integrity—of honesty with others and with themselves. He also endeavors to make them realize that any job which is undertaken deserves their very best efforts, and certainly must be completed. "Never be a quitter once a thing is started!" But his words, however fine, are not nearly as persuasive as his example.

Root displays consistency in all ways. He is as methodical in his subjective thinking as in his objective decisions. Says his friend, Ernie Plesset: "When Gene decided to return to industry, it was characteristic that he would take time to contemplate and to analyze the different directions he might move. Now, it has been my experience with most people that when they are considering an issue which personally involves them, they have a most difficult time being very objective about the decisions they make. They do it on impulse, which they rationalize. Gene, on the other hand, is very realistic in appraising his own abilities. He was both objective and wise in his choice."

Root chose to join Lockheed Aircraft Corporation as Director of Development Planning. It offered splendid opportunity to apply what he had learned at RAND and the Pentagon.

Both Lockheed and the Air Force benefited from his decision. His work with Schriever had entailed putting together the state of the art, and intelligence information to help formulate defense plans. At Lockheed, working for Senior Vice President Hall L. Hibbard, the same technique was employed, except that the information related to the defense market and the general economy. Development planning entails looking ahead at the "state of the art" and at what is being done in research, to consider applications, think of new markets for diversification and expansion, and to specify what new products should be developed by the company to best fill these projected needs.

J. H. Carter, the associate from Pentagon days, joined Lockheed soon after Root did, and recalls that the company was then deeply involved in deciding whether to invest heavily in the development of a jet transport. He relates, "Frequent high-level meetings were held to debate the agonizing technical-economic question. I attended some of these meetings with Gene and watched him with great admiration as he contributed, in a relatively unobtrusive way as the debate proceeded, a pertinent comment here and an interesting technical point there."

Carter points out, "Gene's formidable background at RAND and his involvement on the fringe of Pentagon decision-making stood him in good stead during this difficult period. Although he was a relatively new arrival at Lockheed, I am sure that his judgment and comments were important factors in Lockheed's decision not to proceed with the jet transport, but instead, to go all out on the *Electra,* which appeared to be favored by a combination of technical, economic, and competitive factors. Although as a commercial venture the *Electra* could not be considered an outstanding success, it was perhaps the best decision when one considers the losses incurred by Douglas with the DC-8 and by Convair with the 880 and 990."

Root's first strong planning recommendation was that Lockheed enter the missile field. Compared with other aircraft companies, they were quite late in embracing this activity. A Missile Systems Division was set up in Van Nuys, and Lieutenant General Elwood R. "Pete" Quesada, USAF (Ret.), was named head. Says Root: "Pete took the job seriously and got Lockheed into the missile business in all directions almost all at once."

In accord with the policy of dispersal, it was decided that the plant for the expansion of this division would be located in the San Francisco Bay area at Sunnyvale, California. Quesada resigned before it went into operation, and a search was instigated for an executive to take his place. Lists were scoured and names considered. Root, after helping in this selecting process for some time, made the unguarded comment one day that he thought he could do the job as well as some of the men whose names were finally being discussed. That was the indication of interest that Lockheed executives had been awaiting—Root was offered the job. Though not exactly the kind of "planning" he had been doing, Root immediately moved north and embarked upon administering the Division through a phenomenal period of growth. From an initial manpower of 4800 in late 1956, the size had doubled and redoubled to near 20,000 in 1959.

In late 1959, Root returned to the Burbank corporate offices as Group Vice President with two new operations added—Lockheed Electronics Company in Plainfield, New Jersey, and Lockheed Propulsion Company in Redlands, California. After two years at "headquarters," working closely and intensely under Executive Vice President (now over-all Lockheed Corporate President) Daniel J. Haughton, Root went back to the Bay area location. By this time, its size and importance brought about a change in designation from *Division* to Lockheed Missiles and Space *Company,* and Root was named President.

Dr. Smith J. DeFrance, Director of NASA's Ames Research Center, who has known Root for over 20 years, says, "He organized the new division and did one of the outstanding jobs of the decade in building it to the high level of performance that made it the principal division of Lockheed Aircraft Corporation."

Being heavily engaged in research and development, Root explains the constant battle which his company fights: "We are right at the border line of the 'state of the art' where engineering changes have to be made to bring about necessary improvements. The type of work that goes on these days, with the systems changes, makes it hard to get a weapon completed fast enough for it to have a useful life before it is obsolete. Therefore, there are concentrated efforts to incorporate improvements along the way. We are not really in mass production in the missile and space business—we are in a manufacturing process where we make far fewer units of each thing, but each one requires large amounts of engineering effort.

"It is a higher caliber, more concentrated engineering type of effort than ever required in aircraft. Engineering requirements have so expanded that today they may comprise up to half the total work force of those engaged in research, development, and manufacture. To keep up with new developments, to get items delivered on time, to insure proper reliability and performance—this is all most challenging. It is also an indication of why, perhaps, there are more engineering and scientific people going into management than before—more company vice presidents who are engineers and scientists. A working knowledge of the technical side of the business is almost imperative."

Root's value in his present position is based not only on his present activity, but on the backlog of his reputation for sound judgment and thorough planning which has built up throughout his career. The reason for this emphasis is more fully understood when General Craigie explains what he considers to be the major problem in the relationship between industry and the military: "The military can state its requirements accurately and in a way that can be readily understood, being completely objective in what it wants. Industry, on the other hand, is inclined to oversell because it is profit-motivated. This is not a criticism—it is merely a fact. In order to remain in business, industry must make a profit, and to make a profit, they must get the contracts.

"All contracts, almost without exception, are obtained after competition within industry, so there is a tendency for industry to minimize the difficulties that will be encountered in making delivery on the item. I think they paint too rosy a picture with optimistic brochures and I think that quite often the military is too inclined to buy this too-rosy picture." Craigie continues in this searching comment: "Therefore, each is inviting delays which later on will beset them, and for which both the military and industry will be criticized. Had they really gotten together with a true meeting of the minds, I think they would have faced squarely the series of very great development problems which had to be overcome, and would have set more conservative dates. Then there would not have been the big disappointment of the equipment not being ready on the date that it had been promised."

Craigie admits, "There must be optimism on the part of the military and on the part of industry, of course. But basically there must be awareness of the state of the art, if there is to be intelligent planning—the kind of planning a man would do if it were his own money."

It is in this kind of severe light that Root holds up well, indeed. "His absolute integrity shows through," says Leo Carter, in whose department Root first went to work at Douglas; Carter is now working for Root at Sunnyvale. He continues, "I have had this chance to see him both ways, and can say he is extremely fair in everything he does. You can depend upon his backing if you are right, and can also depend upon his very frank criticism if you are wrong."

This space business has no room for error. The standards of tolerance, both for men and machines, have been calibrated to a minute degree which are more exacting by magnitudes than existed in any prior technology. It has been achieved by the unrelenting determination of those with foresight who snatched figures from the realm of possibility and made them into probabilities—who were willing to pay the personal toll of constant and stressful work to transform a vision into achievement.

The fact that Root understood this is illustrated in an incident related by G. H. Putt, the brother of the General with whom Root worked at the Pentagon: "During the early days after his being appointed General Manager of what was then Lockheed Missile Systems Division, he used a driver to take him to and from work. He also arranged for his executive assistant to ride with him. The half-hour drive each way was used for transferring paperwork requiring action and issuing assignments to the executive assistant. This two-fisted approach kept the executive assistant hanging on the ropes to keep from going down for the count. Since I was the executive assistant, I'm happy to say I survived a most memorable experience." Putt survived to move on to the position he now holds, Director of Central Quality Assurance and Test Laboratories.

In addition to Root's drive and his basic kindness toward everyone, the thing that most impresses his secretary, Kay Fleck, is his memory: "Most people have a memory for details or a mind for big things. This man is the only one I have ever known who has the capacity to go from little details up through the large over-all picture." With memories of many an incident she adds, "Mr. Root is one who asks the impossible—then he not only succeeds in having you perform it, but you like doing it! He produces an intense type of loyalty from his people."

Root expects a great deal from individuals. He expects even more of himself. He is harsh in self-analysis of his shortcomings: "I'm pretty impatient, because there is so much that has to be done. I am strong-minded to the point of stubbornness. A man once said to me, 'Your mind is made up. I may as well get out of your way and watch you make your profile right through that brick wall.' I'm afraid that is a true picture."

With considerable thought, Root continues, "I am too aggressive, and too persistent about things. And I must admit that the reputation is deserved of having 'more guts than sense.' " Without equating the two, it appears that Root is not lacking on either score.

Within the demanding and competitive space business, positions of respect are earned. Lockheed's astronautical activity extends further back than is generally recognized. In 1955 the organization was awarded a study contract for a military satellite system by the Air Force. The following year, J. H. Carter was given responsibility over the program, which progressed from the study stage to an actual contract (won over two other contractors) to proceed with the hardware development of a satellite system. The project nearly starved for lack of funds, and was badly mauled by a succession of discouraging reviews at top government level, but it remained alive.

Schriever was by that time heading the Ballistic Missile Division (BMD) and was deeply involved with the development of this nation's first intercontinental ballistic missile, the *Atlas,* and members of his staff offered encouragement to Lockheed on the project. More than that, the thought came to Lockheed that results might be achieved by the combining of their forces in this manner: by using *Thor,* the intermediate range ballistic missile which BMD was producing, as a booster vehicle, a simplified version of the Lockheed-developed *Agena** could be used as a satellite.

Immediately after the launching of *Sputnik I* on October 4, 1957, Root directed Carter and his staff to put this idea for *Agena*'s utilization in the form of a formal proposal. Carter relates: "In mid-October, it was presented to General Schriever by Gene and me, in the Alexandria, Virginia, apartment of one of the General's good friends. This was a real shirt-sleeve working session, in an exciting atmosphere of urgency, which lasted from 9:30 in the evening into the early hours of the next morning.

"From this, results were produced. In a surprisingly short time, Lock-

* *Agena* is a most versatile satellite vehicle. It is an upper stage booster which can achieve orbit, or put a payload into a deep space trajectory. Whereas the *A* and *B* models have payload integrated, the newly-developed *Agena-D* is a bare model—termed a "standard" space vehicle. *Agenas* have been the upper stages which have placed four-fifths of the total U.S. payload weight in orbit. Its ability to change attitude on orbit, as well as to restart in space, has earned recognition as an ideal mobile launching platform in space for orbital and deep space trajectory missions. An *Agena* placed the *Ranger 4* payload on the moon, the first U.S. vehicle to make a lunar landing. It is used in many other NASA programs including *Mariner* Venus fly-bys; the *Echo* passive communications satellite, where a large rigidized balloon will be placed in polar orbit, and numerous astronomical and geophysical satellite projects. In *Project Gemini,* it will be sent into orbit separately and then joined with a two-man space capsule. This rendezvous-in-space maneuver allows the *Agena* to become the main propulsion unit while the manned capsule is in an orbit of several days' duration.

heed was embarked on the *Discoverer* program of scientific satellites. The *Discoverer* program became perhaps the outstanding satellite program in the world, having successfully launched by early 1962 more satellites than any other United States program, or than *all* the Russian efforts combined. The background for the basic *Discoverer* decision was laid at that night-long session in Alexandria."

Lockheed's major strides have been achieved with other bold actions. Wilbur D. Snow, Director of Market Development at Lockheed Missiles and Space Company says, "Gene is very advanced in his thinking. He has a high degree of capability to interpret the meaning of science in our business." Then he adds, "*Polaris,* for instance, represented a considerable advance. Here again, it was just plain confidence that with the right people and the right amount of effort, we could make it work!"

There were times, both within and without Lockheed, when this confidence was put to severest test. The entire concept of this Fleet Ballistic Missile was a formidable undertaking, and one which could have been accomplished only with the resolute leadership of Vice Admiral William F. Raborn, Jr., and the industrial team which Root organized with Stanley Burris as head. Nuclear submarines now maintain a vigilant "peacc patrol" armed with solid-propellant *Polaris* missiles, providing the nation with a major deterrent to aggression.

"Lockheed Gets Contract for Moon Base Study,"[5] is the headline to a story in the *Los Angeles Times* by Marvin Miles on June 26, 1962, that told of the company's investigations of rocket systems and the various techniques for the establishing and supplying of a permanent lunar base.

Another project, *RIFT* (Reactor In-Flight Test system), has put Lockheed in a whole new area of nuclear-powered satellites or boosters. As the prime contractor for this test program, they are furthering the development of this upperstage engine. It likely will not be flight tested for three or four years, but will be the forerunner of nuclear power use in spacecraft.

Root can carefully ponder "far out" scientific projects which are quite beyond average comprehension and say, "The main problem is in handling a complicated job in a short time, doing it well, and not having 'mental indigestion' as a result of the severely concentrated effort. I feel NASA is taking a most straightforward approach to achieving the lunar landing in a step-by-step fashion, and doing it with all possible diligence."

The advance of technology and the wonders of science do not really amaze Root—but the attitudes of some people do! "I have actually encountered ones who say they feel that there are no opportunities left in this business," he says. "I am inclined to wonder, however, if it is a matter of people not wanting to consider the very apparent opportunities because they entail hard work. This I will admit—it is a tough business, particularly on the scientific and engineering side of it. We are in grave need of more good mathematicians, physicists, engineers. But many people just don't seem to be willing to make the kind of effort that it takes to study for these careers, feeling that things should come more easily, if not automatically.

"Important and worthwhile things are never attained without effort. So instead of feeling this reluctance, I wish that people with able minds could appreciate the possibility that there is far greater compensation—from the fascination that is inherent in the subject, and from the satisfaction of performing a very demanding job. I feel that there should be more nationwide governmental recognition of important accomplishments in the science and engineering areas, to build up the importance of the effort in the minds of the younger people."

Root declares, "We must reverse this present too-prevalent attitude of trying to get by with the least amount of effort, and inspire people who are naturally able, to seek more and more education. In our system, where a person does only what he wants to do, the solution gets down to one thing—motivation. So how do you motivate the individual? This is an important problem—one that needs more attention than others that are being widely discussed. Some of us in the science and engineering professions have been trying to devise the means." The matter of science-oriented high school and college activities has come in for much consideration from Root in conjunction with his function as President of the Institute of the Aerospace Sciences (IAS).

Root and Dr. William H. Pickering, President of the American Rocket Society (ARS), have been earnestly pursuing the merger of the two organizations into one organization—the American Institute of Aeronautics and Astronautics. This would unite some 30,000 professionals, and would be, Root feels, an historic forward step. It is at meetings of such groups that the most advanced ideas are presented in technical papers, that conversations trigger creative thinking, that individual ideas and opinions are molded into an effective policy. To avoid duplication and competition, unity of the air and space groups is obvious and logical; their interests and activities have both overlap and interchange.

Though the preponderance of fact and opinion is in favor of this consolidation, the mechanics of working out a merger which satisfies all has been very time-consuming for the two presidents. Says Captain W. C. Fortune, Commanding Officer of the U.S. Naval Air Test Facility at Lakehurst, N.J., "To me, Gene Root's most impressive trait is his equanimity of spirit in moments of pressure or stress. It has been strongly evident in the midst of all of our recent IAS negotiations with the ARS whenever parochial opinion or misunderstanding threatened to upset the good order of our meetings. Presiding as President, he has remained calm, unruffled, and in complete command of the situation. If these two technical societies are successfully merged, it will be due in large measure to the personal efforts of Mr. Root and Dr. Pickering."

Root and Fortune were associated in 1956, as members of an Office of Assistant Secretary of Defense (R&D) team sent to West Germany to evaluate that nation's newly-born military research and development effort. Fortune explains, "The object was to initiate mutual weapon-development programs."

Through observing Root's conduct in these diverse situations, Fortune says, "His capabilities as a scientist, engineer and administrator are known to many, but I look upon him as a statesman of high order. I thoroughly admire and respect his calm command of temper, speech and outward mien."

Coupled with this serious application is the proper balance of a fun-loving spirit. Fortune relates, "One bright spot of our German trip was a half-day off to help the local Rhinelanders celebrate Vater's Day. It apparently was the custom in the Rhine Valley for all Fathers to arise early on that holiday, dress in gay attire, and proceed from wine garden to wine garden sampling the various wares. They got rosier and noisier as they proceeded along the roads winding up the grapevine-laden mountains. As I recall, Gene's control and equanimity were just as evident at the peak as at the start—as well as that night when we had to get back to work on our reports."

Root joined the Lakeside Golf Club in 1959. Rumor has it that he never hit a ball. "People ask me why I don't play," he says. "It is a simple limitation of time. Any moments that I can possibly spare I want to spend with my family. It is extremely hard to be a good father, a good husband, a good citizen *and* a good manager! Throughout this business, everyone is working long hours. You have no choice—everything is moving so fast that just to keep up technically a heavy work schedule is necessary."

Whatever other pressures or demands there have been upon him, Root has always made the time to be of service to the government. "One of the strongest convictions I have is that a person—particularly one who has had the benefit of special training—should do his part in government to the greatest possible extent."

Between 1944 and 1949, Root served as member of two committees and chairman of three for NACA; the areas of specialty were principally aerodynamics and stability and control. His work with the Air Force Scientific Advisory Board spanned the period of from 1948 to 1959, as a member on five panels and as chairman of the aircraft panel. He had the unique experience of serving on the Nuclear Panel of the late Dr. John von Neumann. "I wasn't a nuclear physicist, but was asked to bridge the gap between the missiles and aircraft panel and the nuclear panel so that they would know what problems were present in the vehicle part. I was honored to serve, and it was a unique experience to watch the workings of exceptional minds such as von Neumann's and others on the Panel."

Since 1954, Root has also served as a member of six groups of the Office of the Director of Defense for Research and Engineering. He is presently active on the Executive Committee and as a member at large of the Defense Science Board, helping as requested to formulate the thinking and planning of major technical decisions at top level.

His tremendous contribution was acknowledged in 1957 when the Air Force bestowed upon him the Exceptional Service Award "in recognition of distinguished patriotic service 1948 through 1956." The Department of the Navy honored him in 1961 with its Distinguished Public Service Award for outstanding contribution in personally directing the organization of the *Polaris* Fleet Ballistic Missile team. Root's dream of a doctorate, sidetracked when he went to work at Douglas, was realized when his alma mater, the University of the Pacific bestowed upon him the honorary degree of Doctor of Science in June, 1958.

Recently, Root called upon his personal physician for a routine checkup. The medical man detected that his patient seemed overly tired and started, in his best professional manner, to track down the cause. "Perhaps the trouble is that you are bored, Mr. Root. Does your work really interest you?"

Summoning the calm for which he is noted, Root quietly recited to the medical man the activities with which he was associated that very day:

"We are hoping to launch not one, but two satellites. We will check out in a nuclear submarine a longer range *Polaris* missile. We should hear today about an important test on our *Polaris* nuclear warhead. We are finishing up a major proposal for NASA on a giant booster that will take men to the moon. Late this afternoon I am attending a briefing on the flight testing of a nuclear rocket—RIFT.

"And you ask me *if I am interested* in my work, Doctor? Here is a question for you: How can I stretch each day to 48 hours so I can pursue all that needs to be done?" The doctor just shook his head. He was not equal to the task of prescribing earth-bound time dilatation.

The same Gene Root who as a child grabbed onto a calf's tail, now has become the man who latches onto stars. His thoughts are in an orderly race toward tomorrow. He has reasoned out, "Most experts have studiously underestimated the future. I don't really believe I am over-guessing it in my thinking."

Those who know Gene Root will bet that he is not unrealistic, and they also will agree that he can put into operation any visionary plan that he proposes in this assault on the universe!

REFERENCES

1. *Flying,* 65:3:40–47+, September, 1959.
2. Goldberg, Alfred, ed.: *A History of the United States Air Force,* Princeton, Van Nostrand, 1957.
3. Adams, Franklin Pierce: *Book of Quotations,* New York, Funk & Wagnalls, 1952.
4. Collbohm, F. R.: *Project RAND,* an address before the Scientific Advisory Board, March 24, 1955.
5. *Los Angeles Times,* Los Angeles, California, June 26, 1962.

Dynamic general manager of the civilian space agency's efforts

ROBERT C. SEAMANS, JR.

"On April 12, 1961, the day that a man first orbited the earth, I learned a great lesson. My enlightenment came not from a scientist, but from my daughter, May, who was then eight years old. I rushed in to tell her the big news, and she responded, 'What's so remarkable about that? Aren't men going to the moon, too?' She regards space exploration as a perfectly natural thing, and couldn't quite understand my being so excited about it."

Bob Seamans stares out of his office window, contemplating the top of the Washington Monument, while his mind's eye reaches beyond distance into time. "When today's youngsters—with their complete acceptance of space—grow up and become tomorrow's leading scientists and engineers and administrators, our whole program will receive added impetus. They are the ones who will give it the stimulus to expand to the planets."

Seamans, as Associate Administrator, is the "general manager" of the National Aeronautics and Space Administration, NASA. His job is essentially that of seeing that the national space program moves ahead as rapidly as possible on all approved projects. Judged in any context, from any viewpoint, it would be hard to find a more immense job. The goals are gigantic.

Seamans' expert judgment and positive attitude were important factors in events on Capitol Hill at the time of the Gagarin flight. In the new United States House of Representatives Office Building, within the Hearing Chamber on the lower floor, the House Committee on Science and Astronautics was holding a hearing. It was for the purpose of reviewing planned NASA activities for fiscal year 1962. A summary of the proposal for *Project Apollo,* the United States program to place three men on the moon, was being presented. At that time, the plan called only for studies—not development—of the actual *Apollo* space craft.

The new Administration had had a very limited time to review the program, having assumed office just three months before, so it was President Kennedy's desire to survey carefully *Project Mercury* and the progress and dimensions of the entire space effort before making judgments on *Apollo.* Also, the President wanted a chance to review international implications of manned space flight before agreeing to a hard-driving development program that would go beyond original planning.

A slight postponement of decision on the space craft, itself, would not delay the actual mission, for it was the development of the huge booster rocket, the *Advanced Saturn,* that would govern just when *Apollo* might make a flight. The space craft (called capsule or module) could be completed at an earlier date than the rocket which would thrust it into orbit.

On the day after Gagarin's orbiting, the furor had grown to such an extent that the hearing was moved to the House Caucus Room. NASA Administrator, James E. Webb, and Deputy Administrator, Dr. Hugh L. Dryden, were called to testify as to "why the United States program was lagging." Several hundred people jammed the room, and television cameras were clustered outside the door. At this point, the purpose of the hearing, consideration of the NASA budget, was temporarily shelved in favor of a somewhat emotional discussion of over-all policy.

Seamans testified the next day that the *Advanced Saturn* was the all-important "pacing" item in the push for *Apollo.* The Honorable Joseph E. Karth joined in the urgent seeking for an opinion when he asked, "If we went to a two-shift operation on *Saturn,* and then gave you more money for the *Apollo* program, how much time do you think we could save or make up in the over-all circumlunar and *Apollo* programs, or the man-in-space flight?"[1]

Seamans, well realizing the magnitude of the question, replied: "I think it would be irresponsible for me to try to give you a definite time in answer to that question." But the Committee, perhaps unreasonably, would not allow him time to formulate a considered estimate. They wanted answers at that moment. Already upset by the USSR's second important space "first," this time achieving manned orbital flight, they now heard rumors of plans toward the next major feat—it was said that our adversary was planning a lunar landing in 1967, to commemorate the 50th anniversary of the Bolshevik Revolution.

Since the United States timetable called for a landing of the *Apollo* capsule in the 1970's, the Committee was insistently pressing for an acceleration of our program. The Honorable David S. King pursued the questioning: "Do you think it would be conceivably possible, by increasing appropriations, by marshaling our manpower and resources and everything else that we have available, to meet this target date of, let us say, 1967?"[1]

Seamans well knew what answer was desired, yet the vastness of the project dictated carefully considered response: "This is really a very major undertaking. To compress the program by three years means that greatly increased funding would be required for the interval of time between now and 1967. I certainly cannot state that this is an impossible objective. If it comes down to a matter of national policy, I would be the first to review it wholeheartedly and see what it would take to do the job. My estimate at this moment is that the goal may very well be achievable."[1]

It had been said! Though a qualified statement, it brought a feeling of encouragement to those in the hearing chamber. Moreover, this was no wild-eyed dreamer who indicated the affirmative. Rather, it was the judgment of the experienced man who would be overseeing the actual working out of the enormous project. Though turning points are difficult to assess at close range, it would appear that Seamans' indication that he was eager to tackle such a stepped-up pace for *Project Apollo* had marked influence on subsequent events. Importance given the program increased.

John F. Kennedy, as Senator, had regarded space as "a great new frontier." As President, on May 25, 1961, he stated his belief that the lunar mission should become a national goal. "No single space project in this period will be more impressive to mankind, or more important for the long-range exploration of space; and none will be so difficult or expensive to accomplish."[2]

Once the policy had been established at top level, what factors reassured the President, the Vice President and Congress that Seamans was the man best qualified to manage its fulfillment? His party affiliation is not that of the present Administration; quite obviously, it has been of no concern in deciding his assignments. He was appointed to his post in September, 1960. Capability is the element that counts. After due consideration, NASA Administrator Webb ruled out the idea of creating a "Moon Mission Czar" to head *Project Apollo*. He has left the responsibility for managing this and all other NASA projects to Seamans.

Seamans is a tall, 43-year-old "North Shore" Bostonian. Both environment and opportunity could have set the pace for a more leisurely life. Yet since young manhood, Seamans has displayed an inner drive of such proportions that his family has felt concern at times for his physical stamina.

Diverse comments paint a character in strong hues. D. Brainerd Holmes, Director of NASA's Office of Manned Space Flight, says, "He has the quality of leadership, plus exceptional technical ability." Another NASA associate, Dr. A. J. Kelley, Director of Electronics and Control, comments, "Bob not only thinks deeply but responds to the ideas of others—traits that are seldom combined in the same person."

Thomas Dixon, Deputy to Seamans, has the proximate view from an adjoining office. "He certainly listens to other people's ideas, but he isn't given to procrastinating while mulling things over. He makes prompt decisions based on wide scientific background plus experience and familiarity with the operations and problems of industry. This makes for good management-in-depth and sound decision-making."

His former employer, A. L. Malcarney, Group Executive Vice President of the Radio Corporation of America, relates, "Dr. Seamans is one of the finest scientists to be associated with RCA's Defense Electronic Products organization. His professional bearing, his personal competence and industry in the field of advanced weapons systems, and his sincere interest in the thoughts and feelings of others earned for him an enviable reputation as an executive, as a scientist, and as a person."

Scientific traits skipped four generations when they fell to Bob Seamans. His great-great-grandfather, Otis Tufts, made a substantial contribution to convenience by his invention of the closed-car elevator. The "vertical railway," as its inventor called it, was not immediately accepted. Some felt the risk of accidental falling was great, and the more hardy souls considered the use of an elevator as effeminate. But these reactions did not deter its appeal as a curiosity. The first passenger elevator was installed in the Fifth Avenue Hotel in New York, and the proprietor wrote in 1882 that "hundreds, even thousands, of persons visited the elevator daily. Men of note such as the Prince of Wales, the Prince de Joinville, and others, as well as eminent foreign engineers and scientific persons, were greatly interested in it."[3]

An article in *Harper's New Monthly Magazine* drew a comparison of the New York skyline in 1882, with that of 1859, prior to the introduction of the passenger elevator. In those early days a quite startling change had occurred, and it is safe to assume that the inveterate stair-climbers ceased their objections long before the appearance of the Empire State Building with its 102 stories.

Two minor notations in the report on the "vertical railway" point up the contrast to present conditions: it was lighted by gas, with attached rubber tubes rising and falling with the car; it was considered very expensive, costing $25,000! (As an interesting comparison, one single office of NASA, that of Manned Space Flight, is currently spending $5 million per day.)

Seamans' great-great-grandfather made other substantial contributions from his laboratory in East Boston. His inventions included the steam-powered printing press in 1837. Eight years later he developed the first compartmented steamship. Two other inventions were the steam-operated pile driver, which was used during the filling of the Back Bay area of Boston, and the babbitt bearings which are still used. Stories of this gifted ancestor as related by the family greatly intrigued young Bob, and undoubtedly influenced his choice of career.

His neighborhood so strongly favored boys in numbers that Seamans smiles in remembering his attendance at his initial major social event which included girls. "I was about 13, and it was the first time I had dressed up to go to a dance. At the dinner party beforehand, I was so uneasy about sitting next to a strange girl that I only stole one quick glance at her. It was not until the meal was over that I really turned to look, and saw it was a classmate with whom I had gone to school for eight years!"

Early years were spent in attendance at Lenox School. The headmaster of this church school was George Gardner Monks, a minister greatly interested in mathematics. He gave Seamans a week of special tutoring on the math standard for the junior year of high school. Monks arranged for Seamans to take the college board examination—which he passed with honors!

After his freshman year at Harvard, Seamans pondered a question—why go to college for four years when it could be done in three? He shrugs it off as a rather obvious conclusion, but this marks a thought-pattern characteristic of him all of his adult life. He recalls, "My parents were not very enthusiastic about the idea, but I finally persuaded them to agree to my doing it."

When drive and independence are partners, effective results can generally be seen. It was fortuitous that it was Seamans whom members of Congress asked for an opinion on speeding the pace of *Project Apollo*—it was a concept in keeping with the traits that he inherited and developed.

To accomplish his accelerated schedule in College, Seamans took a summer course in surveying, his first contact with engineering. "It was a fascinating course, given by Professor Albert Hartlein at Squam Lake, New Hampshire. We lived in tents, roughed it in old clothes. There happened to be a girls' camp across the lake, which added a civilizing effect and an interesting dimension to surveying." (It can be assumed that the shyness he had possessed at 13 years of age had diminished.)

Seamans recalls the final major task of the course: "Each of us had to draw a map of the area, with all the contour lines, showing a projected path of a railroad. We had to work out the excavations and the fills, and the radii of the turns. Most of the 50 of us taking the course were delayed for one reason or another. I know I got sidetracked by reading *Gone with the Wind.*

"The night before the map was due, we were all working in the drafting room frantically trying to meet the 8 A.M. deadline. At about 5 o'clock, Jim Ledgard, my tent-mate, broke out with a horrified yell. He had drawn his railroad—in ink—between two wrong points. His map was irretrievable, and it seemed catastrophic at the time."

What's important? To whom? Where and when?

The variation in the subject and in the degree is as broad as life itself. To the child, his playpen is the world. To the statesman, the entire earth is his domain. Somewhere in between, the remainder of the people range and resolve their level of living.

Seamans had opportunity to expand his viewpoint with an extended trip to Europe in the summer of 1938. "My mother, grandmother, two brothers and I were driving over the Reich Autobahn near the border of Czechoslovakia. Hitler had marched into Austria a few months earlier and was to annex the Czech democracy in September. At any rate, when we topped the crest of the hill, we suddenly came upon an absolute sea of German soldiers. A command was shouted, and they stepped off the Autobahn to allow us to drive on, but I still recall their unfriendly expressions as we went past them.

"We also passed near the military airport at Nuremberg, and counted German fighter planes landing and taking off at the rate of about two per minute. It was obvious that real trouble was brewing."

Another kind of trouble occurred—of a very personal nature. Seamans had planned to spend part of the summer bicycling through Europe with friends. Problems developed. Rheumatic fever appeared and left a temporary heart condition.

He returned to Harvard for his junior and (final) year. It was good to be back at his studies, back among friends. But his activities underwent drastic change. "Football, baseball, and crew were out. I had to have a good deal of sleep and lead a quieter existence than in my first two years of college. This meant more time for study—and an amazing thing happened. The courses, which were mostly in engineering, suddenly came to life for me.

"The teachers were outstanding. I took a course in aerodynamics from Dr. William Bollay, who later did much to put North American Aviation, Inc., in the Aerospace business. I studied mechanical engineering with Dr. J. P. Den Hartog. Den Hartog is an extremely gifted teacher, and I recall vividly the way he used the built-in responses of a cat to illustrate a difficult point: if you hang a cat by its four feet, upside down about

24 inches off the floor, then suddenly cut all strings, the cat will land on its feet. How does the cat do it? This is a very good problem in one type of dynamics. The cat must do something rather clever in order to spin around, because it cannot push on the string. By instinct, the cat will pull in one pair of legs, use the others to stabilize, use its tail, and twist. Thus, from the standpoint of conservation of angular momentum, the cat accomplishes highly efficient mid-air maneuvers to land right-side up."

Seamans was so impressed by Dr. Den Hartog's visual demonstrations in class that he employed the technique in a public speaking course he was taking. "One of the speeches I gave was on 'How Does a Baseball Curve When Going Through the Air?' I took ping-pong balls from my pocket and threw them out into the rather startled audience. I found it helped non-technical people grasp the physical effects I was discussing."

Though Seamans' fascination with engineering had constantly been increasing, even when he received his B.S. in 1939 he had not finally determined his choice of career. He had been prompted to work, perhaps too hard, to complete college in three years simply for the fact of the doing—not because he had set his sights on a specific goal. The trait, a most uncommon one, has served him well by establishing the habit of accomplishing the most possible in the least time.

A return of rheumatic fever dictated that Seamans spend much of the following year in bed. "During this time I was lucky to end up in the hands of Dr. Paul White, the doctor who was to take care of President Eisenhower. I remember when he first came to see me after I had been put to bed. I had a picture of the Matterhorn in my room. I had always hoped that someday I would climb it. I asked him whether he thought I could ever exercise again, thinking I probably never could. Dr. White said, 'It may take six months or a year, but there's absolutely no question about it—you will. In time, you should be able to live a normal life. And that's the way it has been."

That period of enforced rest for Seamans was a time of greatest unrest for the world. Turmoil bubbled in Europe. The rumble of Hitler's march into Poland sounded the beginning of World War II. "That winter," says Seamans, "with all of its ominous events, proved as educational a period as I have ever experienced."

In the compensatory fashion by which partial benefit will so often accompany misfortune, the necessity for rest allowed Seamans the time to sharpen the focus of his thoughts. "Though I would never wish anyone to have to undergo a long period of illness, it proved a decisive experience to me because I had the time and opportunity to read and to reflect. I actually had more opportunity to really talk with people, and to truly think, than one has in normal living."

Contemplation might indeed be termed the lost art of modern living. As men have more to think about, they have less time in which to do it.

In deciding his own future, Seamans considered carefully the ultimate aims. His illness had deeply interested him in medicine. Balanced against that was his long-felt interest in the field of engineering.

The roots of engineering reach deeply into the history of civilization. Until mid-Eighteenth Century the term applied specifically to military works. A new group, engaged in non-military activity, came to be termed "civil engineers." In 1828, the great charter of England's Institution of Civil Engineers defined the work as the "art of directing the great sources of power in nature for the use and convenience of man, as the means of production and of traffic in states. . . ."[4]

The first civil engineers assumed a wide range of responsibilities, but engineering followed the usual developmental pattern. Soon the whole became too great to be considered as one entity, and it was split into various fields of specialization.

The division pertaining to mechanical engineering assumed separate identity; its application at that time was directed in great measure to steam engines. As time went on, mining and metallurgical engineering were established as separate courses of study, as were electrical, chemical, industrial, and aeronautical engineering. Subdivisions of divisions appeared at a rapid rate.

No sooner has expansion fragmented an area than a premium is placed upon abilities to unify. Said S. E. Howland, Educational Consultant to the Dean of Engineering at Purdue University, "The need for men who can view the whole field of engineering, wide and complex as it is, as a single field of operation of relatively few basic laws and methods became increasingly recognized."[4]

Whatever the branch, the basics are constant; this is the view of Linton E. Grinter, Dean of the Graduate School, University of Florida: "Many engineers graduate into the management or administrative function in industry or government since their training and experience encompass the four essentials of handling men, money, methods, and materials."[4]

These four M's have expanded in the Space Age to dimensions surpassing all prior experience, and certainly beyond the imagination of Seamans in 1940. That summer he made his career decision by process of elimination—a medical career was abandoned after a course at Harvard in biology. "I decided after taking that subject that I would be better advised to stick with inanimate objects. Engineering came more naturally and easily for me than biological and chemical work."

With health restored, with the big decision made, Seamans plunged into graduate work at Harvard—only to have it upset by a friend's suggestion: "There's a place down the Charles River where they do a lot more engineering—it's called MIT." The idea nagged at Seamans until he paid a visit to the campus to see Dean Matthew Thresher.

"After Dean Thresher scrutinized my records, he said, 'Well, this isn't too bad—I think we could start you off here at MIT as an undergraduate.' I thanked him and told him I would remain with graduate work at Harvard. Then he produced a form, saying, 'If you will fill this out, indicate the courses you have taken, summarize the material, show what textbooks were included, and go around to the various faculty members here at MIT, you can see what credits they will give.' "

With the tally of his previous schooling in hand, he called upon the "executive officer" of the Aeronautical Engineering Department, Professor R. L. Smith. "When I told him I wanted to do graduate work in his Department, he said, 'Why don't you?' Then came the question of courses. It would take two or two and a half years to get a Master's degree—unless I concentrated on instrumentation and control, I was told. But I didn't even know what that was." Seamans was not alone in his ignorance. Not many did know of the specialty in that day.

The early-day aviators used intuition in their "seat of the pants" flying technique; it was likely more trustworthy than going entirely by the few and unreliable instruments upon their panels. As science took over from "spit n' chewing gum," and daredevils conceded that luck had limitations, a sound assessment of the airplane and its shortcomings pointed toward the development of reliable instrumentation.

"Jimmie" Doolittle (now Lieutenant General James H. Doolittle, USAF, Ret.) performed the first blind take-off and landing in 1929. Though the feat was tremendous, the methods of measurement were crude. While this famed flier was performing in the cockpit, a man with similar determination, Dr. C. Stark Draper, was expending his energies in the laboratory, improving the standards of instruments and extending their applications. During the decade of the 1930's, Draper's tremendously broad scientific knowledge, plus his imagination and energy, led to the formation of MIT's Instrumentation Laboratory. But research budgets were small, and indifference prevailed in commercial application to his advances. Only with World War II was the Laboratory allowed to develop at an accelerated pace when it became evident that there was immediate and grave need for advanced instrumentation.

Seamans was not clear about the nature of this general field when he entered MIT, and there was nothing orthodox about his introduction to the classes to categorize them as routine. Draper is not the standard image of the dignified professor. His physique and energy could more nearly be ascribed to a welterweight prizefighter. His speech is highly individual, and he uses colloquialisms of his native Missouri to color and accent certain points.

Seamans found himself participating in a class in which each member was intensely interested from the first day. "Draper gave excellent examples of everything discussed, and the whole subject started to come to life. I began to see the direct relationship between the work I was doing in college and a professional career. It was realistically pointed out to us that this would probably be a field of limited earnings—but that the expansion and potential of instrumentation were limitless."

The tangible contributions which Draper has made in such devices as the gyroscope have been tremendous. But it would be hard to say that they outweigh his contributions as a teacher, for among his former students are some of today's leading figures in astronautics.

Seamans details his impressions: "Draper is a wonderful teacher because he can relate background theory to the practical problem of getting a job done. In addition, he has the attribute of being a profound student of human nature. He understands his students, the people in his laboratory, anyone with whom he is dealing. He can be of much help to them because he grasps their motivations and their concerns."

Draper's teaching and Seamans' capability brought results. Although it had first been estimated that at least two and one-half years would be required for Seamans to complete work for his Master's degree, he accomplished all but the thesis in two semesters.

Draper inquired, "How would you like to get paid for working on your thesis?" So it was that Seamans found himself in the summer of 1941 as a research assistant to the MIT instructor, Homer "Barney" Oldfield, experimenting with equipment to test engine vibrations associated with aircraft. "It wasn't quite as impressive as it sounds," Seamans recalls. "We worked in a basement next to the place where garbage and refuse were collected."

Two weeks after Seamans became his assistant, Oldfield was called to active duty with the Army. Seamans inherited his position. At the age of 22, while still beginning on his thesis, he became a full-fledged instructor. "I recall how horrified I was," he states, "when I realized that as an instructor, I would have to go into a class and teach."

Draper eased the feeling of panic by allowing Seamans to assist him for the first month. After that, the young instructor was on his own, lecturing to groups who were taking experimental laboratory courses. "There is no question," he believes, "but that in the process of serving as an instructor, the teacher is instructed more than the class—I can vouch for that."

As war drew nearer the United States, the Navy instituted special courses at MIT for new enlistees. The purpose was fast, mass indoctrination.

"They came through in groups of 50 every six weeks. I taught a course in aircraft instrumentation about ten to twelve times during this period, going right through it, then repeating with a new group." But Seamans was not content merely to repeat the same course. He continued to change the presentation to find how best to put across the concentrated course which dealt with gyros, engine indicators, and navigation equipment, and included information for both operating and maintaining the equipment.

The fledgling teacher was presented with problems that demanded resourcefulness to solve. "Among the groups were people who knew a great deal about the subject. Sometimes they relished asking me tricky questions. If one of them started really harassing me, I would announce to the class that we were very fortunate in having in the class Mr. So-and-So who had a great background in this particular area. Then I would call upon him to give a few special talks on the subject. Always it turned out that the particular individual involved was very quiet from then on."

Despite occasional interruptions by obstreperous class members, most of Seamans' teaching experience was extremely rewarding—both for him and his students. One of Seamans' students at the time describes him as "the best teacher I ever had. He organized the material in a logical manner. He presented it in a straightforward, simple fashion. He was able to explain certain elements of the control theory, for example, that I had already studied in other courses, but he laid it out so clearly that for the first time I really understood what it was all about."

MIT's Instrumentation Laboratory held contracts to furnish equipment to both the Air Force and the Navy. Seamans volunteered to help on some of the projects, wanting to contribute to the nation's war effort. After working with Draper on Navy anti-aircraft fire control for automatic firings of 40-mm, 3- and 5-inch guns, he was assigned his own project—installing special equipment on shipboard.

"Draper just said to get the job done, and left me on my own unless I needed help. I had to ransack the Boston area to get parts for this special piece of equipment and get it assembled, then rent a car and drive to Bayonne, New Jersey, where the new aircraft carrier, USS *Bon Homme Richard,* was being outfitted.

"Even though the equipment I brought had been requested, those guarding the base questioned that I should even be there. After we gained entrance, the people responsible for outfitting the ship were most reluctant to install something additional, when the ship was essentially ready to go out into the fleet. We reached a stalemate. Then Commander (now Rear Admiral) Charles B. Martell arrived at the base, and ordered the equipment installed."

The piece of equipment was the target-acquisition gear for the Mark 63 anti-aircraft fire-control director, for use when targets had to be located by other than visual means. It was tied in with the ship's central control, and could automatically acquire targets in bad weather, or (in the case of a Kamikaze diving in directly) in the blinding angle of the sun, or it could be used effectively in a heavily smoke-obscured area.

The task of installation was not completed when the *Bon Homme Richard* set sail. Seamans, together with representatives from Sperry Gyroscope, Western Electric, and other affiliated companies, sailed with the carrier. For a week they cluttered the captain's sea quarters with wiring, using his bunk as a bench for their tasks. "We were crawling all the way from the ship's compass, which was down on the keel, up through the hangar deck to the director, which was up on top of the conning tower. It was about 500 feet of a difficult route. To the relief of all, especially the captain, it was completed and I was put ashore at Norfolk, clutching my oscillographs, wiring diagrams, and other miscellanea."

On Seamans' return to Boston, he was immediately sent out to repeat the process on the destroyer USS *Purdy*. The winter was so severe that the ship's commander, who was a Southerner, inquired if people really lived in Boston through choice!

Although Seamans worked on the Navy's fire-control directors, his principal interest came to be the A-1 gun/bomb rocket sight for the Air Force. Colonel Leighton I. Davis (now Major General, Commander of Air Force Missile and Test Center, Patrick Air Force Base) was then in the Armament Laboratory at Wright Field. Having received a Master's degree in Aeronautical Engineering from MIT following his training as a pursuit pilot, Davis was keenly aware of the nature of the equipment which fighter pilots needed. He was granted permission to establish a project at MIT in Draper's Instrumentation Laboratory to develop a gunsight. The resulting instrument was the Davis-Draper gunsight.

The scheme of operation by which this highly effective instrument was perfected has its amusing aspects in retrospect, for it is so vastly foreign to the formal manner today. The project team designed, fabricated, and installed the sight in a P-38 fighter in less than a year. After the sight was installed Colonel Davis flew the missions and observed, from his engineer-pilot perspective, what the technical problems were as he made attacks upon targets. He would return to the Laboratory in the afternoon. The project team would confer about the information which had been collected, make modifications as indicated, and ready the gunsight for another test the following morning. The process was repetitive but effective. The gunsight had reached such a state of perfection that it was ready to be placed in production by the AC Sparkplug Company when World War II ended.

Seamans explains, "Both the Navy and the Air Force equipment made use of the same basic element—the gyroscope. Much of the geometry and mathematics background was similar. Even though the gunsights functioned as intended, we came to the realization that one of the real problems in achieving intercept was the matter of keeping the airplane on the right course. For the system to function correctly the pilot would have to be given added help in the way of instrumentation.

"To determine the real limiting factors, Davis asked MIT to manage a Tracking Control Project, under the auspices of the Armament Laboratory of which he was chief. The Air Force provided a B-26 airplane for testing, and a lot of special electronics, and we plunged in to work. But we didn't even have a hangar at Bedford Airport, so our Southern pilot spent most of the winter sweeping snow off the wings."

A sub-contract was let to the Cornell Aeronautical Laboratory, Inc., of Cornell University. Dr. W. F. Milliken, who was assigned to the project, recalls, "My initial impression of Bob centered around his outstanding analytical abilities and facility with applied mathematics. I believe he could have made a substantial career for himself in this specific area without going on to the broader aspects of project administration and over-all research program administration. I am sure that Seamans was rated as one of Dr. Draper's most capable dynamicists, and this covers a sizeable range of specialties—from aerodynamics through automatic control and instrumentation dynamics."

Milliken adds, "It should be remembered that Seamans has published some very valuable contributions in connection with automatic flight control." Three notable examples are: *Recent Developments in Aircraft Control** presented before the 22nd Annual Meeting of the Institute of the Aeronautical Sciences; the article published in January, 1950, entitled *The Pulse Method for the Determination of Aircraft Dynamic Performance;*† and the paper, *Automatic Control of Aircraft,* published in the *Comptes Rendus des Journées Internationales des Sciences Aéronautiques.*‡

These writings were the partial culmination of the efforts that began in 1946 with the program to get fundamental information on aircraft and control-system dynamics. Seamans notes that basic questions were investigated mathematically and experimentally. "When you throw the stick to the left, how quickly does the airplane change course? To get answers to such problems, we moved the stick various ways by means of a special control equipment which we had installed in the airplane and measured the airplane response."

After a period of testing, the work came to a climax when the group was invited by the Air Force to transport all equipment to Wright Field and stage a three-day demonstration for industry. Two airplanes were involved

* Co-authors: Frank A. Barnes, V. W. Howard and Theodore B. Garber.
† Co-authors: B. P. Blasingame and C. G. Clementson.
‡ Co-authors: Joseph Bicknell, E. Eugene Larrabee, and H. Philip Whitaker.

—one serving as target, the other to be controlled automatically and fly an intercept course. The demonstration was staged over the Wright-Patterson Auditorium.

Seamans recalls his nervousness: "I will have to admit that we had not conducted this maneuver many times. As the airplanes approached, and the public address system blared out details, I hardly dared look up. But everything worked perfectly. I was thankful that the demonstration had come off in good order.

"Then, to my great consternation, several of the Air Force and industry observers came up and said they understood it was possible to fly in the airplane and really see how it worked. They wanted to see the pilot sit with his arms crossed while the airplane automatically flew intercept course with the other airplane as target.

"As I was about to reply that it could be arranged in the future—allowing us additional time for testing—they asked if the demonstration couldn't be arranged for that afternoon." Relates Seamans, with an attitude that is as nearly fatalistic as his nature will allow, "I said 'Yes,' figuring I could always take up golf, or fishing—so why not? We flew different groups all afternoon, and to our delight everything worked perfectly!" It is certainly to the credit of those who designed and built the equipment that it operated so well from the beginning.

Part of the abstract from one of Seamans' papers conveys much of his approach to the matter of aircraft controls: "In all cases, human beings must select and supervise the mission of the aircraft and must make command decisions when new information becomes available. It is felt that human beings can exercise judgment more effectively when they are relieved of routine operations, especially actions involving muscular fatigue and manual dexterity.

"However, the present trend toward supersonic speeds is introducing more violent changes in the aerodynamic loading of aircraft, especially in maneuvering flight. As a result, large hinge-moment variations are expected. In addition, the center of pressure shifts position with Mach number, causing significant changes in static stability. Consequently, equipment to position the control surfaces and to stabilize the aircraft in the maneuver desired by the human operator appears desirable. . . ."[5]

In retrospect, certain features about any development seem perfectly obvious. Yet it must always be considered that in earlier stages, these very elements are often obscured by the welter of detail. Points appear salient after some individual has had the knowledge and the wisdom to state these fundamentals.

"I first knew Bob Seamans when he became a member of one of the National Advisory Committee for Aeronautics (NACA) sub-committees," says Dr. Hugh L. Dryden. "Even in that casual acquaintance with him, I was impressed with his ability. He was working with Draper in the MIT Instrumentation Laboratory and was a professor during all that period.

"Today in NASA, he is particularly fitted for the position he holds not only because of obvious things, such as the ability to get along with people, but primarily because he has good judgment as well as a background of technical knowledge in research and development that enables him to understand problems relating to space."

Seamans has been with NASA only since 1960, but he went on record a decade ago with strong and positive views regarding space. At that time, conservative scientists considered space travel to be fantasy. But Seamans saw the possibilities and discussed them. "Globe Girdling Satellite Seen Within 10 Years," proclaimed a newspaper headline on December 12, 1952. With amazing perception, Seamans qualified this prediction by adding, "It depends largely on the world political situation."[6] While most who were giving such matters any thought were preoccupied with the technical feasibility of the accomplishment, Seamans pinpointed this foremost consideration. Had we not been subjected to competition from another nation, would John H. Glenn, Jr., have orbited the earth, and would we now be planning to send three men to the moon?

In 1952 also, Seamans was outspoken about the need of this nation to be vigilant in the manner of developing guided missiles. He compared the status then to a chess game, in which we could not actually know what our opponents were doing. He accurately "called the shots" on a need when he said ten years ago that one of the over-all problems in the missile-into-space development is that of coordinating the efforts of many specialists. He foresaw the need of a "systems man." This has materialized as one of the major elements in the management structure of space projects.

In that same period when Seamans was speaking of "way-stations" in space, where space ships might be built and launched, he was actively engaged in *Project Meteor*.

This Navy guided-missile project had been started right after the end of World War II. It was felt that fundamental work was needed on all of the individual missile systems—aerodynamics, propulsion, instrumentation, guidance, and controls. The Navy urged MIT to build up its competence and include this kind of effort in its research and graduate programs. By 1950, the Navy asked MIT to conduct an experimental flight program. A chief engineer was required to take responsibility for the system design and integration. Seamans was selected.

"Having been responsible for the development of several control-system applications to guided missiles, he was clearly one of the few men in that area who had a broad and practical grasp of the relation between the physical problems, the analytical problems, and the detailed hardware problems," says Dr. Allen E. Puckett, Vice President of Hughes Aircraft Company, Aerospace Group. The men first became friends at Harvard, where, Puckett recalls, "Seamans, with his usual vigor and alertness, very rapidly became one of the outstanding students in our classes."

Those qualities, and all others he could muster, were demanded in his triple duties as Chief Engineer of *Project Meteor,* teaching at MIT, and studying for his doctorate. In addition, Seamans bore the responsibility of having a wife and family.

During Seamans' illness, one of his visitors was Rosemary Merrill. When he was recovered, he called at the Merrill home to renew the acquaintance. There he met Rosemary's younger sister, Eugenia (usually called "Gene"). They became engaged on the Harvard-Yale week end in the fall of 1941, and were married the following spring. Seamans relates, "Gene is a very resourceful person, and by nature somewhat independent. She's an excellent housekeeper, and possesses a 'green thumb,' producing flowers wherever we are living. She also has a strong and active interest in community affairs."

Before undertaking his doctoral work at MIT, Seamans thoroughly discussed the matter with Gene. "We certainly realized that it was going to be a back-breaker for both of us. I felt that since my profession was engineering, I should be as well equipped as possible, and she absolutely agreed.

"Gene recognized that I could not do this to the exclusion of everything else. So she endeavored to provide me with counterbalance. She put her effort then, and still does, on making certain that I have other interests, including our family, community, and sports. Though at the time I haven't always agreed with her, she has been right each time with her suggestions."

When Seamans undertook his doctoral study, the household included three children.* The second child, Toby, weighed but 2 pounds at birth, and suffered a two-thirds hearing deficiency. Because of this he didn't have any comprehension of speech until the age of three. It has been a long pull, but with the extra care his mother gave him, together with instruction from a remarkable tutor, Miss Helen Patten, in addition to regular schooling, he has reached the point now that with a hearing aid and through his ability to lip read, one would not be aware of his deficiency. The headmaster of his school recently wrote Seamans, "John Glenn is not the only one to go into orbit—your son has just passed all his subjects."

* There are now five children: Katharine Arlaud, 19; Robert "Toby" Channing, III, 17; Joseph, 14; May, 9; and Daniel, 3.

The fact that Toby has done this well is, of course, due in large measure to the great effort of his parents. But during the year of Seamans' two-fold work of teaching and studying, the bulk of the responsibility of caring for all needs of the family fell to Gene. He recalls one of the countless smaller problems that arose during this period: "Quite naturally, the children wanted to come in and chat with me each evening. I didn't want to ignore them, so of course I chatted. But after each interruption it took me an additional time to regain concentration on my work. So, with time extremely precious, Gene put up a sign at my bedroom door which read, 'Daddy is working—please be quiet.' After that, they would come to the door, and I would hear them reading the sign aloud, but they wouldn't come in. When I finally finished my thesis, we made a great ceremony of burning the sign."

Seamans' doctoral work dealt with the problems of high-speed, high-flying, and high-performance airplanes—and particularly the control of these airplanes for military purposes. He did his thesis in the realm of theory, and he tied the theory to practice by flying airplanes and gathering experimental data. He worked out the theory of control of these airplanes, especially the control that worked in any position—whether the airplane was right-side up, upside down, or in a banked turn.

With such laborious effort, the "Doctor" in front of Seamans' name was attained. There were promises—because of the toll on his family, which concerned him the most—that he would never again involve himself in such an unreasonably heavy schedule. But whether the situation is that those who are most capable are most often called upon, or whether it is that those with conscience feel an inner obligation to assume all that they possibly can carry, the pattern varies but little throughout a career. Extrication from one situation merely leads to different responsibilities.

The automatic control of airplanes consumed Seamans' interest. He was concerned with the scientific aspects, and worked out problems of the mechanism. But his activity was not confined to the laboratory. He went on many of the testing missions himself and studied the proper design factors to put into the guidance equipment.

Draper recalls a phase of this developmental period: "Bob Seamans had the problem of making the control system for an airplane that would work under all circumstances. One of the problems was a puzzle: If you are to have an airplane that can be controlled and flown automatically from any position, it should be possible to connect a button in such a way that no matter at what attitude the airplane might be at the moment, if the button were pushed, the airplane would automatically turn to the correct course. So Seamans took off in the back seat of an airplane, and spent many hours having the pilot put the airplane in various attitudes. Seamans would then push the button to see which way the airplane would turn.

He was very dogged about this testing. He was a little pale when he finally came down, but he had proved that there was no problem."

Equipment to produce collision courses was an important phase of Seamans' activity. In whatever direction a target airplane might be flying, the control system was to set the attacking airplane on a course that would intercept it. When the apparatus reached the testing stage, it was installed in a B-25, and Davis piloted Seamans aloft. The target airplane, a C-47, would be a considerable distance away, but the B-25 would be guided so unerringly to it that Davis would have to seize the controls at the last instant and duck under the C-47. The misses were so close, and the "bump" from the air currents so severe, that the pilot of the target airplane quit his job! His action was really quite a tribute to the performance of the computer devices.

In evaluating the work that Seamans did with aircraft control, Draper says, "Seamans actually established the principles in guidance equipment which have been used since those days. He did indeed make a series of automatic control systems that became the prototypes for much of the high-performance control equipment that has been built since that time. This automatic control equipment really started the developments that later became guidance systems for ballistic missiles."

Utilization of automatic control equipment was being tested at the Naval Air Test Center at Patuxent River by Dr. A. J. Kelley, who then held the rank of Lieutenant. Whereas blind intercepts had previously been done on two-seat interceptors, Kelley was involved in the first project to see if one man in a single-seat jet fighter could use radar and computers to make a blind hit without ever seeing the other aircraft. Relative to this investigation, he made frequent trips to MIT to compare results with Seamans; mutual benefit resulted from the exchange of flight results.

As an adjunct to his teaching at MIT in the Aeronautical Engineering Department, Seamans set up a facility that was called the Flight Control Laboratory, involving about 100 people. There was diversification in the endeavors of this Laboratory. One project concerned guided missile work; another was a project for the Navy called *Sealegs*. "It was the Navy's first really successful experimental hydrofoil boat which utilized the active foil system," says Dr. W. F. Milliken, Jr. "Bob and his MIT group did the control work, whereas the basic boat was a project of Gibbs and Cox, the naval architects. It is now no secret that the behavior of the boat in rough water was remarkable and certainly influenced the Navy's thinking on this type of craft. Bob has mentioned that from a technical standpoint he considers this one of the most interesting projects with which he has been connected."

In November, 1955, the Radio Corporation of America announced that Seamans would head its Airborne Systems Laboratory in the greater

Boston area. This facility, an engineering laboratory for the development of specialized electronic fire-control systems for military aircraft, was scheduled to be in operation by the following February.

While still heading the Flight Control Laboratory and teaching at MIT, Seamans actively participated in setting up this new organization. Seamans screened and hand-picked the staff of scientists, engineers, and technicians. He completed the preparation by overseeing the equipping of the division with the latest and finest research test devices and computing instruments.

Seamans' years at MIT had brought him more than a splendid education—it had provided him with the challenge of stimulating receptive young minds in his teaching. In addition, there was tangible accomplishment from the laboratories in which he worked. So it was with genuine reluctance that he finally resigned his post at MIT to plunge into the full-time, full-energy occupation of heading the new RCA facility.

Says the company's Vice President, A. L. Malcarney, "Dr. Seamans is a tireless worker, and he built a strong *esprit de corps* in the Engineering Department for which he was responsible. His high technical standards and his perceptiveness in assessing the technical competence of others contributed greatly to his success with RCA."

It might be said that a man is known not only by his friends, but by his rivals. "There were a number of occasions on which Bob and I were friendly competitors in proposals on several particular military systems. Among all the competition in these various endeavors, I was most anxious to understand the general approach taken by Bob and his group, as it would very likely be the most ingenious and provide the closest competition." So says Dr. Allen E. Puckett, Vice President of Hughes Aircraft Corporation.

John Rubel relates, "I was working at Hughes at that time, and I recall that people used to talk about trying to hire him into our company. His reputation was outstanding in his running of the RCA Laboratory which was competing with us for certain Air Force contracts. So later, it was most interesting for me to meet him and get to know him." Rubel now holds the position of Assistant Secretary of Defense, and works cooperatively with Seamans on matters which have overlapping interests between NASA and DOD.

The select Air Force Scientific Advisory Board has numbered among its members many of the nation's leading men of science and engineering. In the spring of 1960, the Board met at Colorado Springs. "Professor Courtland Perkins, a good friend of mine, was then Assistant Secretary of the Air Force for Research and Development. He asked me if I would consider taking a job with the government. I enjoyed working for RCA but I had always wondered how governmental agencies were organized and managed. So I told Court yes, that I would definitely be interested in exploring the possibility."

Word spreads with an osmotic quality around the nation's capital; it seemingly seeps across club lounges or edges down the top of conference tables. In this instance it reached the alert ears of a man who—as administrator of NASA—matched possibility with need and placed a long-distance call to Seamans.

"I was surprised when a voice over the phone said, 'This is Keith Glennan. Are you going to be in Washington in the next couple of weeks?' I replied that I hadn't planned to be. Then he said, 'I'd like to have a chat with you. I'll get on the next plane to Boston and see you at the Statler Hotel for dinner tonight—if you are free.' Before I could offer to travel to Washington to see him, it was arranged."

At a quiet corner table, the two men talked. NASA soon would be in need of a new "general manager," with the title of Associate Administrator. Richard Horner, who then held the position, had agreed to serve the government agency for only one year.

There was no necessity to spell out that this was one of the most exciting jobs in the country. There was ample challenge to lure Seamans. Determined to investigate thoroughly, but quickly, Seamans went to Washington, D.C., had a lengthy discussion with Glennan and Horner, then called upon Perkins to clarify his understanding of NASA–Air Force relations. Two days later he informed Keith Glennan that he would accept the job.

Appreciating that it might be a long while before he would again have an opportunity to relax, Seamans took his wife to Maine for ten days of sailing on the *Serene,* an auxiliary yawl which he owns with Sam Batchelder and his brother-in-law, Caleb Loring. Being an accomplished yachtsman, a member and former Commodore of the Manchester Yacht Club, Seamans ranks sailing and skiing as favorite sports (as do his family).

Gene Seamans was completely in accord with the change, for she understood that the position with NASA was where her husband could best serve. Also, living in the nation's capital was not new to her. She had many happy memories from her childhood, much of which had been spent in Washington, D.C. Neither were ties with government strange to her—her father had been in the consular service in Spain, where she was born.

But government has grown more complex and responsibilities for key men have grown enormous in recent years. In NASA, to a greater extent than with any other agency, the areas of work are radically new and little understood by the general public. Career risks are great. Criticism is frequently leveled from one quarter or another. Such is the cold, analytical viewpoint.

It may well be asked: "Why do men accept these positions? Why do they leave the security of key industrial positions, the comfort of homes and surroundings that have been established throughout many years, and enter the arena of government work?"

"It's obviously a combination of things," believes Seamans. "One thing is the national and international aspect. It is important, with the kind of importance that one associates with a great national effort in which we must succeed or find our country in serious trouble. If Russia should pursue space diligently while we did not, the Soviet Union would achieve a dominant technological role. This could mean that mankind could have a somber experience that could last a very long time. There is no question in my mind that a Communist leadership in space, well ahead of our own capability, would be used to bring the world to its knees.

"Thus we have the heavy responsibility to assure that the United States maintains scientific and technological leadership, now and in the future."

In another vein, he says, "There is also a very real fascination for me in this particular job. It arouses a keen sense of curiosity, a sense of wonder at what is happening. Can these space feats really be happening? Will we actually go forward to even greater feats next week, next month, next year, and after? Can it be that this tremendous chapter in human history is fact, not imaginative fiction?"

Comprehension and appreciation of this great new development in mankind's story will continue to grow, Seamans believes. "In a recent sermon, Dr. Theodore Ferris* of Trinity Church in Boston compared this to other great happenings—one being Columbus' voyage, and the second being the Lindbergh flight. He indicated that as far as he was concerned, the advent of space flight was the greatest of the three, because until this point, we were in effect confined to a two-dimensional universe."

So important does Seamans regard the matter of a full cognizance of space that he says, "I am involved in discussing our agency's program in a variety of forums—to groups of engineers, professional people, teachers, and businessmen. True, people are excited by an astronaut orbiting the earth, but often they are not clear on the reasons for such a flight. They don't fully see the advantages of the space program. It is an important part of our job to indicate what the real benefits will be."

In one such address, in the fall of 1961 before the Technical Association of the Pulp and Paper Industry, Seamans stated: "Four major reasons underlie the national decision to marshal the resources required for leadership in space: (1) the quest for scientific knowledge; (2) direct and immediate application of satellites into operational systems; (3) the technological advances and stimulus to our economy that will emerge from the

* Sermon preached by the Rev. Dr. Theodore P. Ferris, Rector, in Trinity Church, Boston, Sunday, March 4, 1962.

space effort; and (4) the risk of delay in our space competition with Communism."[7]

Says Dr. Hugh L. Dryden, "Everyone connected with NASA gets some share of this speech-making in addition to presentations of plans and programs to Congress. But this is not primarily Seamans' concern. He is occupied with internal matters, with day-to-day management, decisions, operations."

It is our President, John F. Kennedy, who determines our nation's over-all space policy—just as he is responsible for everything that the Administration does. Space being but one of his many responsibilities, he designated the Vice President, Lyndon B. Johnson, as chairman of the National Aeronautics and Space Council.

Dr. Edward C. Welsh is Executive Secretary of this group, which has as its members: the Administrator of NASA, James E. Webb; the Secretary of State, Dean Rusk; the Secretary of Defense, Robert S. McNamara; and the Chairman of the Atomic Energy Commission, Glenn T. Seaborg.

In April, 1961, the Vice President reviewed our long-range space goals, and asked the Secretary of Defense and the Administrator of NASA to meet to see if a common program could be evolved which would satisfy both the nation's civilian and military needs. An attitude of determination prevailed at a meeting which involved not only Webb and McNamara, but also included the following: Roswell Gilpatric, Deputy Secretary of Defense; Dr. Harold Brown, Director of Research and Engineering for the Department of Defense; his Deputy, John Rubel; Abe Hyatt, Director of Office of Plans and Program Evaluation, NASA; and Seamans. Dr. Hugh L. Dryden had planned to attend but he was prevented by bad weather following Commander Alan Shepards' *Mercury* flight. At the end of the meeting, Rubel and Seamans were charged jointly with producing a report summarizing the conclusions of the meeting.

This report would have to represent the distillation and culmination of many studies that had been going forward in the preceding months in both the DOD and NASA. The two men established a close and effective working relationship. Rubel is forthright in giving Seamans great credit for the success: "He is very intelligent and catches on to things rapidly, understands what he is talking about, and knows what it is he doesn't understand. Secondly, he has the caution and the precision that you associate with a confident decision-maker. He doesn't make hasty judgments or overcommit himself prematurely. On the other hand, he is not dilatory in making decisions. Once he has made up his mind, he knows why and can explain to others and stick with it.

"Seamans, also, is the kind of person with whom you can have quite a large degree of rapport. You have the feeling you are really communicating. It is necessary to be able to understand what our agreements are, and also what our disagreements are. There have been many occasions to have both, for many problems have arisen between the two agencies. NASA could have taken the attitude that an expanded space program was their responsibility, for their appropriation since the end of the Eisenhower Administration had almost doubled, whereas DOD in the first approximation has not received anything for expansion. But their attitude was one of complete cooperation."

Continues Rubel, "I don't know of any other instance in which two agencies have gotten together as our two agencies have, and successfully laid out joint plans for undertaking programs which in the aggregate are probably going to cost more than 20 billion dollars for their completion. But it was with the recognition that these were very big programs, that they did imply very large future expenditures, and that they would have much to do with our posture in space in the future, that we realized the necessity for close cooperation in planning and implementing our programs."

As one result, NASA and the Department of Defense worked out a general approach for accelerating the national space program. Comments Rubel, "The situation was unique. Both DOD and NASA have the authority to initiate space programs. Both agencies have very substantial resources and the capability to utilize funds that have been appropriated by Congress. So it was clear that unless we had some kind of an integrated approach to this, there was certainly a very serious danger that DOD on the one hand, and NASA on the other, would pursue parallel and overlapping and duplicating courses to the national detriment rather than to the national betterment. So our desire was to see how, with this expanded program, we could get together and lay out a single integrated launch-vehicle program."

It was agreed that neither agency would proceed with a new vehicle without concurrence of the other agency. The purpose, obviously, is to insure that the United States will develop a family of boosters adequate for both civilian and defense needs—from the very small one, the *Scout,* up to the very large one, the *Nova.* Without careful coordination, it is conceivable that both agencies, for example, might develop a launch vehicle for placing 5000 pounds in orbit, and neither would develop one for placing 10,000-pound payloads in orbit. Each takes into account the other's immediate and potential requirements in the planning. By having NASA scientists meet with DOD scientists to consider the individual specifications as one entity, it is possible to arrive at a solution that best satisfies our total national requirements.

President Kennedy advocated a broadened, accelerated space effort, and Congress endorsed it. Says Jay Holmes in his book, *America on the Moon,*

"Congress, in the three and a half years since *Sputnik,* had talked itself out and was impatient to act. Further, the President's declaration had put the nation's prestige at stake."[8] With this "green light," NASA and DOD began marshaling the technical and other resources which the vitalized program requires.

Repeatedly, Seamans has referred to the booster rocket, the *Saturn,* as the "pacing item" in *Project Apollo.* So with the accelerated space program the first item that came up for serious consideration was the big booster.

Webb and McNamara had agreed that DOD and NASA should not both pursue the development of solid boosters. There still remain technical problems to be solved before solid rockets will be well suited to manned space launches. But solid rockets have special advantages to DOD —one being their almost instantaneous firing capability. Therefore, the Air Force is proceeding to develop them as military weapons, with the expectation that as the technology comes along, they will become applicable to manned space flight.

Though NASA and DOD agreed upon the objectives and management procedures, much detailed planning remained. To accomplish this, the Large Launch Vehicle Planning Group was established under Dr. Nicholas Golovin with Dr. Lawrence Kavanau as Deputy. Included in the group were people from NASA Headquarters, representatives of some of the NASA centers (such as the George C. Marshall Space Flight Center, of which Dr. Wernher von Braun is Director), Aerospace Corporation, Air Force, and Navy.

A host of questions had to be resolved on the big boosters. What shape should they be? What size? What were individual requirements for the specific missions? After three months of continuous study the group had laid out long-range plans for our large launch-vehicle undertakings. The agencies were able to say that they had arrived at an integrated program—a most reassuring accomplishment, considering the complexity of the areas. Though, naturally, the plans are subject to change in event of technological progress or altered objectives, they have set very important patterns for a long time in the future.

Says Rubel, "Not only did the group determine parameters for the development of the large boosters, but they also concerned themselves with every phase of the launch operations. Their recommendations included not only what could be done, but also what ought to be done, considering cost, considering reliability, considering the requirements imposed by test programs, considering the missions that would be accomplished, considering what had to be done to man-rate a launch vehicle, considering whether the method was earth rendezvous, direct ascent, or lunar rendezvous. All of those figured in their analysis, and all were criteria against which different proposals were measured."

Even after the committee had determined launch procedures, the matter of launch facilities had to be considered. The laying out of Cape Canaveral to accommodate these mighty boosters presented many problems. Should a second row of launch pads be installed behind the present row, and overflights be made? If it were thus feasible to double up, many additional launch pads could be put into the area.

Studies are required to answer questions of this type. These studies must involve the individuals in the field who have technical and operational experience with this new technology. Consequently, Major General Leighton I. Davis, the Commander of the Atlantic Missile Range, and Dr. Kurt Debus, Director of the NASA Launch Operations Center, worked closely together resolving these issues. These two widely experienced men and their associates delved into great detail reviewing NASA–DOD launch requirements, possible site locations, and launch procedures. As a result, it was decided to enlarge Cape Canaveral by acquiring 70,000 acres of adjacent land, and to maximize the use of this new land by permitting overflights wherever operational criteria permit.

With an objective honesty that works to his strong advantage, Seamans appraises, "This whole matter of joint reviews and planning between NASA and DOD is an interesting and complex matter. Decisions will not be perfect as long as human beings are involved, but there is a great effort being made by all parties to find satisfactory solutions. DOD is an extremely large operation, and NASA is getting larger. To tie these two together is a difficult management task." During the past year, a significant understanding has been reached between the two agencies.

Once the control, structure, and management are instituted so that individuals can work efficiently, the matter of enlisting their interest is certainly no problem. In fact, it has been just the opposite. So great has been the dedication to our country's manned space-flight program, that NASA has been confronted with a most unusual situation—how to keep people from working too long and hard. Says Seamans, "It has been a real problem on *Project Mercury* to keep people from working to the point of sheer exhaustion. Sometimes they work 70 and 80 hours a week. We find that people can work 50 to 60 hours a week without becoming exhausted, when they are interested. But when one works up to 80-hour weeks over a long period of time, it can have serious consequences.

"I think that one of the very significant reasons for this is that *Project Mercury* has been so much in the public eye. Everybody recognizes that it is a very important program. NASA, DOD, and industry people are willing to put in this kind of effort because they see that it is necessary." The fact cannot be overlooked that much of this inspiration comes from the example set at the top of the NASA organization. Long hours are standard practice for Webb, Dryden, Seamans, and other key personnel of the agency.

NASA's individual space projects are divided between four major program offices in this manner:

The Office of Space Sciences, directed by Dr. Homer E. Newell, is investigating the scientific aspects by means of unmanned satellites, space probes, sounding rockets, and balloon flights.

The Office of Applications, directed by Morton J. Stoller, is responsible for space advances with direct benefit—developments such as the communications satellite, the weather satellite, and the navigation satellite.

The Office of Advanced Research and Technology, headed by Dr. Raymond L. Bisplinghoff, is exerting all effort to further the "state of the art" in such areas as propulsion, space vehicles, electronics, nuclear systems, and an area of NASA's interest that has been overshadowed in recent years—aeronautics.

The Office of Manned Space Flight, directed by D. Brainerd Holmes, has charge of the famed *Project Mercury,* and the follow-on projects, *Gemini* and *Apollo.* In addition to the training of astronauts, this office oversees the development and operation of space-craft, launch vehicles, and ground facilities.

Each of these offices reports to Seamans. His method of working with the directors is explained by Holmes: "Seamans and I hold meetings—recently at the rate of one a week. Also present are D. D. Wyatt, Director of the Office of Programs, and Albert F. Siepert, Director of the Office of Administration—two offices that have to do with the administering of all details of the four major program offices.

"Seamans demonstrates in these meetings very outstanding management techniques, and a very thorough understanding of problems—both technical and administrative. He never forces the issues until he has heard you out and understands exactly what you are trying to do. He is free in expressing quite frankly his judgment of the situation, whether it's in agreement or not. I think the way he operates in that small gathering exemplifies a type of really creative leadership, which is perhaps one of his strongest points. We take up personnel problems, not only within Headquarters but in the Centers. We discuss the status of our contracts. In a technical area, we discuss the current status of our systems engineering, where we stand on various projects."

The one ever-present, inescapable element that pervades all segments of the space program is *time.* When? How soon? As the seconds tick by, it hammers at the individuals who are accomplishing these feats. Says

Holmes, "Within this Office, we report on *Project Mercury,* and on *Project Gemini,* the two-man space capsule. But on *Project Apollo,* it has not been possible to come up with a detailed schedule for the lunar expedition until the completion of our mission analysis, until we really know where we should place our emphasis. Now that a prime mode has been selected, we will be able to schedule and cost the tasks necessary to meet our objectives."

The Office of Tracking and Data Acquisition, headed by Edmond C. Buckley, is a support operation to the program offices. It is the function of this office to operate worldwide networks of receiving and transmitting stations, providing communications with manned and unmanned space craft.

All of these offices are located at NASA headquarters in Washington, D.C. The administration, funding, and decision-making on the projects rest with this echelon in the nation's capital. But the facilities of NASA extend to nine field centers located throughout the United States. Of these facilities, which also report to Seamans, he comments, "The major reorganization that has taken place within NASA in the past year has not materially changed these centers, but has added two that support individual offices: the Launch Operations Center at Cape Canaveral, headed by Dr. Kurt Debus, reports to the Director of Manned Space Flight; and the Test Support Office at the Pacific Missile Range, under the direction of William H. Evans, reports to the Director of Space Sciences."

The technical direction for the projects is provided from these field centers, but the major portion of the actual work is performed by industry —to the extent of an estimated 90% in 1963. A reasonable fraction of this is given to small business, both in the form of direct contracts from NASA, and sub-contracts from major industry. Over 4000 separate organizations have been involved in *Project Mercury* alone.

One of the great strengths of America has been our country's mass-production capability. At the outbreak of World War II, the brilliant mathematician, Dr. John von Neumann, made involved computations at the Institute for Advanced Study in Princeton as to the probable outcome of the conflict. The answer confirmed his belief that though the Allies started slowly, the massive industrial strength of the United States would bring them victory.

However, "This valuable capacity to mass-produce automobiles, or refrigerators, or television sets provides a capability that fits in quite well with military requirements," says Seamans, "but it does not answer NASA requirements. It is the individual precision workmanship that is important in our projects."

Individual. The word embodies the key to the success of almost every endeavor, under practically every circumstance. Some of our failures in the launching of multi-million dollar equipment have been traced to some minor component of minute cost. There is no whole. There is only the sum of many pieces. The standard of that sum can be enormously difficult to raise, yet can be lowered devastatingly by one slip.

"The conclusion is inescapable," says Seamans, "that for the years immediately ahead we have set ourselves tasks in space that are worthy of a great nation, but are tremendously demanding. In carrying them out the problem of reliability is a matter of major concern."

Our singular success with manned space shots is outstanding. However, Astronaut John H. Glenn, Jr., in testimony before a Congressional committee following his orbital flight, warned that we must be prepared for some failures as we continue our programs. "Just a few days before Glenn made that statement," Seamans comments, "he had gone through the experience of thinking that his space capsule was disintegrating on re-entry into the atmosphere, as bits of flaming debris flew past the window. So remarks from him about the element of risk entailed carried a most sobering connotation."

Project Mercury has had one great advantage in this matter of reliability —the booster vehicle, the *Atlas* rocket, had undergone extensive testing for the purpose of its original creation, as a weapons system. In the next manned space programs, the vehicles involved will be new and proof of reliability assumes an even greater importance. The *Saturn C-1* is the first vehicle created especially for space missions.

Under Dr. Landis S. Gephart, Director of Reliability and Quality Assurance, a program of intensive study is being pushed forward to analyze meticulously the degree to which redundancy, engine-out capability, manned monitoring, and control should be utilized in the booster vehicles. Not only must performance standards be greatly increased, but they must be accomplished in shorter time—if we are to adhere to the timetable established for our lunar landing.

States Seamans, "We are applying rigorous requirements to all design and testing procedures of our large launch vehicles and space craft, and in addition are giving careful consideration to man's role in enhancing the over-all reliability. We know that a human pilot onboard not only can make in-flight tests, but also in-flight repairs. We have had striking examples of this in missions of NASA's X-15 rocket airplane which has been flying to the fringes of space and has achieved tremendous speed.* In at least eight out of dozens of X-15 flights to date, flights would have failed without a pilot in the cockpit to correct malfunctions of equipment, instruments, or power plant. In at least as many other cases, if X-15 mis-

* Major Robert White, USAF, piloted the X-15 to an altitude of 314,750 feet on July 17, 1962, thereby qualifying as an astronaut. Joseph A. Walker established the speed record of 4159 mph in the rocket airplane on June 27, 1962.

sions had been unmanned, we would have obtained no information because either instruments or telemetry failed. The X-15 pilot, however, was able to land with valuable flight information recorded by his own senses. This experience was corroborated in Colonel Glenn's flight when, upon failure of the automatic yaw control, he manually controlled the vehicle in yaw during the last two orbits."

Seamans emphasizes, "Man's judgment is valuable for certain on-the-spot decisions. He can diagnose equipment troubles and shift to another operational mode. He can control the orientation of the space craft in orbit and during entry into the atmosphere, as astronauts Glenn and Carpenter demonstrated. But how effectively can the astronauts steer the space craft toward rendezvous with another vehicle? Can an astronaut visually judge position and speed precisely enough for rendezvous and docking?

"Scott Carpenter trailed behind his *Aurora 7* a balloon with sections of different colors. By viewing this balloon in tow, and later when it was released, he gained information on the extent to which the pilot's observations can help.

"John Glenn obtained information on the appearance of the horizon from space. Scott Carpenter photographed the horizon with a variety of filters. The data will be of great value to the Instrumentation Laboratory at MIT, which is developing the guidance system for the *Apollo* space craft."

As a step in developing the capability for the lunar mission, *Project Gemini,* the two-man space craft, will remain in orbit for a week or more to study the effects of prolonged space environment on men. It will also test the rendezvous and docking technique—in which two vehicles are brought together in space. The plan is first to place an unmanned craft into orbit, then to launch the *Gemini* vehicle in the same orbit, and through intricate maneuvers, join the two. In this Lunar Orbit Rendezvous (LOR) approach, the *Advanced Saturn* could be used as the launch vehicle, since the total payload could be put up in segments.

However, if LOR does not prove feasible, another means will be employed. This would entail launching the entire space craft, together with the rocket power necessary to return it from the moon to the earth. For this alternate approach another booster rocket even more gigantic than *Saturn* will be required. This is *Nova,* on which studies are now being conducted.

The technological requirements for space hardware are quite beyond any previous concepts of design and manufacture. "There is grave and immediate need," Seamans reveals, "for engineering groups that can design new types of propulsion systems, develop experimental models and flight models, and ultimately produce reliable engines that we can use repeatedly. The process is difficult. It is not handbook engineering—

it is basically creative engineering with good understanding of shop practice. Quality control is also an important factor, because although production-line quantities are not required, the first model certainly must be made so that it can be reproduced. This entire area confronts us today with some of our toughest problems."

The second grave need, Seamans feels, is in our scientific capability. "The work now being performed in Newell's Office of Space Sciences is a reflection of what I mean by the scientific capability. It is the fundamental research needed to understand the laws of the universe. Scientists of this office are searching for many answers: What are the relationships between the sun and the earth? What effect does the sun have on the earth in terms of weather and radio communications? How can we better understand solar flares? How is energy transmitted from the sun to the earth? Is there life on other planets? Some of these areas, we can see, have direct and immediate effect. Others, at the moment, appear somewhat esoteric, but undoubtedly will have greater significance when we know more about them."

However the need is categorized, knowledge and specialization are required. It is Seamans' belief that the person who not only completes a normal college course, but who continues his education to the doctorate level is today the one who has a most unusual opportunity for advancement. Additional benefit is in the reward of knowing he is performing a worthwhile service.

Seamans is heartily in accord with the close liaison that NASA is establishing with a growing number of universities throughout the nation. Through this activity, the unique demands of space research and development are being integrated into curricula. Examples of this relationship are in those which NASA's Langley Research Center has established with the Virginia Polytechnic Institute, William and Mary College, and the University of Virginia.

"Each of the three schools has projects underway that tie in with NASA's research programs at Langley. By tie-in, I mean that they offer courses that our people, while still working on the job, can take in the afternoons or evenings. When these employees approach the time for their residencies, we then provide them leave from their NASA duties to go to the university full-time and work toward higher degrees.

"Some of our staff members conduct courses and seminars. In addition, we assign appropriate research work to universities—in some cases even assist them in setting up the facilities they need."

By these and other active ways NASA endeavors to help meet some of its own demands for outstanding and well-trained personnel. It is recognized that these must indeed be met if the United States is to attain its lofty goals in the exploration of space. Not only must this nation pursue these aims because they are a scientific challenge, and the greatest opportunity that could exist for expansion and progress, but we must in a most practical sense recognize the link that has formed between scientific feats and prestige. It is a fact of international life today that technology plays an important part in the balance of power between nations. A nation's capacity to perform tasks in space is regarded as an index to its strength in carrying out its global policies.

It is no coincidence that Premier Khrushchev proposed shortly after John Glenn's space triumph that the United States and the Soviet Union pool their efforts. The United States has been making such proposals for several years, and there now has been reached a preliminary agreement for cooperation in certain areas of space research. Though these seem limited, this must be regarded as an important first step.

The United States has long had the finest working arrangements with other foreign nations; we have ground tracking stations operating in Africa, Australia, the South Pacific, and Mexico. Further cooperative activities were inaugurated in the spring of 1962 when *Ariel,* the first international satellite, was launched from Cape Canaveral. It carried scientific instruments supplied by the British National Committee for Space Research. NASA and the Swedish Committee for Space Research have come to an agreement for the launching of *Nike-Cajun* rockets from sites near Jokkmokk to investigate the bright night clouds at those northern latitudes.

The tasks ahead in space exploration are mighty enough that there seems promise of unprecedented unified scientific effort between peoples and nations. Men will have advanced to a degree that cannot be calculated mathematically if they learn to work together toward astronautical achievements!

Lunar landing of men is now assumed. It will require incalculable effort, for it is a stupendous undertaking, but it will be done. Seamans is thinking beyond the first accomplishment, to the era that will follow: "There certainly will be explorers who go to the Moon and stay there for extensive periods. Eventually there will be research facilities on the Moon just as we now have scientific outposts at the South Pole."

Enthusiastic about lunar opportunities for scientific study, Seamans believes this: "The Moon offers a wonderful base for scientific measurements. It is a stable platform from which observations can be made of the sun and the stars that just cannot be made from the earth—because of our turbulent atmosphere, for one reason. We also may gain a better geophysical view of the earth by inspecting it from the vantage point of the Moon. I foresee a lunar scientific base as the next important step beyond manned landings on the Moon."

To perform this exploration, to live upon the surface of the Moon and contribute a major chapter to the advancement of mankind will require scientists and engineers. Astronaut-pilots alone cannot perform this job.

As such a staggering adventure begins to assume the status of reality, Seamans reflects, "Ten years ago, I was asked if I would like to fly off into space. I said I would. Now, as the goals grow closer, I realize only those who can contribute the very most should be permitted this experience. All members of the crew must have a significant role, or you cannot afford to take them. You cannot include anyone who might in any way put an extra burden on the others, because in an emergency—as you can well understand—the situation is such that each member of the team must make a major contribution." Thus Seamans places the most stringent requirements on this mission, which well he might.

There are also stringent requirements on scientists, engineers, technicians, and others required to design, fabricate, test, and launch *Project Apollo*. Seamans may, on occasion, still mentally project himself into the space vehicle, but the load he carries as the "general manager" of NASA is too excessive to be boosted into any lunar trajectory.

The requirements for this position are both unique and overwhelming: superb technical understanding, complete management capability, an aptitude in dealing with people, a keen eye for detail yet a broad over-all grasp, utter realism, and enormous vision. The extent to which Bob Seamans fulfills each of the exacting requirements earns him highest respect and cooperation of rare proportions from the countless ones with whom he works. The achieving of our national goals in space is given impetus by the kind of leader who engenders such a feeling of purpose in others.

Seamans' expectation of the future is underscored by a quiet but deep excitement: "I am convinced that we shall be able to utilize space for the service of mankind. I believe that, in the long run, our ambitious adventures in space will repay us many times for all the work, funds, and daring that we can devote to it!"[9]

REFERENCES

1. *1962 NASA Authorization Hearings,* before the Committee on Science and Astronautics and Subcommittees Nos. 1, 3, and 4, United States House of Representatives, 87th Congress, 1st Session, March 13, 14, 22, 23, April 10, 11, 14 and 17, 1961.
2. Kennedy, John: *Special Message to the Congress on Urgent National Needs,* May 25, 1961.
3. *Harpers,* 65:888–894, November, 1882.
4. *Encyclopaedia Britannica,* Chicago, London, Toronto, William Benton, 1957.
5. Seamans, R. C., Jr., Barnes, Frank A., Howard, V. W., and Garber, Theo-

dore B.: *Recent Developments in Aircraft Controls,* New York, Institute of Aeronautical Sciences, January 27, 1954.

6. *Daily Evening Item,* Lynn, Massachusetts, December 12, 1952.
7. Seamans, Robert C., Jr.: *The Role of Industry in Space Exploration,* Address before the Sixteenth Engineering Conference of the Technical Association of the Pulp and Paper Industry, Washington, D.C., October 18, 1961.
8. Holmes, Jay: *America on the Moon,* Philadelphia and New York, Lippincott, 1962.
9. Seamans, Robert C., Jr.: *Space—Friendly or Hostile?,* Address before the Richmond Chamber of Commerce, Richmond, Virginia, January 12, 1961.

Creator of the amazing maser which can illumine the moon

CHARLES TOWNES

Charles Townes gives three explanations for the name "maser": an acronym for Microwave Amplication by Stimulated Emission of Radiation; or, since the technique has now been extended over a wide range of frequencies, Molecular Amplification by Stimulated Emission of Radiation; or, yet another meaning readily appreciated by those enmeshed in our space effort, Means for Acquiring Support for Expensive Research!

Those definitions are tremendously revealing about the man and scientist, Charles Townes. Not only does he have the creativity to have invented the maser, but he has the human qualities to jest about this outstanding work. In his approach to the monumental work that he does, there is zest, and the word "fun" keeps recurring in his description of what science means in his life. Townes speaks of his work on masers as "the experiences and evolving ideas of an individual in the midst of his own hobby."[1]

Comments Dr. S. O. Morgan, who was co-head of the group with which Townes worked at Bell Telephone Laboratories, "Charlie had a genial and friendly manner of talking about physics. He was seldom dogmatic or emphatic. He discussed his work with an attitude of exploring the possible explanations. I always knew, however, that he had thought matters through before discussing them with me and this was his way of telling the facts to a boss who knew less about them than he did."

Professor Ali Javan of the Physics Department of the Massachusetts Institute of Technology, a friend and associate of long standing, has made these thought-provoking observations about Townes: "Charlie Townes is certainly one of our top physicists. However, I am not as enthusiastically impressed by a man who happens to be highly creative and gifted unless his qualities as a human being are just as outstanding. I find Charlie Townes to possess praiseworthy qualities in his human relationships. I have witnessed how many times he has gone out of his way to help others, to get involved and suffer with problems of his own students and his friends in a way that very few people are capable of doing."

Javan continues by imparting this insight into the scientist: "Together with this kind behavior and mild appearance there is at the same time an extremely aggressive personality in his scientific endeavors. This is indicative of his drive and tremendous energy. He works very hard. I remember a time when he used to start his working day at four in the morning and continue almost without interruption until ten in the evening. He is in the midst of one of the highly competitive professions, and hardly allows anyone to step in his way of getting things done—though he is most graceful in the manner in which he accomplishes his goals."

An evaluation of just what Townes has contributed is conveyed laconically by the President of AT&T when he says that "without the maser we do not see how we could even hope for high-quality space communications."[2]

The uses to which this radical new device may be put are incredible. "A pencil-thin beam of light that has the potential to transmit the contents of a multi-volume encyclopedia in the wink of an eye. . . ."[3] Another description terms it "a beam of light a million times brighter than the sun."[4] Townes indicates the fantastic directional qualities and lack of diffusion when he says, "If one puts a series of masers on the Moon and shines them toward the earth, they could be made to cover regions as small as 100 feet."[5]

Several hundred different companies and laboratories are now occupied with diverse applications of the maser technique—such as communications, welding (where surfaces will be touched only by a beam of light), surgery (which can be performed with great speed and precision), the measuring of distance (with an accuracy never before approximated).

Previously, light sources have had upper limits on the amount of energy they will give, dependent on temperature. But in the radio-frequency range there have existed no limits. From a technical standpoint the maser has brought the optical and infrared regions much closer to radio. The effect is to free light from limitations!

Townes explains how the principle works: "The maser utilizes energy from excited molecules or atoms, which is delivered to an electromagnetic field. Excited molecules or atoms have excess energy. They deliver this energy to an electromagnetic field, thereby increasing the energy in the field and providing amplification or oscillation."[5] In emphasis of the maxim that the best things are the least complicated, he adds, "These devices could well have been invented thirty or more years ago. We had all of the theory and they are inherently very simple and use familiar techniques."[5]

The maser was conceived in 1951 by Townes—who is scrupulously careful to credit those whose theories, discoveries, and research laid the scientific foundation for his accomplishment. His attitude extends beyond the sharing of credit with colleagues. Townes possesses a deeply felt conviction that he is an instrument through which scientific contributions might be made; he regards it as a privilege for this greater force to work through him.

Though deeply serious in this belief, he does not carry it as a burden. He reflects, "I think I would emphasize that one does not regard the fulfilling of a potential as simply an obligation—but also as the means of gaining the most pleasure out of life. I think these two things are very intimately connected."

His wife, Frances, helps to clarify his use of terminology by saying, "Charlie talks a great deal about 'fun,' but he does not use the word as I would. He means an intellectual excitement he gets out of his work. He feels an impatience with life—there is so much to do, so much he wishes to experience, that he never wants to waste a minute. He has tremendous self-discipline."

Townes explains, "My problem is to get rid of as many distractions as I can. That's why I gave away the patent rights on the maser." This invention is certainly one of the most commercially promising products of this exploding scientific era, and that is part of the reason Townes made this rather amazing gesture. "If the maser were going to earn a small amount of money, I could have used it. But it will likely earn a very large amount of money, and I really would not need that. So this way I get a small fraction of the income, and the bulk of it goes for research."

Did he consult his wife on this decision? Rather absently, Townes says, "I suppose I did, because I do consult my wife on the most important things. I'm not sure how important I considered this. My primary feeling was that I didn't want to become involved in a lot of business affairs, in having to negotiate with companies on royalties, and having to decide how much should be charged and then take care of the money. I felt it much better to concentrate on things that I regard as being more fun.

"The second consideration was that the Research Corporation, to which I assigned the royalties, is an organization whose aims I very much approve. It is a non-profit group that uses all its income for support of scientific research, and to which many academic people turn over their patents."

The Research Corporation was set up originally by Frederick Cottrell, the famous inventor of the Cottrell Process, used mostly for precipitating dust and smoke from air. Grants, directed principally to universities, were formerly an exceedingly important source of funding for such efforts. With the advent of large-scale space research, the larger universities are now receiving extensive backing from government contracts, and are not as dependent upon such grants. But the Research Corporation is still doing extensive work in supporting research at smaller institutions.

"The work I did at Columbia University to develop the maser was paid for by the government. But neither the Government nor Columbia was interested in patenting the idea, so I patented it with the provision that the government have free use of the idea." Townes' primary interest from the beginning was in sharing the information. He discussed the remarkable maser concept most freely with everyone who came into his laboratory—both before and after it was successful; he also published the information.*

"It is a great pleasure to see other people grow interested, use, and extend one's ideas," he explains. "Most scientists are happy to see this. It makes the field develop more rapidly and pushes the science further. A few centuries ago, there was a certain kind of protectiveness. For example, some scientists and mathematicians used to discover things and keep them secret. They would have challenging contests with fellow scientists, saying 'I know how to solve this problem, and I don't believe you do!' The secret would be kept for some time. But that era has passed."

Though Townes makes concerted attempts to keep himself free of involvements that will detract from his pursuit of science, there is one "distraction" which he considers important and does not avoid—that of serving the government in an advisory capacity. Six of the ten committees on which he now serves are governmental, and he has just completed terms on four panels of the United States Air Force Scientific Advisory Board.†

Committees have been categorically castigated, yet they continue to be formed. "I don't know of a much better way of running things. The

* In order for a patent to be valid, it must be submitted to the patent office within one year after publication of information necessary to reproduce the patents.

† Townes is Chairman of these governmental groups: Professional Committee, Institute for Defense Analysis, and the Department of Defense Committee on Weapons. He is a member of the following: Visiting Committee, National Bureau of Standards; President's Scientific Advisory Committee Panel for Strategic Weapons; National Academy of Sciences Advisory Committee on Strategic Exchanges; Department of Defense Ad Hoc Group on Optical Masers.

difference between a good and a weak committee is the people, including all of their characteristics—how much time they are willing to put on it, how they want to go about things, whether they function in some depth or just skim the surface. Primarily, benefit derives in direct ratio to how deeply the members can delve into the problems.

"Though always questionable, I think committee work is usually worthwhile in some way. There is no way of describing the general operation of committees, because it differs so much. In a very large number of government committees, the people are already engaged full-time in other positions, and they simply give their time with no stipend involved—not even traveling expenses. Since such work is part-time, one is torn between trying to do a good and useful job, and spending an inordinate amount of time. I spend about one day a week on government activities."

Among these high-level duties, Townes has the honor to serve as a consultant and a panel member on the President's Scientific Advisory Committee (PSAC)—the distinguished group of which Dr. Jerome Wiesner is Chairman. Townes' most recent service is on Panel for Strategic Weapons. The average citizen is both vague and confused as to the manner in which the wheels of government turn. Usually only total budgets and final conclusions are reported in the newspaper stories. In tracing the development even the biggest and broadest decisions must start with people saying, "What do we do?"

Townes relates such an instance: "The White House wanted advice on the relative merits of strategic weapons—especially for budget purposes. They asked what kinds of weapons should we really have, how many, and what should one do in planning for the future? PSAC is a group with expert technical training, of course, so their procedure is to make most careful examination of technical parts of these questions, then write a report to Wiesner; he then excerpts the portions he feels are important and passes them on to the President. I have met with the President once in a meeting of PSAC to discuss the general role of science and the government, and particularly scientific and technical problems in relation to international affairs."

Townes points out that PSAC works on some military science, but also on a wide variety of other kinds of questions which have scientific content. "For example, we may be requested to look into the longe-range technical possibilities of making fresh water from salt water—finding and helping decide what kinds of research should be performed.

"PSAC might study the housing problem, to decide if there are new techniques that could help cut the cost of housing—especially in the lower-cost group. It might worry about sudden emergency problems such as what reasons are there, pro and con, that one should consider atomic bomb testing.

"There are less urgent things, such as whether we are spending the right amount of effort in various directions of science technology, are they organized properly, how can people best be trained in science?" Thus does this select group of scientists attack an enormous variety of questions, carefully sift them to decide which are the most pertinent and to which they can best contribute.

The judgment and capability of Townes have been summoned recently by the Institute for Defense Analysis (IDA).* He is Chairman of the Professional Committee whose function is to examine what IDA does for the government—the quality of the technical work, and of the people—and to determine how it can be improved.

This present part-time contribution to IDA is not Townes' first service to the group. In 1959, when he was at Columbia University, the President of IDA, Dr. Garrison Norton, asked Townes to consider moving to Washington and joining the group full-time for two years. Although the assignment involved a complete change in his plans and the uprooting of his family, he felt he must accept this opportunity to serve the government. His only proviso—one he felt highly important, so that he might retain touch with current scientific developments and activities—was that he be allowed to return to Columbia one day a week to continue work with his graduate students.

A man of unusual capacity learns to measure his time, to judge where it can be spent best for productiveness, to be miserly with every hour. There is so much that such a mind is capable of producing that the moments cannot be dissipated; even the usual social activities must be curtailed greatly.

Says Mrs. Townes, "I enjoy entertaining and sociability, but we have always limited ourselves, because Charlie is too busy doing important things. This certainly is not a criticism, for I recognize that this is the way it should be.

"But from a wife's standpoint, it does require some adjustment to live with a man whose work is so absorbing, so important to him, and takes so very much of his time. The compensation is that the hours we do spend together are so much more meaningful. I may be frustrated, because this man never seems to make mistakes—and I feel I make so many; I may be angry, yet that dimension doesn't exist in him—he never gets

* "IDA arose from a 1955 contract between the Office of the Secretary of Defense and the Massachusetts Institute of Technology to supply qualified personnel for the Weapons System Evaluation Group (WSEG). MIT undertook to initiate the work and to organize an association of universities to take over the contract. Five universities, California Institute of Technology, Case Institute of Technology, Massachusetts Institute of Technology, Stanford University, and Tulane University, later formed IDA with the assistance of a Ford Foundation grant of $500,000 for working capital."[6]

angry; but I am never, never bored. It took me ten years of idolatry, five years of adjusting, but now it is fine."

Townes is fortunate in having four daughters* to complete the family side of his life. All share the quality of great adaptability—a necessity considering the family has, to date, lived in many homes all over the world. Not only have they traveled to other countries, but they have truly partaken of the opportunities afforded. The two older girls, Linda and Ellen, spent July and August, 1955, in a summer camp in Sweden—one which presented most severe living conditions and less than abundant food. The eldest daughter went abroad for the summer of 1960 to work in a kibbutz in Israel, and was the only Christian girl in this communal agricultural camp. The summer of 1961 she spent in an international camp in Switzerland. All of the Townes girls have been guided into broad and unusual interests.

Townes' attitude in encouraging his daughters' accomplishments characterizes his attitude toward women. "I think one of the greatest wasted resources in this country is the potential professional efforts of women. The rearing of children is, of course, a very crucial role which must occupy a certain period. But there are many years when women aren't busy with children, and that is when many of them could contribute quite a lot, if somehow our society had the right kind of habits and attitudes about women working.

"I don't think it is possible for a woman, under normal circumstance, to rear a family and at the same time be an outstanding scientist. I do think, however, that women can function in less demanding positions. Science needs a lot of people besides those who work the most intensively —it needs a lot of supporting help. In scientific laboratories, we are very short of the type of skilled assistance, for example, which is rendered in dentistry by dental technicians. It is the kind of job, I believe, that can be done fairly effectively on a part-time basis, and a means whereby women can make a definite contribution to the exploration of space."

Much discussion has taken place throughout the nation about the relative importance of space. This has occurred at curbstone gatherings, in political groups, in scientific conclaves, and much of it certainly has transpired at the top level of government—within such groups as the President's Scientific Advisory Commitee. Everywhere the same basic questions are posed. Should we spend so much money on space? Shouldn't we first solve problems on earth? Should we send a man into space, or can't instruments do the job just as well?

One of the most intriguing viewpoints to be expressed in the space

* They are: Linda, 18; Ellen, 15; Carla, 13; and Holly, 9.

debate has come from John D. Williams, of the Research Council of the Rand Corporation. In his paper, *Anyone for the Moon?,* this leading scientist and thinker puts the lunar expedition in a new frame of reference when he says: ". . . its conspicuous weakness is that it is not really ambitious. While it will doubtless turn out to be distressingly difficult, the prognosis is that the mission will in fact be accomplished, perhaps in nearer to five than to ten years, and perhaps by the Russians before the Americans—someone has remarked that we may have to fight our way to the Moon. Now, goals must be in front, not in back; and this one will soon be in back. There it cannot provide the long stress needed to develop our intellectual resources. If it is put in back by the Russians, we will be frustrated as well as goal-less. On the other hand, if the goal were more ambitious, say to explore the solar system, or beyond, our activities in the next decade would be little affected, but our attitudes would be greatly affected. We would not run out of goals. And we would not be shattered if the Russians beat us on the first short leg. Moreover, we would be less likely to be beaten on the next leg."[7]

Townes also favors a most vigorous space program, saying, "I think the amount of scientific information we'll get from this venture will be enormously large. The intellectual stimulation and the stimulation to our technology will both be exceedingly important. In addition, the impact on our culture and the world generally will be very great. I feel there has been a growing realization of all these things throughout the country—even a growing acceptance among the more conservative scientists."

While it might be expected that the general public would not at first have grasped the full meaning and potential of the space developments, it has been perplexing indeed that the group whose whole orientation is toward the furtherance of science should be less than enthusiastic about space.

Townes explains it this way: "A large number of scientists have been overly conservative about the possible importance of space because it is characteristic for scientists to react carefully about all new developments. Part of the reason is that they have a certain sense of responsibility, a feeling that they must not make statements which are loosely backed or which might mislead the public. It is also because they tend to be a bit tighter in their reasoning, whereas a person who is not a scientist has no compunction about imagining the things that might be attained."

There are two issues involved in the controversies regarding science that should be clearly distinguished. One deals with purely technical capabilities, limits, and feasibility; the other is the interpretation of certain scientific feats, in the area of the sociological implications. Yet, when two scientists debate an issue, it is generally assumed they are always dealing with the area of scientific fact.

Townes stresses that the real issue of such discussions should be clearly recognized: "An example of what I mean is the debate that has been taking place between Dr. Linus Pauling and Dr. Edward Teller. Pauling feels we must cease all nuclear testing; Teller feels we must continue.

"One finds throughout the country that people are terribly puzzled and somewhat upset by this, for they have the impression that these two experts hold opposing ideas. Therefore, they reason, no one really knows what the effects of radiation are. This is not the case. If one only listens carefully to what is being said it is perfectly clear that this is not a disagreement on the scientific conclusions—in fact, the two men are in remarkably good agreement. The disagreement is only in the relative weight of the alternatives." So it becomes a matter of whether all people should be endangered a little by radiation from testing, or to what extent all people are endangered by the possibility of attack if we curtail testing and sacrifice expanding our nuclear capability.

Townes points out, "So it is not scientific facts that Teller and Pauling are disputing, but human values and risks. This is an issue that anyone has the right, and the obligation, to consider. But most people do not grasp that the real area of the dispute is mostly outside of science."

The burden, in this case, rests with the general public to try to understand properly—not with Pauling and Teller to cease their discussion. "I see no reason why scientists can't have views, like other people. In fact, I think scientists must participate in society. But it must be kept in mind that they, too, can make mistakes, and their words should not have tremendous weight in spheres outside of science."

Just as scientists should bear the responsibilities of any other citizen about non-scientific matters, so should the average person today grow more knowledgeable about science, since it has become such a force in our socicty. Townes believes, "People must grow to understand scientific thinking and be willing to examine scientific results; they must learn to raise intelligent questions about these results, so they can make appropriate judgments. As an example of the level of scientific sophistication needed, I think today's informed person should be able to understand a magazine like *Scientific American*. This will probably require a modicum of mathematics; but it will bring them to an appreciation of what science can and cannot do."

To make "Science Appreciation a favorite avocation or hobby would greatly aid development. Townes feels: "I think the acceptance of scientific knowledge depends upon familiarity. Looking back, you learn that gravity was a very abstruse concept in the days of Newton. This great scientist, himself, felt that it was a difficult idea, and that it could not be really right, because it implied action at a distance—two things attracting each other at some distance with nothing in between.

"Though it took a long while for the idea to be accepted, everybody now regards gravity as a normal, natural thing—even though no one really understands it yet. By a slow process, developments and discoveries have come to be ingrained in our societies, and people have come to feel at home with new ideas. Now, with such remarkable things happening, the 'pace of acceptance' must be accelerated.

"A general understanding can be gained with no more effort than we customarily concede as appropriate to keeping up with literature, music or art—for developing an appreciation during school and continuing an interest through adult life. I am convinced that an effort of this order can make quite a large difference in the popular understanding of science, its effect on our everyday decisions, on our political decisions—even on civilization."

In recent years science has pervaded nearly all of society. In the previous generation, science had little connection with the general aspects of living. "But potentially it had great importance," says Townes, "except that then it was more latent. If it had been properly understood at that time, perhaps we would be in much better position today.

"The interaction between science and our society has been developing with increasing rapidity since about 1940. With the onset of the war, there was great increase in the effect of science on our national destiny and on the destiny of the world. Scientists became very much involved in trying to help the government. The two most important and extensive fields of activity were radar and the atomic bomb.

"Since then, there has been a steadily increasing involvement between government, society, and science. The Space Age represents another big step, which furthers inexorably the government's large-scale support of science. Increasing pressure to attain scientific and technical superiority, for economic, military, and other national reasons, has continued to push us in the same direction."

The matter of that direction has become an item of grave concern to many people. There is a degree of fond recollection of another time, and a reluctance to face the reality of now. "This time, like all times, is a very good one, if we but know what to do with it." Those words are no less true than when first penned by Ralph Waldo Emerson.

It would be the easy and simple solution to say that the world has become so complex that we cannot know what to do with it—so we shall leave the matter of decisions to those with specialized knowledge. That kind of rationalizing should not separate us from the privileges that surround free people. The fact that highly talented men such as Townes are exerting their full efforts toward solutions does not lift any of the load from individual shoulders. To let others face the problems is shirking.

To hope that answers will come without effort is fantasy. To think that we can wait until tomorrow to face the issue is madness.

The months, the weeks, even the hours are crucial, when it is grasped that men now circle our earth in 90 minutes. The old standards must give way to a new concept of time. We need all the brainpower we can muster, and need it quickly. Townes proposes giving thought to an altered curriculum for outstanding young men and women—both to the nation's benefit and to their own benefit.

"I feel it would be a wonderful advantage for bright students to get through school at least two years earlier. The ones who continue with graduate study—working for doctoral degrees, in particular—have a very long period of education ahead of them, and it's quite important for them to get through while they are still young and have energy and enthusiasm.

"These youngsters, who are more able and more interested, can go somewhat faster than others, especially in the grade schools. I don't think students are very stretched intellectually in the public schools through high school. I don't mean that they should work so hard that they have no time for any other activity, but on the average I think the intellectually oriented and able child is not moving ahead as rapidly as he or she should. There's a tendency to want to keep them with their age group and not separate them from the other students.

"I can only think of what the added two years would mean in their working life. Not only would they have that much more time in which to advance, but the entire spirit and pace would be enhanced. They would be capable of more, because they would be stimulated all along the line, hence more interested and more efficient in learning. Many students have reached their mid- or late 20's by the time they complete there Ph.D.'s, and they are getting tired of school. By finishing sooner, they would end up with a great deal more drive, and with a feeling of real excitement about starting their careers."

The times have brought another trend which is a consideration: "Many of the students are now married by the time they complete university training. This can become a very distracting element, especially if they begin rearing a family. Let them finish with education sooner, move into interesting work, and they are better able to take on the obligations of a family."

In the instance of Townes' own education, his parents allowed him to skip the seventh grade. With that advancement, his sagging grades were raised. They climbed even higher when he reached the stimulation of college work. Since both parents were actively interested in natural history, there was always an inclination toward science. "My father grew up in an age and a place where there wasn't much science, so he studied law and became one of the leading attorneys in Greenville, South Carolina. In the present day, I am convinced he would have become a very excellent scientist. Mother had enough interest in natural science to put up with the caterpillars my brother and I brought into the house!"

Such encouragement and the warm atmosphere of the 20-acre farm home produced two scientists. (Henry Townes, Jr., the older brother of Charles Townes, became an entomologist and is now in a research position at the University of Michigan.)

"I remember home as having a great deal of intellectual interest. One of the things I think was of great importance was my father's habit of always making information available to us. When there was a discussion about something, he would never drop it without checking the facts in one of a large number of encyclopedias and dictionaries. I think he bought every set that was on the market."

Dividends on such a background were great when Townes entered Furman University. He worked extremely hard—but not on studies, which he did without effort: "It was the extracurricular activities that kept me so busy. I was a Scout Master, was on the swimming team, in the school band, a reporter on the newspaper, was doing a good deal of collecting in my natural history hobby, ran the museum at the school, studied voice, sang in the church choir, and a few other things."

This tremendously active student took a heavy schedule of courses in many different subjects, all of which have proved of value. But it was in his sophomore year at Furman that the revelation and the turning point came, in his first exposure to a physics course. "The essential thing that made me decide upon physics as a career was its logic and its more beautiful structure—to me, at least—than chemistry or biology. Physics makes reasonably clear-cut assumptions in a logical sort of way. Mathematics is, of course, also very logical; but I have always been more interested in the world around me, so I was not inclined toward pure mathematics."

Concurrently with his degree in physics, Townes earned a degree in modern languages. The ability to read French, German, Spanish, Italian, and Russian has materially aided his pursuits. Although currently there are splendid services available which translate foreign scientific papers and abstracts, they do not completely fulfill the need.

He adds, "I think beyond this, the ability to speak and read modern languages has a good deal more importance than just the reading of technical literature, in that they introduce one to a country and a culture. I have always regarded this as quite interesting and valuable. It opens one's ability to learn a good deal more, once you know the language and feel a little bit at home in it."

By the time Townes entered Duke University for graduate work, his brilliant intellect had matured. Full concentration was funneled into physics courses, earning him an M.A. in 1937.

Throughout his years at Furman and Duke, Townes had paid his own way. "I got a scholarship for $100 a year—which in those days was a good deal of money. Also I tutored, I sold apples, I taught in the laboratory, and did almost every other thing under the sun, including teaching kindergarten one summer. For graduate work, I had wanted to enter one of the big schools. Furman was practically unknown in physics. But I could get a scholarship only at Duke, which had not at that time gained any wide reputation in physics. After getting my M.A., I again tried, but could not get a scholarship to the California Institute of Technology. So I scraped together enough money to get to Pasadena anyway; my father gave me the money I had saved on tuition at Furman, and I managed to exist for one term until Cal Tech gave me an assistantship."

Though Townes relates in this experience a certain disadvantage in attending a small and relatively unknown university, he points out that there are also advantages. "I think in many ways the small schools are very good for students, since they tend to prevent overspecialization. A student in a larger school may complain that he is graded in a very severe way, has strong competition, and may end up 20th in the class with a B average —whereas, if he had gone to a small school he would have been first in the class. He thinks this would help in getting a scholarship. But actually I think that aspect evens out, for when a student is applying for graduate work, it is borne in mind that schools grade differently and have different scales of excellence. So I think it doesn't make too much difference except when the school is as small as Furman, where I was the only physics graduate for the year."

Dr. Dean E. Wooldridge, President of Thompson-Ramo-Wooldridge, Inc., relates, "Charlie Townes and I almost went to Cal Tech together, but not quite—I graduated about a month before he arrived. He fell heir to my research project. I had done a thesis on *Separation of Gaseous Isotopes by Diffusion* and had built up a monstrosity of equipment involving large numbers of glass mercury pumps, miles and miles of glass tubes which I had put together with great difficulty." Dryly, Wooldridge adds, "I finally got my Ph.D. degree because I managed to get my tubes free of leaks and get a vacuum in the system—I did a little more than that, but not much."

It was equipment that had unique physical properties for separating gaseous isotopes from one another, and concentrating them; then it made many measurements to learn something about their various properties. The powerful techniques of modern nuclear physics had not been invented at that time, and the matter of separating and concentrating isotopes was difficult and most infrequently accomplished.

But with this equipment, Wooldridge was able to increase concentration of one of the isotopes of carbon with respect to another one, then nitrogen, then to make various types of spectroscopic measurement. It was even seen that the separated isotopes could be bombarded with high-voltage protons, and new things thus learned. Townes carried on the work, using various materials and getting many types of measurements. For that period of development, his doctoral thesis was an advanced document: *The Separation of Isotopes and the Determination of the Spin of the Nucleus of Carbon 13.*

Shoots spring only from seeded soil. The remarkable accomplishments of Cal Tech during World War II with *JATO* and other rocket units were having their beginning during Townes' term at the University. "Frank J. Malina and Martin Summerfield were students involved in the early experimentation. Martin related to me," Townes recalls with amusement "that a professor in the Aeronautics Department gave them instructions not to let the word leak out that Cal Tech was working on rockets. It wasn't secret at that time which was before the War—it was just that rockets had been so discredited over the years that it would give Cal Tech a bad name."

Upon receiving his Ph.D., Townes had planned to go to Princeton University for post-doctoral work on a National Research Council Fellowship. But a representative of Bell Telephone Laboratories visited Cal Tech, and Townes was persuaded by a professor to talk with him. "I was asked to fill out an employment application. I wasn't really interested, and scratched out several of the answers, so it ended up a very messy blank. I asked for another to copy it, but the man said not to bother.

"Soon after, my professor got a phone call from the head of the Laboratory, saying my qualifications looked good, but it was the worst looking blank he had ever seen. My professor reassured him that I was neater with my work, so I was offered a job.

"Though jobs were very scarce and this was an extraordinarily good one, it was only at the strong urging of several professors that I accepted—I still wanted Princeton. When I finally started work, I was amazed and delighted. Physics research had always been the most fun in the world for me. Whereas before I always had had to scrape together the money to do it, suddenly I found I was being paid to do it!"

Bell Laboratories' Physics Research Department was headed by Dr. Harvey Fletcher, and Townes was assigned such projects as thermionic emission and secondary electron emission, in the Physical Electronics Section of which Wooldridge was in charge. Though the two men had never met, the fact that they had "shared" a piece of equipment at Cal Tech made it seem cause for celebration! "We felt we had something of a coincidence going, since Charlie was following along in my footsteps at the time," says

Wooldridge. "The work we were doing was interesting, but short-lived. Some time before Pearl Harbor, it became necessary for both Charlie and me to beat our plowshares into swords.

"Overnight, we were designated experts in airborne electronic computers. At that time we had never heard of airborne electronic computers —mainly because at that time there were none. But what did exist was a ground-based electronic computer that had been developed at Bell Laboratories, which was called the M-9 gun director. For many years there had been mechanical gun directors, but this was the first that was electronic—a combination of vacuum tubes, potentiometers and amplifiers designed to be used with an anti-aircraft gun to control its firing. It had been so highly classified that Charlie and I did not know about it until we were called in and asked to develop something similar for airplanes."

The first unit developed was for aiming torpedoes dropped from the air; about the time it was finished, it was determined that the Army Air Corps would no longer have jurisdiction over this phase of combat. A second unit was developed for use in bombing and navigation with radar. As that was about to go into production, specifications were changed to a more advanced version. The unit which fulfilled those requirements was then considered too complicated, being nearly as elaborate as the radar.

Many years were required before the idea of using very complex equipment in military installations was accepted. But the last system, the APQ-44, was adopted, finally, at the close of the War as standard equipment and was in use for many years. Townes spent five years in this engineering developmental type of work.

E. T. Mottram, now Director of the Submarine Cable Laboratory, Bell Telephone Laboratories, makes this appraisal: "The efforts of Townes and his associates resulted in a series of radar bombsights which became standard in bombing aircraft and completely modified the techniques used during the later years of the War period." He conveys the image of the man in those days by saying, "Townes was an earnest young man with an exceptionally keen mind and an intense interest in science. Serious beyond his years and intellectually alert, he easily assumed a place as a leader of technical people, many of whom were years his senior.

"Townes was always supremely confident that once a natural phenomenon was understood, it could be turned to use. He never felt nature to be a perverse force, but only misunderstood. Doubtless it was this continuing effort to understand, and to make order out of knowledge, that permitted him to achieve distinction in applying natural phenomena. His natural intensity led to long hours in the laboratory and continued application at home. In spite of his drive, however, he seemed to have achieved a nice balance between technical activities and home interests and felt satisfaction in seeing his children living normal, uninhibited lives. I think of this as a period in Townes' career during which he was maturing, learning to work with people with lesser intellects, working in a field where he felt a sense of urgency and responsibility. It was a wartime period when he set aside his major interests."

Wooldridge, too, has memories of Townes' efforts at that time: "Charlie did the work very well. He knew nothing about it to begin with, but his ability was such that it did not take him long to become a very competent electronics engineer. He worked at it with diligence and good humor during the War, as everyone did, but it was definitely not the work that he ever would have chosen.

"Certain things were always very apparent with Charlie. One was that he had set goals for himself. You always had the feeling that here was a fellow who had decided what he wanted to do with his life, and he intended to stick with that course until it led to something successful. I don't think Charlie ever did anything in any offhand fashion—he would sit back and decide things on a long-range basis."

The concerted research efforts of wartime activity produced many innovations and opened a multitude of channels to scientists. One that particularly intrigued Townes emerged from radar—microwave spectroscopy. This analytical tool held great promise in the study of atoms and molecules. With Dr. William Shockley and Dr. S. O. Morgan jointly heading the department, there was formed at Bell Laboratories the Solid State Physics Research Group. As a chemist whose field was dielectrics, Morgan was assigned the supervision of microwave spectroscopy. He recalls, "Charlie promptly turned all his pent-up interest in physics in this direction. At Bell Laboratories, people of his caliber have become directors or even vice presidents. This would have been his lot in time, but he wanted to be a physicist. The senior-scientist ladder, which is being developed to provide the equivalent in prestige and rewards for the scientist as for the administrator, was scarcely considered in his time here.

"But after two and one-half years with our group, Charlie—knowing that he had what it takes—decided that the best place to bring it out was a university. Also, having more ideas than he could develop himself, he turned to the university as the place where graduate students could work with him to develop these ideas while they learned physics. So although I was very sorry to see him leave to accept an offer from Columbia University, I realized that what was a loss for Bell Laboratories was a gain for physics."

Since the founding of the School of Pure Science in 1892, Columbia symbolized a special prestige to scientists—including Townes. The campus also represented an attitude and an atmosphere that Townes desired, though he in no way depreciates his stint with industry. "I gained a great deal from my work with Bell Laboratories, in strengthening my knowledge of electronic techniques in particular. This I used and capitalized on after the War, so that it did help me a great deal in doing physics. In fact, so many physicists went into electronics work during the War that the period following saw a great burst of electronic applications in physics research."

Arriving at the Morningside Heights campus on January 1, 1948, in the midst of a record-breaking snowstorm, Townes resumed the type of research he had been performing at Bell Laboratories, the study of molecular structure and nuclear structure. Soon results were evident. "One of the exciting events," he recalls, "was when we found the spectrum of the first free radical in microwave spectroscopy. At that time it was quite exciting, for it seemed an important discovery with great potential. Another notable time was when we got the first spectrum of molecules at high temperatures. This also opened up quite a new field which I found very promising, and in which we had considerable success thereafter. But I dropped it after a while, because there were still more interesting things to do."

Of all the uneven distributions that exist, there appears no greater disparity than in the matter of brains. Men such as Townes, whom Wooldridge terms, "obviously one of the smart ones," fairly burst with ideas and activities. These men speed through life with both desire and application at full throttle—yet there is never enough time to develop the multitude of ideas that they constantly generate.

The circumstances and setting in which Townes conceived his most remarkable idea seem so dramatically stereotyped that they could have been plotted by a hack novelist! While sitting on a bench in the early morning hours admiring the azaleas in Franklin Park in Washington, D.C., the great idea of the maser seized Townes. Scribbling on the proverbial "back of an envelope," he calculated for a few minutes, then realized that he had found the answer to producing waves in the millimeter and submillimeter range. (In 1945, microwaves of about 5 millimeters in length were the shortest produced.)

Townes and many others of the scientific community had applied thought to conquering this frequency range, with no previous success. But the inspiration that came to him in the Park had supplied the key—for the creation of these short waves, atomic and molecular resonators would have to be employed. In that moment Townes realized what had diverted him from this obvious answer: it was the thermodynamic argument, implying equilibrium, which stated that molecules could not radiate more than a blackbody.

Eager to prove his theory, he presented the idea to two graduate students at Columbia and suggested they carry out the experiment; they were reluctant to devote time to it, fearing it would fail and thereby lose them the doctor's degrees for which they were working. Townes then discussed it with another student who was working toward his doctorate, J. P. Gordon, and with a post-doctorate associate, H. J. Zeiger; they immediately shared his enthusiasm for the possibilities. Thus was the idea which led to the remarkable maser first put into motion.

After two years of work in the laboratory on this approach, Townes was visited by two of his distinguished colleagues, who urged him to cease his ridiculous efforts to develop a molecular oscillator; they felt he was wasting government money, since the activity was being funded by the Signal Corps and the Office of Naval Research.

But no dissuasion diminished Townes' belief in the concept. After a year, Zeiger moved to Lincoln Laboratory, but Gordon remained at Columbia and persisted.

In honesty, Townes admits, "Trying the maser at all looked like a great deal of a gamble, and we worked on it for about two and a half years—which is a fairly normal time for a difficult experiment. We were never sure it would actually work, not because we weren't sure of the theory, but rather we weren't sure that we could get the right conditions for it to work.

"Finally, there were indications that it was close to working. In this state of expectancy, Jim Gordon and I started talking a great deal about what could be done with it, what its ultimate significance would be. We envisioned great potential, but there was plenty of practical doubt about just how far it could be developed.

"One December day in 1953, I had momentarily pushed the thoughts of the maser out of my mind and was concentrating on the graduate seminar that I was conducting, when Jim burst into the classroom to break the news—the maser was oscillating!"

So fresh was this triumph that there was not even time to list it on the program of a meeting of the American Physical Society in Washington, in the spring of 1954. With a deep sense of achievement, Townes appeared and reported on his experiment of the successful operation of the maser. "One good friend reminded me later that he made great effort to attend, just to hear my paper, because he realized its importance at that time. But he was one of the few." Several were quite interested, others were interested from the standpoint of its being a curiosity—but the surprisingly large majority of the members appeared to remain totally unaware of the import of what had been presented. At a later seminar, one scientist blandly posed the question in the minds of many: "Now that you have it, what are you going to do with it?" Myopic imagination has always been one of man's gravest afflictions.

"Such a reception to a new idea is not so unusual, actually. And in fairness it must be conceded that it is not so easy to sort out the best, the ones that are going to develop the furthest, from those that will be stopped in some way. Some things, even after they appear interesting and have gone to a certain point, will fail."

The second paper on the maser, delivered early in 1955, was a specially invited longer talk given by the student who had helped to conduct the first experiment, James Gordon. "On this occasion, much more information was available, and it was received much more cheerfully. In fact, there was a good deal of excitement about it on that occasion."

And well there should have been. Wooldridge points out: "The maser is a big and important development, with a lot of very sound science behind it. But it must be remembered that Charlie's work before the maser had already gained him a great deal of fame. He had a very solid place in the hearts of the scientists and engineers in this country through his earlier work."

Townes' standing was not restricted to national boundaries. Dr. Rudi Kompfner recalls the day that Dr. Brebis Bleaney, professor of physics at Oxford University, said to him, "I'm going to introduce you to Townes—he is *really* bright!" From such a man, the tribute could not have been greater.

Human nature is such that anticipation often generates higher emotion than the actual realization. Through the tedious effort of furthering the maser experimentation, Townes had doggedly persisted. After it was proved, and acceptance gradually accrued to the idea, there came a period of intellectual let-down. Like emotion that has been built to such a key it must have respite, there was a desire for complete and drastic change.

Townes was grateful for the sanctuary of the Columbia facilities, the laboratory which has been partially supported on government contract, and the help of about 25 students and post-doctoral people who had applied their energies to working out his many ideas. He was relieved that the advances of the special field of research were recorded for all to share in a book he had written with A. L. Schawlow. He was honored to have served three years as Chairman of the Physics Department.

But, in 1955, all of this was completed. He had diligently pursued the field of microwave spectroscopy for all of the 10 years of its existence. He felt stale and in need of a new perspective. "I decided I must make a complete break, to stop and consider what were the most interesting and important things which I might do.

"So I took a sabbatical leave from Columbia for 15 months, and went to Europe. I just traveled around from one place to another, stopped at a university that was a reasonably good one, looked around at the physics department, got acquainted with people, and saw what they were doing. I gave a few lectures at Varenna, a little town near Lake Como. After a summer of such wandering with my family—during which time I climbed the Matterhorn—we settled in Paris where I had a Fulbright Professorship at the University of Paris, the Ecole Normale Supérieure. I gave a special seminar once a week to the physics graduate students and some of the physics faculty and others around Paris who were interested."

Habit and circumstance are the two great pitfalls of men. With an insidiousness that is complete enslavement, they ensnare the strong with the weak. Only the wary remain free. By making a change in his routine, Townes' resulting new perspective brought more important and more immediate dividends than he ever could have hoped.

"In Paris, I happened to run into one of my former students, Arnold Honig, whom I had helped to get a fellowship for study there. He and a French physicist, Jean Combrisson, were making fundamental studies on germanium crystals with impurities of phosphorus or of arsenic. At this point, when it was not clear to me what the next stage of development of the maser should be, I suddenly realized that this material was most appropriate for making a solid-state maser."

Creativeness induces a state of euphoria indescribable to those who have never experienced the feeling. Whether it be in the laboratory or at the easel there is a certain excitement that accompanies the procedure of fabricating an entity from ideas and skill. This state of being was by now a familiar one to Townes. He was on the brink of expanding upon his original maser concept.

The initial maser, of the ammonia beam-type, was limited to amplification in a very narrow range of frequencies; it had the added disadvantage of being almost untunable. However, the solid-state maser was tunable, and was operable over a wide-frequency band. Though Townes' remaining time in Paris was brief, he was able to obtain from friends at Bell Laboratories the necessary germanium to conduct some experiments and preliminary tests. They proved the theory! With this success came a marked increase in interest from other scientists. At Bell Laboratories and at the Massachusetts Institute of Technology, for example, research on masers was growing.

Though Townes moved on from Paris, taking his family to the Near East, to India, and to Japan, his work went with him. While lecturing on a Fulbright Professorship at the University of Tokyo, he pursued the development of the solid-state maser. "I enlisted the interest and help of some Japanese physicists, one of whom had worked with me at Columbia University when he was a visitor there."

Townes well conveys the scientist's attitude when he says, "I enjoy exploring things, trying out new things. I'm interested in a wide variety of fields, and have a general tendency to look into many sorts of things for a while, then single out one as a main avocation for a long period of time.

The part of research that I particularly enjoy is discovering new ideas which man hasn't known before, and which have an appearance of permanent validity and use. This new revelation of ideas of permanent value is one of the great joys of science."

It would appear that such broad and alert interest could have the tendency to dilute efforts. But Townes does not regard this as a necessary outcome: "All my activities are more or less related. Some of them I do just for relaxation, but this gives one a certain breadth and understanding of wide variety which usually pays off. I think that knowledge that has been acquired, then almost forgotten, about things a little out of one's primary field frequently turns out to be exceedingly useful. It may prove the key to something that might otherwise be missed.

"A lot of the things with which I've been occupied and have enjoyed in unrelated sequence all fit together, eventually. I'm never sorry for having spent time on something. Intense interest, activity, and a certain amount of objectivity are traits which are important to any scientist. To a certain degree I think I have them."

An instance of how one of Townes' earlier activities proved useful is in the matter of radio astronomy. While he was a graduate student at Cal Tech, Townes worked under the direction of Dr. Fritz Zwicky, and did some additional studying unrelated to his doctoral work; in part, this consisted of taking pictures with a telescope and looking for a supernova. The thread of this endeavor was picked up again when, during the latter part of the War, Townes endeavored to interpret the results of the work in radio astronomy by Jansky—who was the first to discover radio waves coming in from outside our own earth.

"When I wasn't too busy on war work, I took this up as a hobby at night, looking for an explanation to these radio waves. I found one which I think is correct for many astronomical sources of radio waves. What I worked out was the radio waves produced by random collision between ions in a plasma, or ionized gas.

"Later I resumed this interest through masers; they were used as very sensitive receivers to pick up these extremely weak radio waves. So I began to study Venus, Mars, Jupiter—their temperatures, behavior, and atmospheres—with radio waves."

Flexibility and scope are great assets in a time which paradoxically demands more specialization, and at the same time more generalization. The problems that exist are so numerous and formidable that no route can be ignored in searching for their solution. Townes' approach is highly compatible with the nature of Space Age science. In keen attunement to conditions, he writes, "Considered as an invention, the maser epitomizes the great change that has recently come over the character of technological frontiers. It was worked out and predicted almost entirely on the basis of theoretical ideas of a rather complex and abstract nature. This is not an invention or development which could grow out of a basement workshop, or solely from the Edisonian approach of intuitive trial and error; it is rather a creature of our present scientific age which has come rather completely from modern physical theory."[1]

Within the memories of living men have occurred many upheavals and revolutions. None has surpassed in magnitude the one which gripped physics in the early decades of this century. The science exploded to dimensions undreamed of by Galileo, Newton, and Maxwell. The century began with Max Planck's quantum of action. Within five years, Albert Einstein's theory of relativity redirected all thinking.

No previously stated concepts could cope with the atom of Niels Bohr and Ernest Rutherford. The decade of the 1920's brought the emergence of the laws of quantum mechanics, and produced great strides by small numbers of brilliant avant-gardes. The new world of physics was evolved largely in the Old World. Much of its impetus was imparted to our nation through the wonderful minds of the emigrees who bolted from the Fascist vice which gripped Europe in the 1930's. The intellectual challenge inherent in the unfolding of the new physics elevated the theoretician to a pinnacle—both of esteem and attainment.

Lest today's aspirant conjure that era with yearning, it must be considered that it may in future come to be regarded as the prologue to the solving of nature's great riddles. The secrets of anti-gravity and the creation of matter may be scribbled "on the back of an envelope" at some near date, when expert training, genius, and inspiration merge in the brain of tomorrow's physicist. The battle for knowledge never ends. It scarcely has begun—all the universe awaits conquest.

No decision is more important to Townes—nor to any other man—than how he will spend his time. It was his intention to complete his 2-year stint with IDA in Washington, D.C., then to return to the laboratory at Columbia, from which he had been on leave. But from the Massachusetts Institute of Technology came an invitation to join as provost and professor of physics. Though the honor was great, the decision was still difficult to make.

Townes had held administrative positions in government work, but had done it through a sense of responsibility. Now he was faced with making the choice for his own work and life. Wooldridge smilingly recalls, "Charlie wouldn't have been caught dead becoming a provost 20 years ago." But in 1961 Townes so chose!

His viewpoint was altered by these considerations: "This is one kind of administrative work which I consider particularly important, for it requires someone who is thoroughly familiar with science and engineering. Usually the difficulty is that the man who enters such work finds it most difficult to maintain his touch with current discoveries—the very thing that initially made his judgment worthwhile. By remaining in administrative work very long, he becomes stale and out of touch with the very scientific ideas he must know how to properly judge.

"But at MIT, I have safeguards against that, through some teaching, through having time for my own work, and through the nature of the MIT community." Guided by this line of reasoning, Townes resigned from Columbia and moved to Cambridge.

"I find it an exciting kind of community. MIT is a place of great flexibility, and the nature of its present growth makes good administration even more important. Though, true, this present endeavor is a diversion in the strictest sense from what I had previously decided—to settle down to a life of research and teaching—I think it carries with it an opportunity to bring in activities of a somewhat different sphere. Much hard thought is required to try to understand the different fields of science and engineering, the problems of education, and the kinds of policies an institution like MIT ought to follow. I expect to be working in these directions for a long while; however, this plan may change overnight.

"I can be sure of only two characteristics of what I am likely to be doing in the long run. One is that I expect to work in the field of science, where there are so many interesting things to be done, and where most of my experience lies. The other is that I hope to make contributions in some way useful to civilization and the society around me. In choosing goals, one must weigh two aspects: he has to consider what things he can possibly succeed in doing, and what is their relative importance. The roads which are eventually the most satisfying to an individual are those which most challenge him, allow him to exercise his abilities for something worthwhile, develop new abilities, and thus realize his greatest potential."

Through strong purpose and through orderly planning, Townes has put the 47 years of his life to rather splendid use. The extent of his scientific accomplishments is, of course, within the capability of only those with rare mental ability. But other facets of his life and career stand more as products of industry and energy.

The multitude of his activities in boyhood and throughout school years set a pattern which has never abated. While living in Pasadena, his competence as a bass baritone gained him a place in a very fine choral group, the Bach Choir. After he joined Bell Laboratories, he furthered this talent by studying evenings at the Juilliard School of Music. Home at that time was an apartment on Claremont Avenue, one that he shared with several musicians. Each would practice individually on his instrument—piano, clarinet, violin—producing a total effect somewhat more cacophonic than symphonic.

Townes was adept at sports—fortunately. His wife recalls, "I was organizing a skiing party when I was working at International House. I simply had to have 20 people signed up or the excursion would fall through. I was at a point where I desperately needed someone to complete the number; then I got a lead on Charlie. I didn't let up until I had persuaded him to join us. He has since laughed about the incident, saying he had never seen such enthusiasm as I evidenced for skiing!"

The courtship was a period of alternate delight and dilemma for Frances. Townes would give her a tremendous rush, during which time they would explore New York in the most exciting fashion—visiting foreign restaurants, attending the theater and concerts, staying up all night to go to Washington Market and watch the fruit vendors come in, going to Harlem and dancing all night. Then weeks would elapse during which time she neither saw nor heard from him. Suddenly he would appear, offering no excuses, and resume the rush. The alternating so disconcerted Frances that she refused to see him for several weeks. When she did, it was to marry him and fly away to an exotic honeymoon in Haiti.

Their first "enchanted cottage" was a sub-basement in Greenwich Village. It was embellished with a fabulous array of silver and crystal wedding presents from friends of their two socially prominent families. But the furnishings were a bit austere at the beginning—they consisted of two sleeping bags, and a tablecloth spread out on the floor. This trivial matter of no furniture proved no influence on the state of their happiness. "Money, or lack of it, has never been a problem. We have simply lived on whatever we've had, and never worried about it," says Frances. (Townes' name for his wife is Squita, from the diminutive of her name, Francesquita.)

Though work has placed heavy burdens upon Townes, the spirit of fun has always awaited him in his home. It is brimming with the lively activities of four daughters, with music and an abundance of family traditions and rituals, to which Frances has made a point of adhering. There are two loves in this man's life—physics and family.

What makes a scientist?

Men have laboriously and ingeniously delved into every aspect of the world and the things upon it, producing comprehension of it to incredible degrees. The most enigmatic, ambiguous, and equivocal of all the puzzles remains man himself.

The University of Utah, under contract to the Air Force, recently published a survey which probed quizzical fingers into the morass of human qualities, characteristics, and behavior of about 200 scientists. In summarizing the interviews, they state in part:

"The most predictable criteria, in terms of number of valid scores, were likeableness as a member of the research team, professional society membership, current organizational status, judged work output, supervisory ratings on over-all performance, and peer rankings on over-all productivity."[8]

The psychological characteristics which could be correlated to the criteria in the greatest number of instances were: ". . . creativity, inner directedness, discrimination of value, professional self-confidence, cognition, desire for principles, drive, self-sufficiency, flexibility, independence, intuition, aspiration in quantity of research reports, aspiration in theoretical contributions, aspiration in high level of original work, and intellectual thoroughness."[8]

Though the well-organized research into the nature of scientists continues, though the conferences produce voluminous reports and the generally expected tallies, they do no more than write the first syllable toward answering the riddle. Some results of the survey served only to deepen the dilemma: "Undergraduate grade-point average correlated significantly with only four of the seventeen criteria, with three of these barely at the level of significance."[8]

If the era of a man's education is to be a steppingstone to the period of his career, should not the system of grading better indicate his capabilities? Are employers justified in giving great consideration to an applicant's ranking in his class in the face of this finding? Must the finding itself be challenged, with further investigation into its significance? Answers are not easily acquired.

Townes believes there is a characteristic shared by scientists: "One of the very great joys of this profession is that one can usually arrive at a reasonable understanding of a situation—or at least decide where you have an understanding and where you don't. Most scientists approach problems with the attitude of playing a very serious game, and very genuinely try to arrive at what might be called, provisionally, the truth. They will earnestly try to get at the scientific background of a particular problem, and will appraise the technical questions involved. They will discuss things with each other, and eventually arrive at a consensus much more successfully than any other group of people that I know.

"This doesn't mean they don't argue, but their arguments are almost always directed at finding the truth. It generally results in an eventual recognition of what the truth is, or what it is that one does not know. It takes this form, instead of personality conflicts and arguments at cross purposes that don't lead anywhere."

An aura of exaggeration is generally built up about any public figure. Heroes are braver, fighters are stronger, comedians are wittier—than reasonably can be expected. Because of this inclination, together with the fact that those who are the objects of adulation usually do little to dispel the myth, the role of infallible pantologist has been ascribed to many scientists.

With refreshing candor, Townes said during a talk about the maser at a meeting of the Research Corporation, "I must confess that when Gordon, Zeiger, and I first started work on this new type of device, I—at least—had little idea of its value either as a very low-noise amplifier, or as an atomic time standard—aspects which might appear now to have been the prime reasons for our effort. As for the millimeter waves—well, we haven't gotten around to them yet. My only consolation and excuse for such a bumbling approach is that others have had similar experiences—perhaps one can even say that this type of indirect and unexpected development is typical of research."[9]

In continuing, Townes makes clear a vitally important point, "I believe the value and practical effectiveness of research which is not clearly directed towards some recognized practical end is well recognized here, even though doubts would certainly be found among a different selection of people, who have not had close contact with research. The most important practical results often come indirectly and as by-products of very impractical intellectual curiosity."[9]

Two vital factors are clear from Townes' experience—he initially furthered the idea, without having specific applications in mind, but his vision was such that he clearly perceived wide application once the concept had materialized.

The crusade for support of pure research is one that has gained momentum in recent years. The transition from the attitude of "who cares why grass is green" to the present level of funding and furtherance is a marked improvement. Yet it remains a misunderstood area, often the first to be regarded with mistrust and disapproval when cutbacks are to be made.

The Research Corporation has earned a position of esteem by having been one of the first foundations to support the search of scientific knowledge for its own sake. Frederick Cottrell, in setting up the organization, determined that it should maintain the openness to "bet on long shots" in scientific research. The manner in which the Corporation has carried out that aim has made an enormous contribution to science, to scientists, and to the technology of our country. Impetus and encouragement have also been given to individual scientists through recognition by their colleagues. In 1958, Townes was the recipient of the Research Corporation's Annual Award—the single honor bestowed for that year.

He was also recognized with the Page One Award for Science from The Newspaper Guild of New York. The third honor to come his way that year was from the Institute of Radio Engineers, in the form of the Morris Liebman Memorial Prize, given for outstanding work in electronics.

The following year brought an additional three prizes—the esteemed Comstock Award from the National Academy of Sciences, which dates back to an outstanding civil engineer of Civil War times, and is given only once in every five years for the most important work in electricity and magnetism; the Stuart Ballantine Medal of The Franklin Institute; and the Exceptional Service Award of the United States Air Force, which is rarely given to citizens not directly in military employ.

Maintaining the precedent of receiving three prizes during a year, Townes, in 1961, received the Arnold O. Beckman Award of the Instrument Society of America, the David Sarnoff Award in Electronics of the American Institute of Electrical Engineers, and the Rumford Premium of the American Academy of Arts and Sciences.

Townes relates interesting sidelights on the last prize: "It was originated by Count Rumford who lived in Revolutionary times. He was an American who was scientifically inclined, whose greatest honor came from abroad. In his paper, *Enquiry Concerning the Source of Heat Which Is Excited by Friction,* he was the first to dispel a view that heat was a material substance. After becoming quite a well-known scientist and public figure, he decided to establish an award to be given once every two years, and presented the American Academy of Arts and Sciences in Boston with a number of government bonds to be used for the endowment of the prize, and an accompanying cash award."

The Award itself is most impressive. Count Rumford is pictured in profile on a gold medal which contains a silver medal. And since it was specified that the value of the medallion was to be $300, it is not small, as is usually the case with modern medals; rather, it is about 3 inches in diameter and is quite thick.

On April 23, 1962, the Great Hall of the National Academy of Sciences building in Washington, D.C., was filled with some of the nation's most distinguished scientists to witness the awards ceremony. Townes was the recipient of the John J. Carty Medal, and Dr. Mervin J. Kelly said in making the presentation, "His generosity in making available to all who came to him his valuable time and his penetrating suggestions characterize his approach to science and to life as a whole."

Frances Townes has arranged her husband's medals on the mantelpiece. But she observes that any time guests are coming into the home, the medals mysteriously disappear until the friends have departed. The only things that Townes will allow to remain on display on the mantel are the prizes which he has brought from the bottom of the sea—coral, star fish, sea urchins—that he obtained while engaging in one of his favorite sports, skin diving.

Townes relates the story of one member of the scientific community whose curiosity about the value of his Nobel Prize and his Rumford Prize prompted him to send his wife to Tiffany's to get the medals evaluated. "The woman was led into a little room. An expert sat down and studied the medals. He read the inscriptions, then looked up at the woman—whom he presumed to be a grieving and destitute widow—and said, 'He must have been a wonderful man.' "

Frances wears a piece of jewelry that is utterly unique and beyond monetary value to her—a large and very beautiful pink ruby that came out of the maser which Townes used on the 50-foot radio telescope at the Naval Research Laboratory, and with which he measured the temperature of Venus, Mars, and Jupiter.

These large radio telescopes, which normally have peered farther into the universe than any optical telescope, have their range increased by a factor of 10 with the use of masers as an amplifier! Time, as well as space, has undergone a transformation with this new device. Whereas formerly the best possible timepieces were accurate to within 1 second every 10 years, with the maser oscillator, clocks can be controlled so that they will accumulate an error of 1 second in but every 10,000 years—and work is being done toward even greater accuracy!

In every dimension the maser is a startling development. Said Townes at an address in Los Angeles, "Because we've obviated thermodynamics, we have no fundamental limit in power which can be obtained. The limit is simply a matter of engineering and heat dissipation."[5] The transmission of the power via the maser light beam over long distances can be expected, with Townes' amusing suggestion that 10 kilowatts of power could be beamed to a 6-inch spot at 1000 miles distance to heat the spaceman's coffee pot.

In a serious vein, the statistics continue: in amplification (the controlled release of stored energy) it has been customary to measure the inherent noise properties as "noise temperature." A good microwave amplifier might have a noise temperature of 1000°–2000° K. A maser amplifier will have a noise temperature of less than 1° K.

If a maser beam of 10 kilowatts were put into a 200-inch telescope, it could be seen by the naked eye at a distance of $\frac{1}{10}$ light year.* If a good telescope were used to look at the beam, it could be detected at a distance of 100 light years!

Townes says, "It's brighter than the sun, in the sense that if we have a filter which takes out wave lengths excepting those in a narrow region about this wave length, it would be some several hundred times brighter than the sun at a long distance. Yet the total amount of light is not necessarily large. The brightness comes about because even though the energy

* A light year is approximately 5.88 trillion miles.

is much less than the total output of the sun, it is highly monochromatic and highly directional."

The focusing of this maser light beam can, because of its coherence, be condensed to the size of one wave length, about $1/25{,}000$ of an inch. So with its use, such unrelated applications as to measurement—attaining accuracy of one wave length over 100,000 miles—or to surgery are possibilities. In the skilled hands of a doctor or biologist, the light beam can be reversed through a microscope and be localized on a *particular spot* of a *particular cell.*

Says Townes of its medical possibilities, "It will mainly be used for destroying certain tissues, such as a cancer in the back of the eye. Experiments have also been done with it for welding on detached retina. It might be used for brain surgery, or for surgery inside the stomach, since light tubes can be sent down into the stomach. Surgery on any exposed surface is certainly a possibility."

Just as the knife that is used to heal can be used to kill, so can many scientific advances assume this alternate purpose. A recent magazine article classifies the maser as one of the death-ray weapons, surpassing the imaginings of science fiction in its potential. It states: "This death-dealing capacity and its future promise in warfare were explained by one anonymous scientist in a DOD (Department of Defense) report: 'The ability of the optical MASER, or LASER, to transform electrical power into a single optical beam makes it possible to achieve a suitably fine focus of concentrated amounts of wave energy sufficient even to destroy enemy missiles at relatively long range.'"[10]

The penetrating beam of a maser is used in drilling holes in diamonds, it may well be used as a radar to shoot up to the Moon and explore it—by shooting the beam to the lunar surface and recording the varying lengths of time it would take the beam to travel there and back as it was moved over the surface, up mountain sides and down into valleys. A preliminary experiment which detected a maser light beam reflected from the Moon has already been run.

This fantastic technique is best known as maser—the name Townes christened it. The acronym laser* has been used frequently in place of the term optical maser. "I think this name is perfectly appropriate," says Townes. "Other names have appeared in the literature—iraser for the infrared frequencies, uraser for ultraviolet, and raser for radio-frequency masers. The latter sounds like something you shave with, and the others may become confusing. So I think it would be better, generally, to use the term maser for all, then specify the frequency range."

By whatever name this may be called, the invention is expected to exert

* Light Amplification by Stimulated Emission of Radiation.

the greatest single influence in the change and expansion of the electronics field for the decade to come. The maser is a principal element in the new area of "quantum electronics," the field which deals with the production and the control of electromagnetic waves through their interaction with the electrons in atoms or molecules.

Though Townes' maser work tends to eclipse prior accomplishments, his stature was established with outstanding accomplishments in the field of microwave spectroscopy—he considers his work with the maser a continuation of this investigation. Another important contribution has been his utilization of nuclear effects in molecules to examine the structure of molecules and the structure of solids.

This man's great intellect has not been restricted to the technical nature of science, but has crystallized some excellent considerations in the philosophical aspect of science and its relationship to broader goals. While recognizing that we must have the military strength to defend freedom and to deter aggression, he strongly disagrees with the concept of tying a long-range science program to the limiting factor of competitiveness. In Townes' view, far different motivation is required for real achievement:

"We need to create in the United States the type of atmosphere where intellectual creativity and research become the natural by-products of a general interest in and eagerness for knowledge and ideas, rather than a protective reaction."[9]

He points out, "Americans often like to think of themselves as very practical and realistic, and not fooled by impractical idealism. But such realism amounts often to just lack of imagination—particularly the variety sometimes recognized as hard-boiled realism, which is often a disguise for hard-shelled, thick-headed shortsightedness."[9]

Charles H. Townes, who imparts the spirit with his every thought, urges other Americans to catch the thrill of scientific advancement and discovery: "Why should we not have undertaken, and why can't we now sell an exploration of space as an adventure and a challenging extension of the human spirit, rather than be forced reluctantly and grudgingly into a belated development of space devices? I know that the political realist would immediately recognize such suggestions as idealistic and impractical. I can only reply that he may be right, but that so little confidence is usually shown in the intelligence of the American public and in the effectiveness of genuine idealism, that we should give them an occasional good try before abandoning ourselves to hard-boiled realism—that is, I mean, thick-headed shortsightedness."[9]

REFERENCES

1. Overhage, Carl F. J., ed.: *The Age of Electronics,* New York, McGraw-Hill, 1962.

2. Ramo, Simon, ed.: *Peacetime Uses of Outer Space,* New York, McGraw-Hill, 1961.
3. Associated Press, *Los Angeles Times,* Los Angeles, California, February 5, 1962.
4. Pacific Telephone, *Telephone News,* March, 1961.
5. Townes, Dr. Charles H.: *Optical Masers and Their Aerospace Application,* Address, Air Force/Aerospace Corporation Symposium on Ballistic Missile and Aerospace Technology, August 28, 1961.
6. *Organization and Management of Missile Programs,* Eleventh Report by the Committee on Government Operations, September 2, 1959.
7. *Congressional Record,* Proceedings and Debates of the 87th Congress, Second Session, April 2, 1962.
8. *Air Force Technical Report,* ASD-TR-61-96, 31–32, April, 1961.
9. Townes, Charles H.: Address, Research Corporation Annual Meeting, January 23, 1958.
10. *Space World,* 2:6:49, May, 1962.

Forceful administrative figure who furthered numerous space projects, including Tiros, the weather satellite, and Transit, the navigation satellite

ROGER S. WARNER, JR.

"A teacher named Reginald Nash taught me the value of using energy as well as intellect in approaching problems," says Roger Warner, Jr.

The lesson has carried through into his life with such effectiveness that Warner assumed on his powerful shoulders the burden of furthering two of the primary concepts of the Space Age—the weather satellite and the navigation satellite. Warner's driving manner, though brusk, conveyed such enthusiasm for them that it might well be said that his momentum brought these projects into fruition.

They are involved and complicated concepts, which, obviously, require enormous contribution and cooperation of great teams of men. But someone of broad technical know-how and solid scientific background must combine with them the ability to first transmute proposals into programs. In this context, the credit for both *Tiros* and *Transit* is given to Warner.

Reaching this man can be compared with re-entry from space. He is engulfed in a layer of business-like atmosphere which is difficult to penetrate. Warner, the scientist-administrator, is regarded as highly competent, and is a figure with a tremendous reputation for setting programs into motion and achieving results. Warner, the man, is known and understood by only a very few friends of very long standing.

It becomes an obscure matter to try to trace back the formation of many of Warner's influences. But he clearly recalls the association from which his strongest characteristic resulted: "It was at the Milton Academy in Boston, which I attended throughout high school years, that I had Reginald Nash as a teacher. He was a short wiry man who walked on his toes at a great rate of speed and spoke with endless fire.

"Whatever I am able to do now to supply impetus to certain areas is directly traceable to his guidance from those early years. He was the athletic director and pushed me into football; he also taught me history. In a combination of those two activities, he taught me that unless you employ both stamina and a singleness of purpose, you probably are doing only a part of the job."

The job which Warner is currently undertaking is one of high significance; it is as Director of Research at the Institute of Naval Studies, INS, at Cambridge, Massachusetts. He has alternated his interest between the sea and space, and in this current endeavor is combining them uniquely.

INS was in the planning stage for three years prior to its emergence about two years ago as an analysis and planning group, comprised of both civilians and Navy personnel who are engaged in deciding what the Navy will be like in 1975. They are considering what big issues the Navy needs to begin to decide upon now against its requirements in the future.

It was initially set up under contract with the Institute for Defense Analysis, IDA, the group that runs various analytical operations for the Department of Defense, DOD. IDA operates several study groups, all pointing toward supplying the Secretary of Defense, Mr. James McNamara, with objective information. Since all of IDA's other activities are thus oriented toward the DOD level, it was felt that a possible conflict of interests existed in its handling Warner's INS group.

He explains it this way: "Each of the military services is a component of DOD, but each should have the opportunity to let its own thoughts develop; the views and objectives of each are, necessarily, quite different. The Pentagon is a place in which it is difficult, as you know, to get a body of thought collected and furthered without its being squelched by opposing forces. It is quite proper and necessary, therefore, that there should be a little administrative privacy within the individual services."

That is one of the reasons why the contract on INS was transferred on July 1, 1962, to The Franklin Institute in Philadelphia. The second reason is that this Institute already is the contractural agent for three or four other study groups for the Navy. By coordinating them all under one contractor, it is possible to achieve an interchange of people, which in turn allows for the handling of projects of greater magnitude.

The INS group, whose total attention is directed to techniques that are not yet in existence and on projects that are not yet funded, has a companion organization, the Operations Evaluation Group, OEG, which has as its objective the optimizing of techniques for equipment currently in existence. Both report to the newly created Center for Naval Analyses, CNA, the Chief of which is Dr. Frank Bothwell, with offices in Washington, D.C.

If the structure seems complicated, it must be considered that the tasks to be approached are giant. Warner explains: "We work for the Chief of Naval Operations, Admiral G. W. Anderson, Jr., and in a sense are at his elbow, trying to identify problems which have a technical content, which are capable of being analyzed, and which are capable of being projected into the future. We set up a series of projects to study some of the problems.

"The first project we undertook was to study this: What kind of characteristics might the Navy be able to use in the development of power—main propulsion power for submarines and ships, but not aircraft. This is one area that already has made an enormous stride in the last decade, in that Vice Admiral Hyman G. Rickover has brought into being a nuclear power plant and utilized it with magnificent success. So we approached other questions regarding power: Should there be more speed, more compactness, greater endurance? Where does nuclear power fit? What are the characteristics that one can get from nuclear power? Is it essential that the Navy begin to think of going all out for nuclear power, or are there areas where advances in conventional propulsion techniques are better suited?

"This is a curious kind of study for those of us who are technically trained," says Warner, "because once you have determined what might be technically feasible, then you must consider what the posture of the country will be. We cannot simply consider planning improved characteristics in power, but must take into account what is the general picture of Europe, the uncommitted nations, and our own economy."

Thus is it pointed up that all facts and events are interrelated. One question cannot be isolated from other factors. Warner continues, "We could extrapolate, think only of technical trends, possibly, for a few years ahead. But in covering the span of 20 years, broad considerations apply. This is the kind of study which Dr. Theodore von Kármán has conducted with such great success. At the end of World War II, at the request of General H. H. Arnold, he gathered a distinguished group which prepared the massive 20-volume work *Toward New Horizons*. He has recently prepared a similar but not as comprehensive study for AGARD,* entitled *Von Kármán Committee Long Term Scientific Studies for NATO,* on future prospects and needs of NATO."

The technical portion of the INS study has been completed, and the

* AGARD is the Advisory Group for Aeronautical Research and Development to NATO, the North Atlantic Treaty Organization.

group is now concentrating on its utility in a series of obvious operational tasks that the Navy might have to perform. Meanwhile, economists and political scientists are sizing up the impact from other viewpoints; the study will be completed in all of its phases in 1963.

The second project of INS has exciting prospects! *Project Starlight* is "far out," for it is looking at the impact of astronautics on the Navy. From June 18 to July 20, 1962, approximately 75 people gathered at the Naval Training Center in Santa Barbara, California, for concentrated work on the subject. "It was a very comprehensive and senior group," Warner points out, "including civilian scientists, Navy personnel and some from the other services.

"Discussed were the types of missions that the Navy might be expected to undertake, and whether astronautics could supply better tools for such needs. In no way was it suggested that the Navy is trying to get into a position of strength in relation to the Air Force—it was merely a look to see if the Navy can perform its own tasks better with the aid of astronautical developments. It might be indicated that the Navy even use operational information obtainable out of certain Air Force programs, or request that certain new missions be started with the Air Force as the agent to carry them out."

What was discussed and projected at this top-secret conclave can be speculated only. Even deliberately freed imagination, stimulated to rampant roaming by the incredible events of this new Space Age, will likely fall short of actual developments in the next two decades. Says Dr. H. Guyford Stever, Professor of Aeronautics and Astronautics at the Massachusetts Institute of Technology, "No one accurately foresaw the shape of things to come for the airplane. . . . The parallel between the story of the airplane and that of the applications of our space technology is obvious. . . . The lessons in prognosticating the technical possibilities of space flight that can be learned from this brief consideration of another great technology are numerous. For example, most people, over the long run, fall short of the mark in their predictions. . . .

"I can best describe my attitude by telling an anecdote about a foreign visitor who took a taxi tour of our national capital. When shown the Archives building, on which there is inscribed a quotation from Shakespeare's *The Tempest* which reads 'What is past is prologue,' the foreign visitor was a little puzzled, for he did not have a good command of the English language. He asked his taxi driver if he knew what the saying meant. The taxi driver answered, 'Sure, bud, that means you ain't seen nuthin' yet.' "[1]

With dynamic resolve, Warner's group has undertaken yet another project. Number three has to do with inventorying all shipping on the

Atlantic Ocean, particularly. Over the years, people have known when a vessel has left a European port and when it has arrived at an Atlantic port. Within the tempo of life that existed in another day, nobody was really interested if a vessel showed up a day or two late. Nobody cared if vessels did not report their noon position.

"Now, however, it has become necessary to see how to conduct a fairly comprehensive positioning of all shipping. All of the various information channels that have existed since time immemorial—including Lloyds of London as well as a number of voluntary services that exist in the maritime nations bordering on the Atlantic—must now be updated."

The concept Warner terms, "A SAGE* of the sea, in a sense—very definitely a NORAD of the sea, and any successful venture might ultimately be operated by a NORAD type of center for the benefit and protection of the maritime industry from the perils of the sea. Such an undertaking would, of course, require the cooperation of all the countries bordering on the North Atlantic, and presumably would involve techniques and equipment which all maritime services possess.

"We ran an actual exercise which was completed in June, 1962, in which we took inventory of what was on the ocean, with the aid of all contributing government-operated shipping. We are knee deep in data which poured in from all the sources." It is rather obvious that satellites will surely play an important role in the future. With its reputed "spy in the sky" military capability, *Samos* could have a worthy role in peacetime; for example, ships could be kept track of during their voyages. It can be speculated, also, that *Transit,* the navigation satellite, could well have utilization in this long-range plan.

The INS has a staff of about 40 people. These are loanees from industry, consultants from industry, from MIT, from Harvard, and other universities, a few scientists on sabbatical from Naval laboratories, and about eight Naval officers. The Director, Rear Admiral E. E. Colestock, has his offices at the Naval War College at Newport, Rhode Island. Warner is "in command" of the Cambridge facility, in its day-to-day operation.

In addition to all other projects, he has instituted yet another group of studies of major scope. He describes it this way: "We are trying to define how one might want to select nuclear weapons under the constraints of limited war. A project like the use of nuclear weapons is in itself a very big project, but at the moment we are regarding it from the point of view of military effectiveness, not from the point of view of escalation, and not from the viewpoint of its impact on international relations or even how one presents a situation to the White House for permission to use it. We

* SAGE is the SemiAutomatic Ground Environment installation operated by the Air Defense Command of the Air Force for the purpose of detecting incoming missiles. SAGE, and other warning systems, report their findings to NORAD, the North American Air Defense, located at Colorado Springs, Colorado.

will not consider any of these problems, but will restrict our present efforts to an issue that is sufficiently complex: How are nuclear weapons militarily helpful?"

There are difficulties in this particular project that go beyond the intellectual conception. "Even in the limited context in which we are studying, it is amazing how strong are the emotions of the people who have been brought into that program.

"The very strong emotion is engendered by any consideration of using a weapon which may have all sorts of dire effects that we can't possibly control. It is the 'Brinkmanship' philosophy, which does not allow people to retain much reason about the matter of nuclear weapons. If we can be logical about this, it might prove useful."

Warner traces the background of events which led to this study: "When President Kennedy and Secretary of Defense McNamara assumed office, there had been little emphasis on limited war. The need to update plans for limited war became extremely important. There is pressing need to update conventional weapons."

Whereas, two years ago it was felt that nuclear weapons would have to be used when it was impossible to detect or isolate the target precisely, today a different approach is in order. Conventional weapons have increased in the order of tens of times in accuracy. This prompts Warner to consider a dual philosophy, of perhaps putting nuclear weapons aboard some vessels so that there would be the capability of using the proper tool for any given situation. Though the subject has been neglected, Warner feels that the long-overdue limited war philosophy is taking form.

All of this effort by the Institute for Naval Studies is aimed toward the objective of looking ahead to future problems. Warner explains, "We are not spending large amounts of money, and not building new hardware systems. We are generating the beginnings of policy. We are trying to describe the pros and cons and what position the Navy might well consider as the more promising approach. We are erecting guide lines for the Chief of Naval Operations."

What habit is to an individual, tradition can be to an institution. It can alter in time from being a benefit to becoming a liability—yet the changing of it requires effort far out of proportion to its importance. In this insecure and ever-changing world, there is a certain comfort in continuing the things that have been done before. They may not be right, but they are familiar. Today's boosters and missiles and fuels are spoken of as "sophisticated," which indeed they are. Now it is man, himself, who must gain in sophistication and maturity, if he is to cope with his creations.

Some of Roger Warner's unusual capability to look ahead was implanted by his boyhood fascination with looking back. His uncle, Langdon Warner, was an archeologist of note who spent a considerable portion of his life in the Orient. He was deeply interested in the early culture that was discovered in the Gobi Desert. His long and frequent letters to his young nephew about his discoveries in this arid land between China and Mongolia filled the boy's imagination with a yearning for adventure.

In the proper surroundings of Boston, where young Roger's father practiced law, there was little opportunity to satisfy the desire. But an opportunity for travel and new surroundings occurred in 1927, just at the time Roger Warner was ready to enter college: "My father had a job to do in England, so I went there with him. After spending the summer in one of their tutoring schools, familiarizing myself with their atmosphere and methods, I entered Cambridge." For a year Warner attended Gonville and Caius, one of the nineteen colleges of Cambridge. The lectures of the scholars in the atmosphere of this European-type institution opened new and promising vistas to Warner.

"It was all very strange, but I had an extremely interesting time with other students who were also thrust into this environment. Some were from Belgium, Switzerland, Scotland—through them, the international picture began to take on some significance to me. I began to learn the difference of one country from another, and what particular problems each faces. At this impressionable stage I started to realize how other people were thinking, how people from different environments approached life.

"Several of the friendships I formed then I still maintain. When I am on the Continent, or in Scotland, I visit with them. I am rather amazed by how easily we pick up and go on from where we left off, as if there had been no break in the association. We talk of things that interest us today. We talk and think in the world of ideas, not things." Warner adds, "In our visiting, we never hark back to 'school days' or the times that first brought us together."

Those first days at Cambridge were not without difficulty for Warner. Though he quickly adapted to the personal relationships with other students, the scholastic phase was drastically different from his experience in Boston. "The disciplinary demands and educational demands taxed me. The accomplishments that were expected from casual conversations in informal sessions were much greater than one would encounter in this country. Their educational process involves much more discussion in small groups, aimed toward developing in the student an analytical approach to conversation, rather than just an absorbing of the facts. This, in retrospect, is what I remember finding difficult; at the same time I feel I profited from the training."

Warner, who claims he was "a pretty poor student in grammar and high school," admits that he got acceptable grades at Cambridge. Quite evidently they were acceptable, for they gained him entrance to Harvard for the remainder of his university training. From his sojourn in Britain, and from the early influence of the teacher, Nash, Warner had started as a history major. But half way through, he switched to chemistry. His absorption with the present does not even allow any recollection of why he made the change. "I was simply fascinated by chemistry—that's all."

"Immediately out of Harvard, in 1931, I embarked upon a research project to attempt to find a way to use paper in the manufacture of shoes. I finally managed to lick the problem, but not at a profit. My next venture was to make meteorological balloons out of latex—that is the milky white sap before it is reduced to rubber. This endeavor was more successful, and it became the basis for making meteorological observation balloons."

Warner attended Graduate School at MIT for additional training in chemical engineering in 1934. "Monetarily it was a hard period. I went for a year, but that was as long as I could manage it."

His next major assignment was one that was to supply this country's wartime needs in a major way—the research which led to synthetic rubber. Though war had not yet erupted in Europe, perceptive ears could hear the rumblings, and even a cursory assessment revealed our dependence on rubber imports.

The forethought that our nation would have a great need of this substitute started with the DuPont Company, and investigation was taken up by all rubber companies. Warner joined the staff of the B. F. Goodrich Company in a pilot-plant operation. The research involved an endless series of tests, and a constant repetition of failures. To the untrained individual, it would have been a sadly discouraging experience. To the scientists who were doggedly persisting, it was a mighty challenge—though, also, it was hard, dirty work. Progress appeared intolerably slow, but it did occur.

"During this whole preliminarization process of building synthetic rubber out of the basic ingredients, the greatest problem was learning how to control the reaction. In the telling, it seems a small step in the business of building synthetic rubber, but in the doing, it was really quite intriguing," says Warner. Experiments finally began to prove out on a small scale. Finally they were tried on a larger scale—and worked!

Warner reminds us, "Our country ran out of natural rubber stock; this was in spite of the fact that rubber was being flown in from Brazil, and all sorts of extreme measures were being used to increase the import. Synthetic rubber eventually satisfied 80% of our wartime needs.

"There was a second purpose behind the extensive research for a synthetic rubber, and that was to develop a product which would resist oil and gasoline to increase its utility. The man-made product came through on that basis, also."

Windmills led Warner into his wartime position. "Palmer C. Putnam was an interesting fellow with a wild imagination. We talked for many years about his idea of building updated windmills, using modern techniques which might generate power in places where there is constant wind." It was Putnam who guided Warner to the National Defense Research Committee, NDRC, of the Office of Scientific Research Development, OSRD.

In 1940, Dr. Vannevar Bush was appointed by President Roosevelt to the post of Chairman of NDRC, which was a government agency established to supplement the work of the Army and Navy in developing military devices and instrumentalities. A year later, OSRD was formed, and took in NDRC as one of its two main divisions. Bush was named Director of OSRD, which assumed broad and vital responsibilities—mobilizing the scientific effort of the country, initiating broad programs of research in cooperation with the Army and Navy, advising the President as to the status of defense research and development, continuing research in the field of medicine, and performing research on military weapons and materials.

Warner was appointed as an aide to the NDRC—a great tribute to a young scientist, most certainly. This gave him an opportunity to work with one of the recognized leaders in the scientific community, Dr. Bush. When the threat of World War II was looming, he assumed these government appointments in addition to his regular duties as President of the Carnegie Institution. Though Bush's training and activities were mainly in the mechanical and electronic fields, his influence and pronouncements on broad scientific policy were highly regarded.

The first assignment handed to Warner was a test of his resourcefulness, for not only was it a difficult problem, but it was outside of his specialized area of training as a chemist. He was appointed Project Manager on the development of equipment for amphibious operations. Here was a prime example of the philosophy of "intellect plus energy" coming into play, as Warner relates: "I must have traveled 200,000 miles during this period to push the program beyond the research and development stage. It moved very fast. There was a rapid round of meetings with naval architects, a review of paper and model studies, and suddenly within 90 days we built an amphibious vehicle at the Yellow Coach Division of General Motors (the Division that builds school buses).

"The first test was at Ft. Belvoir near Washington, D.C., and it was immediately obvious that we had some interesting problems—mainly, we didn't really know how to make a wheeled vehicle go over soft ground. Our next approach was to develop a tire and a method of inflation which behaved essentially like a camel's foot in its action. The degree of inflation and deflation was determined by the softness of the ground, to give a sort of flotation. In this way, the tire would not just sink in and get mired, but would spread out like a flat tire and help to get the truck going." DUKW (pronounced "duck") was the name given to the project by General Motors.

From that point, momentum increased. Warner had joined NDRC in April, 1942, and by Christmastime had achieved limited production of the trucks. At Ft. Story, near Norfolk, Virginia, the vehicles were put through their paces. They were driven through sand dunes, into water, out of water—every possible test to determination limitations. An added 50 trucks were sent to the Army Corps of Engineers at Camp Edwards on Cape Cod; there troops trained unloading from a vessel in an amphibious exercise. NDRC then ordered 1000 of the trucks. An unusual feature of the project was that there had not been stated any military requirement for DUKW—this endeavor had started as a research project, but was growing to the proportions of a major order.

Ingeniously, Warner and others at NDRC hit upon a plan to create a "need," feeling they had a piece of equipment of which good use could be made: They gathered together a number of dedicated people who started spreading the word of this truck to all the amphibious forces that were in existence, those who were training or conducting exercises in either Europe or the Pacific. The results from this private campaign were amazing! Forces were eager to adopt the advanced design. Relates Warner, "I even have a letter in my files from General Eisenhower, saying that he was wondering how it had happened that these amphibious trucks had been shipped, displacing so much cargo for which previously the forces had been pleading." Lord Louis Mountbatten, Admiral of the British Fleet, was among others who wrote to Warner telling him how importantly DUKW had figured into their efforts.

Warner had accomplished a tremendous task in moving so far so fast with the development of the vehicle, and this was not his only responsibility. Simultaneously he was involved in several other problems—among them the operation of the amphibious vehicles and the demolition of landing obstacles. "At Ft. Pierce near Cape Canaveral, we built about nine miles of obstacles, such as our intelligence reports indicated our landing forces would encounter in the Normandy invasion. Once we had developed operation techniques for getting through these obstacles, we trained assault troops in the methods."

Thus, beyond developing a vehicle, the NDRC provided operational understanding and provided for logistic support. Warner set up a supply line directly from Detroit to the Omaha beachhead to keep the trucks in repair. In every phase he worked closely with those who were planning the date, the hour and the strategy for Overlord, the Normandy landing.

The results achieved by Warner's driving and determined efforts were startling, even in context with the wartime atmosphere where seeming-miracles constantly were being performed. The number of lives which DUKW saved, and the amount of help that was given by these remarkable vehicles are beyond estimating; the project clearly stands out as a vital element in the success of the invasion.

In addition to the "duck" there was an animal in Warner's life during this wartime period—it was WEASEL! "The British asked Vannevar Bush to suggest means of carrying troops and a small amount of equipment in aircraft, drop both down onto snow, have them attack downhill, and escape uphill. That was the assignment called WEASEL." Warner was named Project Manager.

So important was it considered that Prime Minister Churchill sent over one of his top advisors. Warner relates the circumstances of his first meeting with him: "I called upon him at a hotel in Washington, D.C., and found hot water pouring out from under his door. I knocked, he answered. There was never any comment or explanation about the hot water that was flooding the room." As if trying to explain it to himself, Warner adds, "He was a poet and wore a goatee."

Warner continues his recollecting, "A few days later, on Memorial Day, 1943, we were working at the Carnegie Institution all day, and it was unbearably hot. Most of the time was spent on long distance phone, calling up people all over the world to round up a force for a test of WEASEL. We found a meteorologist from Norway, a glacier expert who was a former Minister of Education in Austria. With these, and others, we flew the backbone of North and South America, looking over all the possible ice fields in an attempt to select a test site. Incidentally, the commanding general abruptly asked us to leave Alaska. Two days later we understood why —the attack on Anchorage took place.

"We finally picked the site to make our test—it was the fantastically lovely Athabaska Glacier in the northern part of Alberta. After locating the spot from the air, we trekked up there with some special troops training in Alberta. We set up camp at the foot of the glacier. Then we flew up some vehicles to start field testing, and moved in special combat troops. In the testing, which lasted all summer, we dropped all the unsuccessful pieces of equipment down crevasses. By October we retired having met with simple failure. Needless to say, the British lost interest."

But Warner did not. The strength of his features well reflects the dogged persistence he applies to any undertaking. He stuck with the problems all through the winter, and by spring had managed to achieve such reliability and utility that the newly perfected utility vehicle was put into production! As an unexpected benefit, it had broader capability than was intended originally—its primary use being not as a snow vehicle, but rather as a vehicle for crossing mine fields. The WEASEL was used in the marshlands behind the Normandy beachhead, both for crossing marsh regions and as a vehicle that would move ahead of troops and kick off mines. It was used in Sicily and going on up into Rome; it was used in Salerno, and also in the Philippines.

It is a smart man who doesn't know when he is licked, and who finds the way to turn defeat into an even more important triumph. The problems that had faced Warner in Project WEASEL had been threefold: "First was the environmental problem of correlating air temperature with moisture in snow, the second was that of developing a tread which would go through snow, and the third was that of designing a vehicle that would support an engine and some troops.

"To lick the problems, we first had to measure the 'shear' that one could develop in snow. Shear is what develops when you walk in snow—it is not just the downward pressure, but the sideways pressure which supports you. It is the amount of resistance."

Warner goes on to explain, "When an average man with an average-sized foot steps on the ground, he probably produces a pressure of about 7½ pounds per square inch on the ball of his foot. Our problem here was to produce a vehicle tractor tread which was as close to 3 pounds—just exactly half of what a man would produce—in order essentially to float over very soft ground, whether it be snow or mud."

Each such endeavor leads to some most interesting experiences, as Warner relates: "We got enthusiastic in our belief that this vehicle could ford small streams, and made the body watertight. Then we tested it. I made a bold attempt in Lake Erie—and had to swim ashore. It was less than successful."

There were other tests even more attention-getting. Once WEASEL had been successfully developed, the British resumed their interest in the concept, and asked for a demonstration of the vehicle. Warner was pleased to have the opportunity, for he saw in it a strategic benefit. Up to then the utilization of DUKW was dependent on the word being passed among the amphibious forces; he had not seen the means of bringing the proper attention to WEASEL. He had not managed to bridge the huge gap between his office and the Pentagon, just across the Potomac River in Washington, D.C. This demonstration would provide the means.

He managed to arrange for the Coast Guard to patrol around Roosevelt Island, a small poison-ivy patch that lies in the middle of the Potomac between the Chain Bridge and the Memorial Bridge. Then he brought a delegation of about 50 Britishers to the spot for the demonstration. Those in the Pentagon were suddenly very interested and alarmed at this activity, for this was wartime and the Island was government property.

Warner told Dr. Vannevar Bush of his plan, received his cooperation in keeping the Pentagon guessing about what was going on, and staged the entire demonstration for the British only—the Coast Guard followed instructions to keep out all other visitors. Warner muses, "By means of this strategy, we finally got good recognition and proper attention. It is unfortunate to have to promote something in this 'Madison Avenue' style, but it achieved results."

Warner has strong memories of his close association with Dr. Bush: "To me he is an extraordinary person. He has a constructive, sort of 'weaned-on-a-pickle' approach to problems—a sour approach with a smile. He is a severe person, most interesting and highly motivated. He would always find a way to shake out action, to guide you into useful applications of what you were doing. He certainly pulled me out of lots of problems during the period of my work with NDRC. I don't think the military always loved him, but I did."

Warner's instructions for his next phase of activity were cryptic. Dr. Bush told him, "Go see Major J. H. Derry in the New State Building. Do anything that you can to help guide the Ordnance activity on a project that is underway."

The name of this mysterious program? The Manhattan Project. At that time, Warner had not even heard of it.

He was promptly flown to Albuquerque, met at the airport by a WAC driver in a beat-up car, and was taken to Los Alamos. "We arrived there well past midnight on a very cold night," Warner recalls. "My passes were not in order, so I was put in the stockade for the night. At least it was warm in there, and I didn't lack for company—it was filled with G.I.'s who had misbehaved. The next morning I got in and started to work."

The Manhattan Project may well rank as history's best-kept secret. News of the dropping of an A-bomb on Hiroshima on August 6, 1945, utterly astounded the world. Though the scientific work that led up to this colossal weapon stretches far back into history, the events that triggered the actual project occurred in 1939.

In January, the great Austrian woman scientist, Lise Meitner, explained that the uranium atom could be split. The significance was enormous. Two months later Dr. George B. Pegram arranged for representatives of the United States Department of the Navy to come to Columbia University and discuss the matter with Dr. Enrico Fermi, who had received a Nobel Prize the previous year for his research on artificial radioactive substances.

By the fall of 1939, prescient individuals recognized that such a momentous possibility as harnessing the power of the atom necessitated consideration at the highest level. A comprehensive letter was written, explaining the meaning and potential of this scientific breakthrough. By prior arrangement, the letter was taken to Dr. Albert Einstein to sign—so that the prestige of his name might give added emphasis to the message. The letter was then delivered to President Roosevelt.

In response, the first fund for research toward the A-bomb was set up. The unbelievable part of it was the small amount—$6000! But it was a beginning, and it soon expanded. The effort, initially in the Bureau of Standards, was transferred in 1941 to the Office of Scientific Research and Development, of which Dr. Vannevar Bush was the Director. Then it was transferred for the final time—to the War Department. "It is to their everlasting credit that Bush and his colleagues had the discernment to recognize the limitations of their own organization as well as the moral fortitude to admit them in the national interest. Very few men, confronted with a similar situation, would have done so."[2] So writes Leslie R. Groves (now Lieutenant General, USA, Ret.) who was placed in charge of the project in September, 1942.

From the beginning, it was a giant gamble. Taking chances is not consistent with the nature of scientists, but the risk of Hitler's laboratories' achieving an A-bomb first was a threat of such proportions that our scientists were convinced they had to try for the development of an A-bomb.

Facilities, operating quietly under different guises, expanded. In 1943, an isolated mesa in New Mexico became the site of the secret Los Alamos Laboratory, and Dr. J. R. Oppenheimer took over as Director. Great Britain and Canada cooperated with the mighty effort by contributing some of their leading scientists. An ironic note is that among them was Dr. Klaus Fuchs, a British subject born in Germany, who later confessed he was engaged in espionage for the USSR.

Warner joined the mighty effort in October, 1944. "My usefulness there was in making concepts take shape into hardware," he relates. "I found myself operating not only in the mechanical engineering department and working in the field testing of non-nuclear portions of the system, but also in setting up of plans for the Nevada flight testing of Project Y."

Project Y was the designation given to the development of the A bomb, the end product of the Manhattan Project. Two methods were being followed in parallel for the design of the bomb—the Thin Man and the Fat Man.

The former method fired one sub-critical mass of fissionable material like a projectile into a second sub-critical mass of fissionable material. The latter employed the implosion method, that of directing the blast of conventional high explosives in toward the fissionable material. There was never sufficient plutonium available to run a test on the Thin Man design. Theory alone indicated that it would detonate when it was released over Hiroshima.

The Fat Man bomb, which had first been regarded with skepticism, was the first A-bomb ever tested in the Trinity Test at Alamogordo Air Base in New Mexico. The strain of the frightful schedule of work was heightened as unfavorable weather threatened to delay the test. But Groves and Oppenheimer held up the procedure for only a matter of hours, then decided to go ahead. When the clocks reached zero minus 30 minutes, the five men guarding the monster bomb started racing back to the control dugout in their jeeps—several of the vehicles were used, since in a prior TNT test the single jeep had broken down.

Warner, as Director of Ordnance, remained in the dugout, binoculars trained on the brightly illumined steel tower 10,000 yards away which had been constructed under his supervision. At the base camp, General Groves and the others stretched on the ground, face downward and eyes closed. As the seconds approached zero, the minds of most of these men were battlegrounds, where confidence and apprehension struggled for upper place. There were thoughts of the previous night, when the great scientist, Fermi, had been willing to take bets on the possibility that the bomb might ignite the atmosphere! (If it did, would it destroy the world, or merely New Mexico, he asked, quite academically?)

Questions were pounding for answers, and they concerned not only technical matters relating to this enormous scientific undertaking, but were asking the meaning of the moment in terms of humanity's viewpoint. Thought was shattered when the most brilliant flash men ever had created penetrated through closed eyelids. Even mountains ten miles away were sharply illumined by the detonation of the world's first A-bomb!

The heat wave surged across the desert, followed by sound waves that carried the noise of a thousand thunders! The ball of fire was rising, followed by the mushroom cloud that has become the signature of these blasts. In that instant, the surface of the desert for a radius of 800 yards was fused to glass. The giant steel tower that had held the test bomb was completely vaporized. The detonation of the first A-bomb was an unqualified success!

The race against time was accelerated. The targets had been selected, the support to place the bombs on those targets had been secured. It was the decision of General Curtis Le May that a single unescorted airplane would deliver the A-bomb. The plan, though at first utterly startling, had sound logic—the Japanese would likely pay little attention to one airplane flying at high altitude.

Tinian was selected for the base of operations, largely because it was 100 miles nearer to Japan than the alternate, Guam; the B-29 would be loaded to a critical point, so this was a major consideration. An airfield was already in existence on Tinian, though Warner arrived at the Island to find it in dire condition: "In inspecting the runways, I found them scattered with a huge number of metal bits and fragments. Since our airplane had rubber tires, I didn't relish the possibility of a blow-out on take-off. The kind of cargo we were carrying deserved every consideration. I prevailed upon the commanding general to assign all of his prisoners the job of going over the runways on their hands and knees, cleaning them up. The pile of metal they collected was beyond belief—nearly a ton."

As soon as the success of the Trinity Test was known to President Truman, he issued his Potsdam Ultimatum to Japan. To give reaction time, he did not wish the A-bombing of Japan to take place before July 31, 1945. On August 1, the weather would not permit the flight. It was not good on August 2, 3, or 4. Nerves became strained to unbelievable tautness. Warner and his colleagues, bivouacked in tents on the humid island, spent the hours in tedious checking and rechecking of all preparations. The forecast on the 5th was good. Activity erupted, and in 24 hours the Thin Man (also called Little Boy) was assembled—except for the final loading of the gun and the insertion of the red plugs which was accomplished in flight by Rear Admiral W. S. Parsons, Head of the Los Alamos Ordnance Division.

The *Enola Gay,* piloted by Colonel Paul W. Tibbets, flew the 1700 miles from Tinian to Hiroshima, and arrived but 30 seconds off schedule. The A-bomb was released and the *Enola Gay* performed a maneuver then unknown to bombers—a sharp diving turn to gain speed for the get-away. The airplane had reached a point safely beyond the 10-mile danger radius on detonation.

Warner says, "I have a photograph of that moment, taken from the tail gunner's position." Though it was the moment that indicated a quick victory for the Allies, acceptance of our ultimatum was not immediately forthcoming.

Preparations surged forward on the Fat Man. Just as the date of the dropping of the Thin Man had been controlled by the moment that sufficient U-235 was available, the delivery of this second bomb could not be accomplished until there was a sufficient amount of plutonium; the complete supply had been used up in the Trinity Test.

Warner headed the Fat Man Assembly team. Writes General Groves: "The job of the Los Alamos group on Tinian was to provide and test bomb components and also to supervise and inspect the actual assembly of the bombs. They were to inspect the bomb prior to take-off, test the completed unit, and coordinate the various project activities on the Island."[2]

The 509th Group, created for the delivery of the A-bombs, had been practicing the drop of the Fat Man with Pumpkins—a training bomb containing 5500 pounds of explosives. The pattern for the bomb run was unlike any previous experience; in altitude, for instance, it was made at an unprecedented 30,000 feet.

With the prospect of getting sufficient plutonium, the date for the second bombing was set for August 11. On August 7, it was rescheduled to August 10. Then the elements played against this date, when a forecast for bad weather spanned August 10–14. Though such pressure induced added elements of risk, the date was advanced to August 9. The vital plutonium was flown to Tinian in a C-54 and under Warner's expert supervision, the bomb was completely assembled. The nature of its design did not permit the precaution taken with Thin Man, of final assembly after take-off.

(A senior officer demanded a signed statement to the effect that if the airplane should have an accident in take-off, the fully-armed A-bomb presented no danger. Writes Groves: "Parsons and Ramsey* signed such a statement promptly though with some trepidation, possibly with the thought that if they were proven wrong they would not be there to answer."[2])

A series of difficulties plagued this mission. The B-29, which was piloted by Major Charles W. Sweeney, was discovered to have a faulty fuel pump, which would prevent the use of 800 gallons of gasoline in a bomb-bay tank. Despite this, the decision was made to proceed. Then, the three airplanes involved in this flight failed to rendezvous properly at Yokushima, and 30 minutes of time and precious fuel were wasted. Sweeney proceeded to the primary target for this second A-bomb, Kokura. There he made three bomb runs and wasted 45 minutes; weather prevented sight of the target.

As the B-29 headed for the secondary target, Nagasaki, it was determined that the gasoline supply had grown so critical that only one bomb run could be made. Again, the overcast was present. There appeared no alternative but to disobey orders and use radar to locate the target. At the last instant, a hole opened in the overcast and visual sighting could be made. A-bomb number two was dropped.

On the return dash, the crew prepared to ditch, but luckily made it to the alternate air field on Okinawa—though after landing Sweeney did not have enough gas left in the tanks even to taxi off the strip!

As electrifying word of the second successful bombing reached Warner and the other weary personnel on Tinian, there was little doubt that the gigantic effort had paid off. The surrender of Japan was at hand. Operation Olympic and Operation Coronet—in which Warner's amphibious equipment would have been utilized for assault landings at southern Kyushu and Tokyo—were abandoned, and thereby countless American

* Ramsey was Scientific and Technical Deputy.

lives were spared. Instead, the amphibious force that landed on August 28, 1945, was one of occupation.

The men on Tinian had done their jobs, and done them well. Now they waited. Says Warner, "We remained on that island for a solid month, with absolutely nothing to do. With time so heavy on our hands, we found the most entertaining thing we could do was to start a rumor factory. Life was spent creating constructive rumors of any sort!"

Warner was disturbed by the condition in which he found Los Alamos when he returned in September, 1945. A transformation had occurred at this great and productive laboratory. "The place was completely demoralized. Almost everyone was trying to leave. I took on the job of stabilizing a certain number of people—at least those people who had been working directly with me and knew the hardware, knew what it took to assemble a bomb, knew how to get it into operational use. With them, and with a corps of engineers, I set up Sandia Base, which eventually became Sandia Corporation."

There were good reasons for instituting this new Laboratory, as Warner explains: "In the first place Los Alamos was running out of space, and in the second it was not a proper postwar operation for the University of California to manage. There were all sorts of people who were in ordnance activity who really belonged in a line organization. So the Sandia operation was built up to about 150 people and took over much of the Los Alamos ordnance function. The following summer the Bikini tests were held."

The splitting of the atom ushered in the age of inadequate adjectives. Proportions, intensities, meanings, potentials—all increased by such magnitudes that words, as men had used them, became meaningless. In the Bikini tests, it is a curious commentary that witnesses reacted in a manner which is similar to Geiger counters—blanking out when they are overloaded.

The most fascinating portion of the excellently written *Bombs at Bikini, The Official Report of Operation Crossroads,* is that in which the Historian of Joint Task Force One, W. A. Shurcliff, relates that few eyewitnesses to the blasts could recall what happened. Astutely he analyzes it in this manner: "Without question one reason why observers had so much trouble in retaining a clear impression of the explosion phenomena was the lack of appropriate words and concepts. The explosion phenomena abounded in absolutely unprecedented inventions in solid geometry. No adequate vocabulary existed for these novelties. The vocabulary bottleneck continued for months even among the scientific groups; finally, after two months of verbal groping, a conference was held and over thirty special terms, with carefully drawn definitions, were agreed on. Among those terms were the following: dome, fillet, side jets, bright tracks, cauliflower cloud, fallout, air shock disk, water shock disk, base surge, water mound, uprush, after cloud."[3]

Thus the group struggled to comprehend what they had seen, heard, felt—with very considerable aid from the records of the thousands of instruments, and by seeing the film of the explosions run in slow motion so that receptivity was not swamped. But even after this great post-Bikini study had given them channels of communication between one another, it did little to funnel any true picture to other people. The deaf man can learn to read music, but he will never truly know the crashing crescendo of a Mahler symphony.

The test was a project of the Joint (Army and Navy) Chiefs of Staff, carried out by Joint Task Force One, which was created January 11, 1946 —the day after President Truman approved the detailed plan of action prepared by Vice Admiral W. H. P. Blandy. Blandy was named Commander, and 41,963 men and 37 women were sent to the Pacific area to participate in the program.

So apparent was the value of this effort that the natives of Bikini were willing to evacuate the island that was their home, feeling that the tests were a contribution toward world peace. It is curious that though these unsophisticated people clearly grasped the significance of the tests, not all Americans were as perceptive. In the rush to return to peacetime living, the very roots which would help to insure the peace were being trampled. Manpower, resources, and budgets for defense were dwindling at an alarming rate. So it was under compensating pressure approaching that of wartime intensity that Warner and countless others carried out the involved plans.

Preparations for this most elaborate and extensive scientific test in recorded history were seemingly infinite. A voluminous Operation Plan, consisting of thousands of finely printed pages, contained 29 plans—among them were Movement Plan, Logistics Plan, Communication and Electronics Plan, Security Plan, Safety Plan, Air Plan, Instrumentation Plan, Bikini Evacuation Plan.

The author of the *Official Report* makes the rather amusing comment: "The Operation Plan was so complete that the writer, who studied it with some care, had throughout the Operation the impression of attending a good Technicolor motion picture of a recently read book."[3] Nothing was unanticipated, nothing was impromptu in execution.

Some of these arrangements were obvious, some obscure, and some surprising—for example, first-class repair jobs were performed on war-damaged ships, which were to be taken to the Pacific lagoon and blown up!* The reason for this was to be able to exactly determine the amount of damage from the Bikini blasts, without being misled by any prior damage.

The task of accurately and usefully evaluating the damage still remained a Herculean undertaking. For instance, to have described the thousands of compartments and installations of the battleship USS *Independence* as either "wrecked" or "partially wrecked" would have had little meaning in the later interpretation of data. Therefore, especially worked-out forms were prepared for the inspection teams, in order to give uniformity and clarity to their observations.

Another of the preparatory steps was to take a fish census! It was vital for botanists to know accurately the effects of the blasts on fish, animals, and plant life in the area.

The 26 islands of the Bikini Atoll were renamed—Bokonfuaaku was changed to Bokon, Romurikku was changed to Romuk, as examples. Eninman ended up being renamed Prayer, after its first designation, Eman, became confused with the new name for another island, Amen.

The *Sumner* and the *Bowditch* were the first ships to reach the area in late January; their mission was to make oceanographic studies. As the weeks passed, other vessels swelled the fleet to a total of 242, augmented by 156 airplanes. Warner, as Assistant to Dr. M. G. Holloway, Head of the Los Alamos Group, had among his responsibilities the outfitting of one of the vessels, the *Albemarle* (AV-5).

Rear Admiral W. S. Parsons, as Deputy Commander, directed the technical and scientific work for the tests. The questions to be answered were seemingly endless. From a military point of view, the A-bomb "shakes the very foundations of military strategy."[3] Naval architects needed new concepts. Scientists and engineers were reaching into dark areas with only flickers of knowledge to guide them.

When one speaks today of the sciences involved in space, the list virtually includes all disciplines. This pattern was first set with nuclear research. Vitally concerned with the tests at Bikini were nuclear physicists, mathematicians, chemists, spectroscopists, biophysicists, roentgenologists, biologists, veterinarians, piscatologists, hematologists, oceanographers, meteorologists, seismologists, geologists, and others.

These men of different disciplines, together with the officers of different services, concentrated with great congeniality and effectiveness on the very big job to be accomplished. Admiral Blandy established a reasonably in-

* The repair even had to surpass normal requirements, in that the ships had to be rendered nearly watertight—a condition not usually required of manned vessels where leakage can be pumped out. In these tests, where the ships might have to remain unmanned for weeks while the tests were readied, leakage could have proved serious.

formal and democratic procedure which facilitated the night-and-day schedule of work. Launches furnished a taxi service to take the thousands of men from their ships to the target vessels each morning to work on the installation of testing devices and various other equipment. Conferences of every nature were endless; for example, briefings to the press corps of 124 on the port deck of the *Appalachian.* To satisfy the journalists, who were always pressing for more details, Dr. R. A. Sawyer, Technical Director, brought Warner to one of the press conferences. He introduced him as "the man who will tell you almost anything about the bomb—except what you want to know."[3]

There were 90 vessels arranged in the target area with the battleship *Nevada* as the hub; the ships that radiated out formed curved lines, so that one ship would not protect the next from the effects of the blast. Test animals that were put aboard constituted an extensive zoo—204 goats, 200 pigs, 5000 rats.

Final checkout of equipment was completed on June 30, 1946, and the ships weighed anchor to leave the lagoon and take up new positions ranging between 10 to 25 miles from Bikini. The catastrophic contingency of inadvertently leaving someone behind in the target area was dealt with by having the senior officer—who was the last to leave each target ship—hoist the Y, "Yoke," signal flag to signify evacuation by all personnel. The appearance of other flags would have been the signal for rescue operations. Writes David Dietz, one of the correspondents who was present, "We watched the proceedings through binoculars from the *Appalachian* hoping to see some ship break out like a Christmas tree, but the operation proceeded smoothly without incident."[4]

When the bomb-bay doors of the B-29 named *Dave's Dream* opened at 9 A.M. on July 1, 1946, the bomb for Test A hurtled toward its massive target. While still several hundred feet in the air, Mike Hour (the instant of detonation) arrived. The energy release was about 1,000,000,000,000,000,000,000 ergs, equivalent to approximately 20,000 tons of TNT.* The annals of science were provided with an accumulation of valuable data which would require the efforts of thousands of man-years to analyze; within *2 hours* after Mike Hour, the first of the manned boats re-entered the Lagoon to begin that task.

The President's Evaluation Commission sent Mr. Truman a preliminary statement immediately following Test A which said, in part: "We are of the unanimous opinion that the first test amply justified the expenditure required to conduct it and that the second test is equally desirable and necessary."[3]

The A-bomb was yet a scientific innovation. To detonate this second

* The H-bomb exploded July 9, 1962, by the U.S. in the Pacific area was equivalent to more than a million tons of TNT.

bomb underwater was a giant problem which taxed the collective brainpower of the personnel with a series of major difficulties. But all technical aspects were surmounted, and the ships of the target fleet—the ones still afloat after Test A—were rearranged for this history-making underwater detonation of an A-bomb.

The *Official Report* states: "Among the last persons to leave the lagoon was a group consisting of Admiral Parsons, Dr. M. G. Holloway, Mr. R. S. Warner, Jr., and a few others."[3]

The A-bomb in Test B produced almost exactly the same amount of energy as Test A, but due to the near incompressibility of water, the shock wave produced by this explosion was greater—probably the greatest that had been produced on earth—in excess of 10,000 pounds per square inch near the bomb. The wave traveled at the speed of sound during most of its course—only a third as fast as in Test A, where it encountered the lighter resistance of air.

Detonation formed a brilliantly illuminated gas bubble beneath the surface of the water. As it rose, it produced the incredible sight of an inward illuminated dome, atop which was riding the LSM-60! When the dome burst, the vessel became a shower of small steel fragments! The 2000-foot diameter, two-million-ton column of water rose to an altitude of about a mile and a half before it unfolded into a fantastic cauliflower!

The scientific story of what happened during those two blasts at Bikini was recorded by 750 cameras, 4 television transmitters, 5000 pressure gauges, 25,000 radiation recorders. What cannot be tallied in statistics is the effort of men such as Warner, who realized these tests were vital to guarantee this nation's future defense posture. They laid a foundation of incalculable value for the expansion of our nuclear capability.

Roger S. Warner, Jr.

His story is not an account of what he is, but of what he has done. His name is recognized and respected in many, many circles. But who knows this man—really knows him? "Interesting man. A solid scientific background. Gets things done as few ever have around Washington. Seems to be in the middle of—or behind—a lot of things. Must be highly regarded at top levels. Knows how to slash through red tape. He's good at banging heads, if need be, to promote a solid idea. Always works to do things for the Navy."

The comments go on and on: "In meetings, he is sort of like he looks—sort of like a bear. He's intolerant of delays. Has a great sense of humor, but not in the manner of laughing at someone else. There's a real motivation there. He won't stand for a lot of beating around the bush—likes for people to come to the point and say what they mean. Extremely competent. He's a doer. Also has great creative thinking ability. A real nautical type.

He's capable of hiding his inner feelings to everyone. He puts up a façade to those who work with him. I worked with him a long time and got to know him as well as did anyone—and I never really knew him."

One colleague adds, "I think he is a lonely man."

Many scientists are devoted to work, fewer earn the description of being dedicated. Warner is the stage beyond—he is utterly absorbed. He is so much his work that the line separating the emotions and feelings of the man has been inundated with the flood of responsibilities he has been willing to assume. It is unlikely that any psychologist would ever consider his a well-balanced life, with appropriate divisions of work and play and interests. But no one could ever question that it is a productive life, and one that perhaps brings greater rewards to this man than the arbitrary "patterns of living."

Unusual men don't fit usual molds. Even self-description comes hard with Warner, but it is most revealing of all: "What have I contributed? I don't know. I seem to have gotten into many things, yet I don't fit any category. You wouldn't say that I am a nuclear physicist, nor a marine designer capable of turning out amphibious craft, nor an operations analyst suited to head up an operation like the Institute of Naval Studies. Since I'm none of these things, I really can't say what has gotten me into those positions. I get in the middle of them, and get tremendously enthused. They all have required a very great amount of effort—it is never easy getting something started.

"Every so often I just burn myself out and have to go vegetate for a couple of months. I'm operating a boat right now in Massachusetts which will take my attention for a month—then back to work. I don't know what single thing I enjoy the most. I enjoy each of the activities. And I can't really say what the characteristic is that ties all this together. Something must exist—I don't know what. I'm only glad that, for whatever reason, a great many people will let me help, will listen to what I think about things, and will come along with me to get a job done."

After many years of government work, Warner rejoined industry in 1948—the well-known research firm in the Boston area, Arthur D. Little, Incorporated. As Assistant to the President, he was involved both in management of engineering programs and in consulting services. But even that did not lead far away from what had become his primary interest: the support and strengthening of our military defense forces. "The first real job that descended on me there was to develop equipment for supporting the liquid-hydrogen program at Los Alamos."

Warner continued in the design, development, and manufacture of cryogenic engineering equipment, switching in 1951 to the Cambridge Corporation. This company performed all of the design and development on the critical components of the first hydrogen bomb! Warner's firm also supplied the liquid-oxygen equipment and ground-support equipment for the development of the nation's first intercontinental ballistic missile, ICBM, at both the Vandenberg and Cape Canaveral facilities.

It must be noted that both the H-bomb and the ICBM were the most advanced possible developments, straining at the very limits of reliability. To have a major element supplied by a man who had fought the battles and pushed the frontiers of research—and had done it with an incredible amount of success—was one important victory in their over-all developmental process.

Though Warner has found his vast experience to be of enormous value to industry—as witnessed by the growth of the Cambridge Corporation in two years to a total sales of $30 million—he has never hesitated to return to government work when he was needed. He had been with Allied Research Associates, Inc. but two months when the Department of Defense indicated need of his help. He joined the Advanced Research Projects Agency, ARPA, for an important episode in his own life, and for a period of influence upon our nation's space effort which was decisive!

Events make their imprint upon the vast majority of people of the world. A very, very few are able to reverse the process—to make their imprint upon history. Sometimes this is accomplished with a revolutionary discovery or a creative product of magnificence. Sometimes a mighty contribution is made by looking ahead to what will most surely evolve in time, and greatly accelerating its advance.

At first, the whole idea of space was so fantastic that it was regarded with awe and wonder. But simple amazement at that which is new generally has a low satiation point, and is soon replaced by a blasé attitude. Then, in order to excite, yesterday's prodigy must "do something." In this regard, space can "deliver." Whereas the scientific research aspects may be incomprehensible, the military potential frightening, and the manned flight achievements unbelievable, there is yet this one facet that is completely understandable—the utilization of space for practical purposes.

It was into this area that Warner plunged when he again made his offices at the Pentagon in April, 1958. Our first satellite, *Explorer I,* had gone aloft the previous January 31, and an organized national space effort was still suffering the pangs of creation. There was no shortage of suggestions as to what should be done. Formal proposals were bulging from the briefcases of every bright-eyed man who hurried into the inner offices of the policymakers.

There is a humorous saying to this effect: "If you can keep your head when all those about you are losing theirs, you just don't understand the situation!" It is likely that Warner did understand the situation—more thoroughly than the majority—and still managed to keep his head. He felt that the best dispeller of confusion could be produced by positive results: "I wanted to work on projects that would have a fairly immediate opportunity for success. I felt this would also give some impetus to the Congressional support that we needed at that time."

Such thinking was wise, for many legislators on Capitol Hill were not too sure about the new agency, ARPA, even though President Eisenhower had said in his State of the Union Message on January 9, 1958: "In recognition of the need for single control of some of our most advanced development projects, the Secretary of Defense has already decided to concentrate into one organization all the anti-missile and satellite technology undertaken within the Department of Defense."[5]

ARPA was conceived as a small task force or management team—operating above the level of the Army, Navy, or Air Force—using its own budget for the furtherance of advanced research in space projects of potential military significance.

The House Appropriations Committee issued a statement of caution by saying: "If it is to be successful, the Advanced Research Projects Agency must not be allowed to become just another layer of paperwork in the Office of the Secretary of Defense. It must be clothed with the authority and the control of funds necessary to conceive, coordinate, and implement research and development of essential programs of advanced science. If this is done, it could assist in large measure in bringing order and efficiency out of the chaos which has characterized efforts in this area in the past."[5]

There was a question as to whether ARPA should be based on the authorization of Congress, or the Secretary of Defense; Mr. McElroy made moot this question by formally establishing the new agency on February 7, 1958, before either the construction or the appropriation bills had been signed.

There were other hurdles. In view of the Agency's stated objectives, would the individual military services still be permitted to initiate their own advanced research projects? The answer was not clear, and did not enhance the appeal of ARPA to many military officers.

Since the 1958 Defense Reorganization Bill had created the powerful, high-level post of Director of Defense Research and Engineering, which Dr. Herbert York occupied, there arose the question as to whether ARPA should be granted equivalent authority. McElroy resolved it by deciding that ARPA's projects would be subject to supervision and coordination by York.

As a staff to manage the individual space projects, ARPA had the assistance of the Institute of Defense Analysis, IDA. This group of scientific specialists had been formed in 1955 to assist DOD, and assumed the ARPA assignment as an extension of its duties. Though initially IDA had been made up largely of university personnel, the emphasis had shifted. Roy Johnson, the Director of ARPA, selected the people he felt were best qualified to join IDA, and they happened to be from the ranks of industry.

Since ARPA soon would be administering an annual budget of $500 million, it was patent that a "conflict of interests" could exist. This consideration, which has come to plague retiring military officers who might want to join industry, is an equal burden to the men of industry when they enter government service. Though, admittedly, it is necessary to guard against such a possibility of influence, it has restricted the utilization of the abilities of countless experienced and valuable people.

As precaution against abuse, Mr. Johnson made a division in his structure. Both IDA and ARPA personnel would take part in the technical evaluation phase, but only ARPA civil service personnel would award the contracts and administer the funds. All of the staff were very much aware of the problem, Mr. Johnson said: "We make this a way of life, morning, noon, and night. This is a constant discussion, and every man we have is very aware of this, and very aware that any indiscretion on his part can put the whole concept in jeopardy."[5]

Under such elaborate safeguards, and after such a turbulent beginning, ARPA began to gain stature in the spring of 1958. Although Warner's involvements were numerous, there were two special projects which fitted perfectly his criteria of usefulness and rapid results: the navigation satellite and the meteorological satellite. These were worthy of every ounce of his drive, resourcefulness, and tenacity. It was good he possessed the qualities and was willing to give in abundance, for either project alone was a backbreaker—yet he furthered both simultaneously.

Here the characteristics noted by colleagues and acquaintances came into important play. To wage a victorious campaign in that concrete jungle called the Pentagon is an accomplishment of no small proportions. To promote a new concept, secure the budget, and tie together the individual participating agencies or contractors was a giant undertaking—and this was preliminary to the very real and major technical problems of "making it work."

Many a theoretical brainchild has suffered a sad demise when it faced the cold scrutiny of the laboratory. But Warner had substantial reason to feel that these projects could be developed to fulfill all their inherent promises. There had been discussion about the advantages of observing the weather over extensive and inaccessible areas for many years.

In 1951, the discussion was put into a formal proposal: *Inquiry Into the Feasibility of Weather Reconnaissance From a Satellite Vehicle,* by S. M. Greenfield and W. W. Kellogg. This document, which remained a classified Air Force Project RAND report until 1960, set forth three pertinent questions: "(1) What extent of coverage can be expected from a satellite viewing system? (2) In terms of resolution and contrast, what can be seen from the satellite? (3) Given proper coverage and resolution, what can actually be determined regarding the synoptic weather situation from this information?"[6]

Another very early and important paper was the one presented by Dr. Harry Wexler of the United States Weather Bureau on May 4, 1954. Entitled *Observing the Weather From a Satellite Vehicle,* it, also, faced up to the limitations but did not minimize the potential of such a system: "A satellite vehicle traveling about the Earth outside the atmosphere would not assist in portraying the pressure, temperature, humidity, and wind fields by direct measurement. However, by a 'bird's-eye' view of a good portion of the Earth's surface and the cloud structure, it should be possible by inference to identify, locate, and track storm areas and other meteorological features."[7]

There were, in addition, a great number of scientists reporting to the National Academy of Sciences who felt they, also, had very good ideas as to what a weather satellite should contain and how it should perform. So the need and the use were clear. The technology had progressed to the point that such a system was feasible. Warner performed the remaining, vital step—to pick up the ball, buck a seemingly impenetrable line, and run with it.

"I was in a continual hassle to try to generate meaningful requirements. Not just requirements, not just military requirements, but something really significant which would develop interest among the services. I remember a briefing I gave at top level in which I displayed a half-scale model of a satellite which would light up and revolve. It was only a trick of the scientists, but it intrigued the distinguished group and they began to wonder if all this talk could really mean something. This helped to get through a paper which purported to be a requirement, but really was only a hunting license.

"Finally I got hold of $18 million to get the operation started and into hardware." For the next step, Warner turned to the Signal Corps. The Director of ARPA, Mr. Johnson, had specified to Congress that the Agency had "no intention of building an empire"—that they would not set up new field contract agencies of their own, but would utilize the military services for contract work.

In 1870, the Secretary of War, William B. Belknap, gave to the Signal Service (which became the Signal Corps) the responsibility for the weather service. So the involvement of this group had a certain history behind it—if not necessarily logic—for coordinating the weather satellite program.

"ARPA allotted the funds to the Signal Corps, who acted under my direction," says Warner. "They contracted with Radio Corporation of America to build the satellite. Ground stations had to be designed, built, and positioned to read out the information; this, also, was handled by RCA. The tracking station and the launch trajectory were handled by Space Technology Laboratories, Inc. The booster rocket was handled by the Air Force Ballistic Missile Division and Douglas Aircraft Company.

"At the end of two years from the date I joined ARPA, we had the project really going—the booster had been delivered and paid for; the payloads were bought, delivered, and tested; teams were working on projections of what kind of information would probably be relayed back from the satellite; experts had determined exactly how the camera should be set; all that, and a million other details, had been carried out."

The stage was set, the star was poised—but the curtain never went up. At least, not for Warner. Very shortly before *Tiros I* was launched, on April 1, 1960, the entire project was transferred to the National Aeronautics and Space Administration, NASA.

"It was not a very great shift, really," Warner says, and then adds with unusual honesty, "except to my ego. Having sweated buckets to get it going, it just bothered me to have it taken away. But it is very good and very appropriate that it happened—for the project belongs in the civilian space agency.

"When the project had been under the military, many NASA people had been on the steering committee, and when the transfer was made to NASA, the top Signal Corps men transferred with the project to lend continuity. Among them was Bill Stroud, whom I knew from the days at Los Alamos and with whom I work so well; another was Herb Butler, an extremely enthusiastic kind of fellow who always gets along well anywhere."

Though it left Warner's jurisdiction with that move, the program has never left his interest. He has strong ideas about the manner in which the project has developed: "After *Tiros I* went up, the battle to convince certain elements in the Pentagon of its value still had not been won. But in four months, after the satellite had sent back over 400 pictures and the public press was taking great notice, the fact of its great potential began to filter through to all levels.

"When recognition finally came, it was in the form of, 'Gosh, these pictures are magnificent! But what do we do with them?' The first *Tiros* was really at a 'Gee Whiz' stage, and to a large extent that is where *Tiros* is today, still going through the 'Gee Whiz' stage. There is a weather map, but we have a very great distance to cover before really substantive information begins to appear out of these photographs."

Warner explains further, "I'm interested in seeing that we really get some data out of these photographs just as fast as we can. I would like to spend much more money in the software at this stage than in the hardware, and learn how to get more than a small per cent of the information out of these photographs."

The furtherance of the meteorological satellite program was a night-and-day preoccupation that required great attention and tremendous energy. Yet, simultaneously with that development Warner managed to advance a second major program in answer to a need which existed within the Navy. Warner explains it this way: "The *Polaris* missile is one of the most significant advances of this era, but to have real value as a deterrent, it must be coupled with the nuclear-powered submarine. That gives the best military example of the radical change of technique in providing deterrents. A number of needs come out of it—the most immediate being for precise navigation. *Polaris'* ability to perform as planned hinges on knowing exactly where it is to be fired from, as well as where the target is.

"Consequently, with the arrival of the *Sputnik* era, and the arrival of the organization of ARPA, it was only natural that one of the significant projects to consider would be navigation by means of an artificial satellite. This was a stimulating new tool which was provided for a rather old art."

Warner explains that at the beginning of the considerations, there were two basic approaches to a navigation satellite: "*Pathfinder* was the most straightforward, most obvious and most classical one: to put up a satellite at a very high altitude and have it give off radio signals, then take a radio sextant and get an angle from the vertical straight overhead down to the satellite, and solve the navigation problem just as one solves the problem of navigation by the stars or the sun.

"Though this was the solution with which many people agreed, it had four or five major holes: one was that we didn't have the booster rockets capable of putting up that kind of satellite at that time. Another was that nobody had really figured out what would be done with the data after it came down to the ground. It was a lot more complicated than it first appeared."

Warner names another shortcoming of this system: "You can measure optically the height of a star pretty well; but the real error is in knowing where the vertical is, for ultimately what you measure is the horizon to the star. So by the measurement-of-angles method there is an uncertainty of maybe 3 to 5 miles.

"I knew that if we were going to get any navigation-satellite scheme considered and accepted, we'd certainly need the possibility of greater precision over anything which existed. This was important, because the military services were certainly spending tremendous amounts of money on installing Loran Systems and Omega Systems—these are ground systems that send out radio signals, the ship takes bearings from several stations and from that gets a fix."

The second possible approach to the problem came in the form of a proposal from The Johns Hopkins University Applied Physics Laboratory. It was a startling and revolutionary concept, put forth by Dr. Frank McClure, Chairman of the Research Center, based on the Doppler shift technique.* The idea had been presented to Rear Admiral Levering Smith, the Technical Director of the Navy's Special Projects Office, where *Polaris* was created. Smith liked it, and supplied a small amount of funding to prepare the proposal.

Now the crucial decision faced Warner. Should the nod be in favor of *Pathfinder,* an approach that entailed not too much risk, but might not give too much gain? Or should he seize upon the radical and untried Doppler shift theory, hoping that the vast and numerous problems might yield to solution; they ranged from massive technical problems to ones as basic as geodetic uncertainties about the earth's shape and gravitational field.

Judgment-making is an unenviable act; responsibility carries with it little forgiveness for a misjudgment. A man must consider all sides, weigh every advantage and drawback, guess at the elements which will doubtless appear to alter the course, estimate the investment in effort and funds, and then be humbly aware that the task is actually beyond his own capability to perform. No excuses will alleviate his position, whatever transpires after he has pronounced his decision.

Warner took the gamble. He chose the Doppler shift theory to use on the navigation satellite (which later came to be called *Transit*). "I knew if it worked at all, it would be remarkable. Theoretically, there was a hundred-fold increase in precision capability; even practically, it promised ten times greater accuracy than anything that had been devised. Also, this approach had the advantage of operating from a satellite orbiting at a very low altitude, and therefore could be launched with the booster capability that then existed. Considering all aspects, I felt that the amount of developmental work which remained to be done was probably within the state of the art, with the exception of how to compute the orbit with all the variables which go into its determination. The effects due to earth's gravity on the satellite's orbit were expected to be profound and there seemed to be no way to understand the problems except by observing at many points the position of the satellite itself and working the problem backward. It seemed to me that this point could be solved with time and effort, but few agreed."

Warner met with violent objections as to his choice. Except for the

* The principle is explained in the chapter on Richard Kershner.

confident few at the Applied Physics Laboratory, and the faith of Admiral Smith, the ranks formed against him. The "believers" pointed out that it was Warner's steadfastness that kept the project alive. He was the determined catalyst, between the dream of the Laboratory, the need of the Navy, and the funds of ARPA.

Transit came into being through the joint efforts of thousands of people, but individuals can be singled out for rich credit. It was the scientific excellence and enthusiastic spirit of Dr. Richard Kershner, who headed the Project at the Applied Physics Laboratory, that created a piece of hardware out of an idea. But this could not have been done without funding, in great amounts, from a governmental level. There, Warner is largely responsible. It is by no means automatic that every worthy idea will see the light of fulfillment. The competition is too keen, the appraisals at too great variance. There has to be a powerful supporter to put the idea through. This was Warner's role.

When a man sticks his administrative neck out—that far—it gets pretty chilly in the gray dawn of reflection. But as the days and weeks accumulated, confidence rose that even the first launch would prove to be a minor triumph. All laboratory testing indicated full vindication of the principle.

On September 17, 1959, the date of the first scheduled launching of *Transit,* Warner remained in Washington, D.C., in order to be at the site of the telemetry equipment that would report on the progress of the vehicle. The countdown was completed, and the giant *Thor* booster lifted off its pad at Cape Canaveral. As it climbed into the night sky, hopes soared with it! The pinpoint of red against the black sky became smaller and smaller until it vanished. Instruments told the rest of the story. It was a failure.

Even though the first *Transit* failed to go into orbit, it flew over the corner of Newfoundland, and Warner relates, "During that brief period of powered flight, we got some encouraging data. We managed to get another booster very rapidly, and this launch, on April 13, 1960, was a complete success."*

From the beginning of *Transit*, the technical direction was assigned, obviously to the Navy. The following month after the first successful launch, the management of the *Transit* program also was transferred to the Navy for the second phase of the program.

* It was performed by the Douglas Aircraft Company's faithful *Thor* booster—that has been employed in launching more satellites and space probes than all other booster vehicles combined. Among the many successful launches have been: March 11, 1960, the *Thor-Able* launching of *Pioneer V,* which transmitted data over a distance of 22,500,000 miles, the longest direct radio transmission ever achieved; August 12, 1960, the *Thor-Delta* launching of *Echo,* the passive communications satellite; July 9, 1962, the *Thor* boosted the payload for the first thermonuclear test explosion in space; and on July 12, 1962, the *Thor-Delta* launched *Telstar,* the first active communications satellite which transmitted the first transoceanic television.

Reports Captain Robert F. Freitag, the widely respected and knowledgeable Astronautics Officer, Bureau of Naval Weapons, "This system is currently under development within the Navy at top priority and, based upon present schedules, is expected to be operational in late 1962."[8]

Warner's remarkable contributions have brought him the highest civilian award given in this country, the Presidential Medal of Merit. Two of his outstanding activities, those associated with *Tiros* and *Transit,* have yet to mature to the point where their benefits will be fully reaped. They are truly space projects which will substantially influence certain features of living here on earth.

Though programs of this nature have absorbed a larger degree of his time, and the preponderance of public attention, Warner is most concerned over another aspect which he feels is not appreciated: "Space is an environment all its own; ultimately most of the space activity will have relatively little relation to earth-bound needs and objectives.

"It is a long way off, but the Air Force is actively pushing toward the objective of treating space as an environment all its own. This concept does not look down on the earth, does not support earth-bound activities, but institutes projects self-sustained in the space environment. The very large funding which Congress has given to NASA for activities which assist us here on earth are in effect a 'pay-as-you-go' policy. I think Congress soon will expand into a broader support of space for its own sake."

Warner continues by saying, "Meanwhile, I feel our all-out effort to land on the moon is moving too rapidly. The mission may well be successful, but I think it is going to leave too many things undone. It is pushing not the state of the art, but reliability—pushing it far too fast.

"But it is national policy, and the people are in favor of it; they are willing to go all out to achieve some sort of national superiority in space activities. They don't want to be caught napping by another *Sputnik* kind of event—and I have to admit that there is no fun in being second."

Two highly interesting observations are to be made from this attitude: first, Warner, as one of the leading figures in space developments, is perfectly free to speak his mind and express thoughts that do not fully agree with the national policy; second, even though he does not agree in all respects, he is most willing to abide by the will of the majority and will expend his very greatest efforts and talents to carry out the policy which the government has established.

The very essence of our way of life is contained in this dual condition. We are made up of a group of individuals who are not required to submerge any of their thoughts and beliefs. But we recognize that no order or progress can be made by 180 million individuals each pulling in his independent direction.

Civilization's first magnificent experiment in democracy, in early Greece, floundered and failed because order, the element which makes independence workable, was absent. The high resolve and intelligence of our founding fathers were demonstrated when they ingrained discipline into our republic.

We are paying a great price in money and in effort for our advances in space. But the fact that men may speak their minds freely gives proof that the toll has not extended to any of our liberties. We have made great gains, and are continuing with the most gigantic scientific program that mankind has ever witnessed, by means of a free system. It is this system which ultimately dwarfs even the atom in its power!

REFERENCES

1. Bloomfield, Lincoln P., ed.: *Outer Space,* Englewood Cliffs, Prentice-Hall, 1962.
2. Groves, L. R.: *Now It Can Be Told,* New York, Harpers, 1962.
3. Shurcliff, W. A.: *Bombs at Bikini, The Official Report of Operation Crossroads,* Prepared under the Direction of the Commander of Joint Task Force One. New York, William H. Wise, 1947.
4. Dietz, David: *Atomic Science, Bombs and Power,* New York, Collier Books, 1962.
5. *Organization and Management of Missile Programs,* Eleventh Report by the Committee on Government Operations, September 2, 1959.
6. *Meteorological Satellites,* Staff Report of the Committee on Aeronautical and Space Science, United States Senate, March 29, 1962.
7. Wexler, Harry: *Observing the Weather From a Satellite Vehicle,* presented at the Third Symposium on Space Travel, New York, May 4, 1954.
8. *Naval Institute Proceedings,* 87:5, 1961.

Index